OVER
1500
FANTASTIC
JOKES

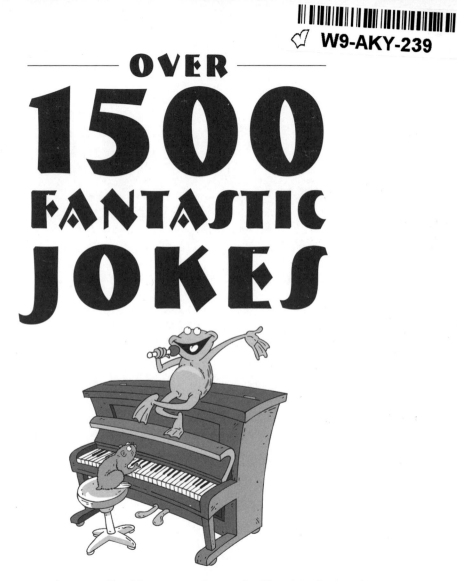

Written and compiled by Guy Campbell & Mark Devins
Illustrated by Paul Moran & Simon Ecob

First published in Great Britain in 2002 as three separate books
(*The World's Funniest Animal Jokes for Kids, The World's Funniest School
Jokes for Kids* and *The World's Funniest Disgusting Jokes for Kids*)
by Dean.

This edition published in Great Britain in 2002 by Dean,
an imprint of Egmont Books Limited,
239 Kensington High Street,
London W8 6SA

ISBN 0 603 56084 9

Printed and bound in Italy

1 3 5 7 9 10 8 6 4 2

PART ONE
ANIMAL JOKES

**What do Paddington, Rupert and Pooh
pack when they go on holiday?**
Just the bear essentials!

How do you get six donkeys in a fire engine?
Two in the front, two in the back and
two on the top going "Heehaw Heehaw
Heehaw"!

**What do you get if you cross a centipede
and a chicken?**
Enough drumsticks to feed an army!

**A man walks into a pub with a tiger.
"Do you serve Welsh people in here?"
he asks the barman.
"Certainly, Sir." the barman replies.**
"Good. A pint for me, then, please, and two
Welsh people for the tiger..."

**What happened when the chef found a daddy
long legs in the salad?**
It became a daddy short legs!

What do ants take when they're ill?
Anty Biotics!

What is a newly hatched beetle?
A baby buggy!

A little turtle begins to climb a tree slowly. After long hours of great effort, he reaches the top, jumps into the air, waving his front legs frantically, then crashes heavily into the ground. After recovering consciousness, he starts to climb the tree again, jumps once more, but again crashes to the ground. The little turtle does this again and again, while all the time his heroic efforts are being watched with sadness by a couple of birds perched on a nearby branch. Finally, the female bird says to the male bird,
"Dear, don't you think it's time to tell Tommy he is adopted?"

What do you get if you cross a glow worm with a python?
A 15-foot strip light that can strangle you to death!

Where did Noah keep his bees?
In the ark hives!

What do you call a vet with laryngitis?
A hoarse doctor!

How do you change tyres on a duck?
With a quackerjack!

What does Tarzan say when he sees a herd of elephants in the distance?
"Look, a herd of elephants in the distance!"

What does Tarzan say when he sees a herd of elephants wearing sunglasses in the distance?
Nothing. He doesn't recognise them!

Why shouldn't you take bears to the zoo?
Because they'd rather go to the cinema!

**What noise does a cat make
going down the motorway?**
Miaooooooooooooooooooooooooooooooow!

**What is the difference between a flea-bitten
dog and a bored visitor?**
One's going to itch and the other
is itching to go!

**Hickory dickory dock,
the mice ran up the clock.
The clock struck one,**
the rest got away with minor injuries!

**A penguin walks into a bar and
says to the barman,
"Have you seen my Dad?"
"I don't know," says the barman.**
"What does he look like?"

A man and his dog sat in a movie hall, both enjoying a movie. When the film ended, the dog applauded until his paws were sore. The man sitting on the next seat was wonderstruck.
"That's amazing!" he exclaimed.
"Yes, it is," agreed the dog owner.
"He hated the book..."

What do you get if you cross a cat with a parrot?
A carrot!

What's big, grey and mutters?
A mumbo jumbo!

Where do monkeys make toast?
Under a gorilla!

How do we know elephants are always unhappy?
Because of their great sighs!

How do bees get to school?
By school buzz!

11

Last time David went to the zoo he got into trouble for feeding the monkeys...
He fed them to the lions!

What do you call a woodpecker with no beak?
A headbanger!

What is green, sooty and whistles when it rubs its back legs together?
Chimney Cricket!

Where do you weigh a whale?
At the whale-weigh station!

What do you call a vampire's dog?
A werewoof!

What do you get if you cross a skunk with a boomerang?
A horrendous smell that keeps coming back!

A duck walks into a pharmacy and says "Got any bread?" The pharmacist explains he has no bread because it is a pharmacy. Then he tells the duck to try the supermarket nearby. Fifteen minutes later the duck comes back and says, "Got any bread?" The pharmacist again tells the duck he doesn't sell bread and to try another shop around the corner. A few minutes later the duck is back again and says, "Got any bread?" The pharmacist screams that if the duck asks him for bread one more time he will nail its bill to the floor. The duck leaves. Twenty minutes later the duck comes back. "Got any nails?" he says. The pharmacist explains that NO, being a PHARMACIST, he doesn't sell NAILS either. "Oh," says the duck, "in that case... Got any bread?"

What do you get if you cross a tiger with a kangaroo?
A stripey jumper!

A baby blackbird fell out of its nest and went flying through the branches of the oak tree towards the ground.
"Are you all right?"
called out a magpie as the chick went hurtling past his perch.
"So far!" said the little bird.

What do Alexander the Great and Winnie-the-Pooh have in common?
They both have "the" as their middle names!

A tortoise is mugged one day by a gang of snails. The police asked him what his attackers looked like and he said,
"I really don't know, it all happened so fast!"

What's black, yellow and covered in blackberries?
A bramble bee!

**What has ten guns
and terrifies the ocean?**
Billy the squid!

What has six legs, four ears, two trunks and three tusks?
An elephant with spares!

What's brown and sees just as well from either end?
A horse with its eyes shut!

Why do elephants have grey skin?
To keep their insides from falling out!

Why aren't elephants allowed on beaches?
They can't keep their trunks up!

Why did they make two Yogi Bears?
Because they made a Boo-Boo with the first one!

What do you get if you cross an elephant with the abominable snowman?
A jumbo yeti!

What has antlers and sucks blood?
A moose-quito!

What's grey and wrinkled and lights up?
An electric elephant!

What did one centipede say to the other centipede?
You've got a lovely pair of legs, you've got a lovely pair of legs, you've got a lovely pair of legs, you've got a lovely pair of legs...!

What did the bee say to the naughty bee?
Bee-hive yourself!

Why do elephants have big ears?
Because Noddy wouldn't pay the ransom!

A man goes into a pet shop and asks to buy a wasp. The shopkeeper tells him they don't sell wasps. "That's strange," says the man.
"You had one in the window yesterday!"

**What does a caterpillar do on
New Year's Day?**
Turns over a new leaf!

Which fly makes films?
Stephen Speilbug!

**What's pretty, delicate and carries a
machine-gun?**
A killer butterfly!

**Why didn't the two worms get on
Noah's Ark in an apple?**
Because everyone had to go on in pears!

**What do you get if you cross a fish
and a Ducati?**
A motor pike!

Why don't centipedes play football?
Because by the time they've got their boots
on, it's time to go home!

What wears glass slippers and weighs a ton?
Cinderelephant!

A Shaggy Dog Story

A local business looking for office help put a sign in the window saying: "HELP WANTED. Must be able to type, must be good with a computer and be bilingual".
A short time later, a dog trotted up to the window, saw the sign and went inside. He looked at the receptionist and wagged his tail, then walked over to the sign, looked at it and whined.
Getting the idea, the receptionist got the office manager. The office manager looked at the dog and was surprised, to say the least. However, since the dog looked determined, he led him into the office. Inside, the dog jumped up on the chair and stared at the manager, who said, "I can't hire you.

You have to be able to type."
The dog jumped down, went to the typewriter and typed out a perfect letter. He took out the page and trotted over to the manager, gave it to him and then jumped back on the chair. The manager was stunned, but then reminded the dog, "The sign says you have to be good with a computer." The dog jumped down again and went to the computer. He then demonstrated his expertise with various programs, producing a sample spreadsheet and database. By this time, the manager was totally dumbfounded! He looked at the dog and said, "I realise that you are a very intelligent dog and have some fantastic abilities. However, I still can't give you the job. The sign also says that you have to be bilingual."
The dog looked him straight in the face, and said, "Meow."

ANIMAL JOKES

The world's funniest

What do you call a camel with three humps?
Humphrey!

Why is a baseball team like fish and chips?
They both need a decent batter!

What do you get when you put a fish and an elephant together?
Swimming trunks!

What has four wheels and flies?
A wheelie bin!

What do you call a cow with no sense of direction?
Udderly lost!

What do you get if you cross a skunk with an elephant?
A smell you never forget!

What do you get if you cross a cow with a crystal ball?

A message from the udder side!

How do snails get their shells so shiny?
Snail varnish!

Why did the fly fly?
Because the spider spied 'er!

**How can you get a set of teeth put in
for free?**
Smack a lion!

**If a four-legged animal is a quadruped
and a two-legged animal is a biped,
what's a tiger?**
A stri-ped!

**What do you call a lion who has eaten
your mother's sister?**
An aunt-eater!

**What do you get if you cross a rabbit
and a flea?**
Bugs Bunny!

Upon entering the little village shop, a tourist noticed a sign saying "DANGER! BEWARE OF DOG!" posted on the glass door. Inside he noticed a harmless old hounddog asleep on the floor beside the cash register. He asked the shop manager, "Is that the dog folks are supposed to beware of?" "Yep, that's him," the manager replied.
The stranger looked amused.
"That old thing? He's got no teeth and he must be 35 years old! Why in the world would you put up a sign saying 'Danger! Beware of the dog'?"
"Because," the owner replied, "before I put that sign up, people kept tripping over him."

How can you tell if you are looking at a police glow worm?
It has a blue flashing light!

The Tramp and the Hamster

A tramp goes into a restaurant and orders a burger. The waiter says, "No way. I don't think you can pay for it." The tramp says, "You're right. I don't have any money, but if I show you something you have never seen before, will you give it to me?" The waiter agrees, and the tramp reaches into his pocket, and pulls out a hamster. The hamster runs to the end of the counter, climbs down to the floor, runs across the room, and gets up on to the piano and starts playing Elton John tunes. The waiter says, "Wow, that hamster is a really good piano player!" He brings the tramp a burger, which he eats, and he asks for another. "Money or another miracle," says the waiter. The tramp reaches into his coat again and pulls out a frog. He puts the frog on the counter, and the frog starts to sing Ricky

Martin songs brilliantly. A stranger from the other end of the counter runs over to the tramp and offers him a hundred pounds for the frog. The tramp says, "OK", and takes the money. The stranger takes the frog and runs out of the restaurant. The waiter says, "Are you crazy? You've just sold a singing frog for a hundred pounds? It must have been worth millions!"

"Nah," says the guy. "The hamster is also a ventriloquist."

What's more dangerous than being with a fool?
Fooling with a bee!

What do you get if you cross a cat with a canary?
Shredded tweet!

What do you call a Russian flea?
A Moscow-ito!

What do you get if you cross an elephant with a whale?
A submarine with a built-in snorkel!

What were the only creatures not to go into the Ark in pairs?
The maggots, they went in an apple!

If you get referees in football and umpires in tennis, what do you get in bowls?
Goldfish!

What time is it when an elephant sits on your fence?
New fence time!

What would you do if an elephant sat in front of you at the movies?
Miss most of the film!

What do you get if you cross a shark with a parrot?
An animal that talks your head off!

What wobbles and eats peanuts?
Jelly the Elephant!

What's grey, has a wand, huge wings and gives money to elephants?
The tusk fairy!

Why do you need a licence for a dog and not for a cat?
Cats can't drive!

What's worse than raining cats and dogs?
Hailing taxis!

Why did the cat join the Red Cross?
Because she wanted to be a first-aid kit!

Why did Mickey Mouse get shot?
Because Donald Ducked!

What do polar bears have for lunch?
Ice burgers!

How does a bird with a broken wing manage to land safely?
With a sparrowchute!

What do bees chew?
Bumble gum!

Why did the muddy chicken cross the road twice?
He was a dirty double crosser!

What do you call a cheerful frog?
A hop-timist!

Why did the cat sleep under the car?
Because she wanted to wake up oily!

**What is the difference between a
fly and a bird?**
A bird can fly but a fly can't bird!

**What should you give a
nervous elephant?**
Trunquillizers!

Waiter, there's a fly in my soup!
What do you want for 85p, an ostrich?

What book tells you all about chickens?
A hencyclopaedia!

**How do you make a statue of
an elephant?**
Take a piece of rock and carve away
everything that doesn't look like
an elephant!

The Brave Pig

A man is visiting a farm when he notices a pig with only three legs. When he meets the farmer, he asks him how the pig came to be so disabled.

"That pig is a marvel," said the farmer, "an absolute gem. He once saved my chickens from a couple of foxes! He heard a noise one night and saw the foxes about to get through the fence and scared them off by banging a wooden spoon on a bucket." "That's amazing," said the man. "Did the foxes bite off his leg?" "No, no," said the farmer, "I tell you, that pig is worth his weight in gold. He once stopped burglars robbing my house. We were all out in the village one day and armed burglars broke into the house. He dialled 999 and let the tyres down on their car. The police caught them and recovered all our stuff." "Good Lord!" said the man. "But tell me, how did he lose the leg?

continued overleaf

Did the burglars shoot him?" "No, no, no," said the farmer, his eyes filling with tears, "I tell you, that pig is an angel sent from above. Do you know he saved my daughter's life? She was only six years old and she fell asleep in the barn one evening while feeding the new lambs with their bottle by lamplight. The lamp fell over and set fire to some hay, and before you know it the whole place was in flames. That pig went into the blazing barn and pulled my daughter out. Then he went back in eight more times and rescued every single lamb as well!" "Incredible!" said the man. "And he lost his leg in the fire?" "No, no, no," said the farmer. "THEN HOW DID HE LOSE HIS LEG?!" said the exasperated man.

"Well," said the farmer, "when you have a pig as truly exceptional as that... you don't want to eat him all at once, do you?"

There were four cats in a boat, one jumped out. How many were left?
None. They were all copy cats!

What did one flea say to the other after a night out?
Shall we walk home or take a dog?

What is worse than finding a maggot in your apple?
Finding half a maggot!

What's got eight legs and can fly long distances?
Four geese!

What do you call a flea on the moon?
A lunar-tick!

What do you give an elephant that's going to be sick?
Plenty of space!

**What is the difference between a
cat and a comma?**
One has the paws before the claws
and the other has the clause
before the pause.

**What do you get if you cross a parrot with
a centipede?**
A walkie-talkie!

**What chases the Roadrunner and
sings disco pop tunes?**
Kylie Coyote!

Where do birds meet for coffee?
In a nest-café!

What do you call a crate of ducks?
A box of quackers!

What is a parrot's favourite game?
Hide and Speak!

What happens when a bomb goes off in the middle of a herd of cows?
Udder destruction!

How can you tell which end of a worm is which?
Tickle it in the middle and see which end laughs!

What is the best advice to give to a worm?
Sleep late!

What is an asset?
A small donkey!

**Two hunters find some tracks in the forest.
"Those are bear tracks," said one.
"No way, those are moose tracks," said the other.**
And then they were run over by a train...

What do you get if you cross an elephant and a kangaroo?

Great big
holes all
over
Australia!

Harry was trying to smuggle a skunk out of America to sell it abroad; he asks his friend the best way to do it. "Just stick it down your trousers," his friend said. "He won't bite unless you sit on him." "But what about the terrible smell?" said Harry. His friend thought for a moment. "He'll get used to it eventually!"

What is out of bounds?
A knackered kangaroo!

What did the bee say to the flower?
Hi honey!

What do you get if your budgie flies into the blender?
Shredded Tweet!

How do you start a firefly race?
Ready Steady Glow!

What did the spider say to the bee?
Your honey or your life!

What do cows play at parties?
Moo-sical chairs!

The Mighty Tiger

A tiger corners a monkey one day and roars: "WHO IS THE MIGHTIEST OF ALL THE JUNGLE ANIMALS?" The poor monkey replies: "You, of course! No-one is mightier than you, Tiger!" A little while later the tiger finds a deer, and bellows out: "WHO IS THE MIGHTIEST OF ALL THE JUNGLE ANIMALS?" The deer is shaking so hard it can barely speak, but manages to squeak: "Oh Great Tiger, you are the mightiest animal in the jungle!" The tiger, feeling good, swaggers up to a female elephant that is quietly eating some weeds. He roars: "WHO IS THE MIGHTIEST OF ALL THE JUNGLE ANIMALS?" The elephant grabs the tiger with her trunk, slams him down, picks him up again, and shakes him until his teeth rattle. Finally she throws him hard

into a nearby tree. The tiger staggers to his feet and looks at the elephant and says: "Just because you don't know the answer, you don't have to get so upset..."

What happens when ducks fly upside down? They quack up!

What's grey on the inside and clear on the outside? An elephant in a plastic bag!

What do frogs eat with their hamburgers? French flies!

Why do elephants wear sandals? To keep from sinking into the sand!

Why do ostriches stick their heads in the sand? To look for elephants that weren't wearing sandals!

What happened to the hyena that swallowed an Oxo cube?
He made a laughing stock of himself!

What did the woodworm say to the chair?
It's been nice gnawing you!

What happened when the owl lost his voice?
He didn't give a hoot!

What do you get when you cross a python with a porcupine?
Ten feet of barbed wire!

What do you call a cat who does tricks?
A magic kit!

How do you get two whales in a Nissan Micra?
Straight up the M4 and over the Severn Bridge. (To Wales.)

How do you get four elephants in a Nissan Micra?
Two in the front, two in the back!

How do you recognise an elephant's house?
There's a Nissan Micra outside!

Two monkeys had a dare, to paint a lion's bottom blue as he slept. Bobby monkey crept up to the sleeping beast and carefully painted its hindquarters, but suddenly the lion woke up. Bobby shot off like a hare, being chased by the angry lion. Through the jungle they sped, until Bobby jumped over the wall to a house. Quickly, he sat in a garden chair and pulled a newspaper over his face. The enraged lion wasn't far behind: he came leaping over the wall and stopped in front of the trembling monkey. "Did you see a monkey come through here?" said the lion. "What?" said Bobby, still shaking. "The one that painted that lion's bum blue?"

"Oh no!" said the lion. "Don't tell me it's in the papers already!"

How do you make an elephant stew?
You keep it waiting for a few hours!

How can you tell an elephant from a giraffe?
Say "Hi giraffe" and if it doesn't answer, it's probably an elephant!

I went to the dentist yesterday. He said, "Say Aaah." I said, "Why?"
He said, "My dog's died."

What looks like a horse and flies?
A flying horse!

Who clucked and conquered half the world?
Attila the Hen!

What did the buffalo say when his son went on holiday?
Bison!

How do you find out how many cows you have?
With a pocket cowculator!

What part of a fish weighs the most?
The scales!

What did the banana do when the monkey chased it?
The banana split!

Farmer Brown meets his friend in the village pub. "Harold, what did you give your bull when it had colic?" "Vinegar and Fairy Liquid," said Harold. A week later they met again. Farmer Brown says, "Oi, Harold! I gave my bull vinegar and Fairy Liquid, like you said, and it died!"
"So did mine!" said Harold.

Which dinosaur had one leg?
All of them!

What do you get when you cross a cow and a duck?
Cheese and quackers!

Why don't owls sing when it is raining?
Cos it's too wet to woo!

The Rude Parrot 2

A lady was walking to work and she saw a parrot on a perch in front of a pet shop. The parrot shouted,"Oi! You're really ugly!" Well, the lady was furious! She stormed past the shop to her work. Going home that night, she saw the same parrot and it said, "Oi! You're really ugly!" She was very angry. She went into the shop and told the owners that she was going to sue them and have the bird put down if they didn't make it stop insulting her. The owners told her they would make sure he didn't do it again. The next morning, she again passed in front of the shop. The parrot was still on his perch. When she walked by, the parrot said, "Oi!" She stopped and turned to the parrot and said, "Yes, what?" The parrot looked at her and said: "You know..."

What is white, sugary, has whiskers and floats?
A catameringue!

What did the slug say as he slipped down the wall?
How slime flies!

What is the difference between fleas and dogs?
Dogs can have fleas but fleas can't have dogs!

What did the clean dog say to the insect?
Long time no flea!

What goes clomp, clomp, clomp, squish; clomp, clomp, clomp, squish?
An elephant with one wet shoe!

What happened when 500 hares got loose on the main street?
The police had to comb the area!

A vicar was reading Bible stories to his Sunday school class. He read: "The man named Lot was warned to take his wife and flee out of the city, but his wife looked back and was turned into a pillar of salt." One of the children asked, "What happened to the flea?"

What became of the man who was swallowed by a cow? He became the man in the moo!

What do you give a dog with a fever? Mustard, it's the best thing for a hot dog!

Why do baby giraffes walk softly? Because they can't walk hardly!

What does an elf get in a cow field? A pat on the head!

What do you get if you cross a pig and a laundry?

Hogwash!

Teacher: If I gave you three rabbits today and five rabbits tomorrow, how many rabbits would you have?
Jackie: Nine.
Teacher: That's not right, you'd have eight.
Jackie: No, I'd have nine. I already have one rabbit at home!

What did the fish say when he swam into the wall?
Dam!

What do you call a story about young horses?
A pony tail!

Why don't you see elephants in lifts?
Because they hide in the back corners!

Why do elephants drink so much?
To try to forget!

A vicar is buying a parrot.
"Are you sure it doesn't scream, yell, or swear?" asked the preacher.
"Oh absolutely. It's a religious parrot," the shopkeeper assured him. "Do you see those strings on his legs? When you pull the right one, he recites the Lord's Prayer, and when you pull on the left he recites the 23rd Psalm." "Wonderful!" says the preacher.
"But what happens if you pull both strings?"
"I fall off my perch, you fool!" screeched the parrot.

Two fleas were running across the top of a cereal packet.
"Why are we running so fast?" said one.
"Because it says 'Tear along the dotted line!'"

Why should you never buy dogs that are going cheap?
Because a healthy dog should go "Woof"!

The Talking Dog

A man and his dog walk into a bar. The man says to the barman: "I'll bet you a round of drinks that my dog can talk." The bartender says, "Yeah! Sure...go ahead." The man says to his dog, "What covers a house?" and his dog says, "Roof!" The man says, "How does sandpaper feel?" and the dog says, "Rough!"

The man asks, "What percentage of the Earth's surface is water?" and the dog says, "Arf!" "There!" said the man. "I told you he could talk!" The bartender, annoyed at this point, throws both of them out the door. Sitting on the pavement, the dog looks at the man and says, "Or is it three-quarters?"

What's big, white and scary with a hole in the middle?

A polo bear!

What do you get if you cross a frog with a traffic warden?
Toad away!

Why did King Kong climb the Empire State Building?
Because he couldn't fit in the lift!

What's pink and grey and has four feet?
A hippopotamus poking its tongue out!

Rachel: How did you like the parrot I sent you?
Michele: It was delicious!
Rachel: You ate it? I paid 500 dollars for that parrot, and it spoke seven different languages!
Michele: Then why didn't it say anything when I put it in the oven?!

Who took ten thousand pigs up a hill?
The Grand Old Duke of Pork!

Who steals soap from the bath?
Robber ducks!

A magician was working on a cruise ship performing tricks for the guests. But his act was ruined every night by the captain's parrot, who would shout out, "It's up your sleeve!" or "She's gone through the hidden trapdoor!" during his act, and give the tricks away. Unfortunately, the ship struck an iceberg one night and the magician and the parrot ended up in the same lifeboat. After a week of silence, the parrot turned to the magician and said,

"All right, I give up - what did you do with the ship?"

What should you do if you are on a picnic with King Kong?

Give him the biggest bananas!

How do you stop a cockerel crowing on Sunday morning?

Have him for lunch on Saturday!

The Antique Saucer

A famous art collector is walking through the city when he notices an old cat lapping milk from a saucer in the doorway of a shop.
He notices that the saucer is extremely old and very, very valuable.
So he walks casually into the store and offers to buy the cat for £2. The shopkeeper replies, "I'm sorry, but the cat isn't for sale."
The collector says, "Please, I need a hungry cat around the house to catch mice.
I'll pay you £20 for him."
And the shopkeeper says, "Sold!" and hands over the cat. The collector continues,
"Hey, for the 20 quid I wonder if you could throw in that old saucer? The cat's used to it and it'll save me from
having to get a dish."
And the shopkeeper says,
"Sorry, Mate, but that's my lucky saucer.
So far this week I've sold 68 cats!"

What happened when the cat ate a ball of wool?
She had mittens!

Customer: I'll take this parrot. Could you please send me the bill?
Shopkeeper: I'm sorry, but you'll have to take the whole bird!

What do you get when you cross a pig and a centipede?
Bacon and legs!

A Ring-Tailed Lemur goes into a tea shop and orders a jam scone. "That'll be £2.50 please, Sir," said the waitress. "I must say, we don't get many Ring-Tailed Lemurs in here!"
"I'm not surprised," said the Lemur. "Two and a half quid for a scone?!"

What's grey and squirts jam at you?
A mouse eating a doughnut!

What do you get if you pour boiling water down a rabbit hole?
Hot cross bunnies!

What has six ears, twelve legs and can't watch telly?
Three blind mice!

The Bragging Horses

Some racehorses are chatting in a stable. One of them starts to boast about his track record: "In the last 15 races I've run, I've won 8 of them!" "That's nothing!" another horse breaks in, "In the last 27 races I've run, I've won 19!" "Oh that's not bad," says another, flicking his tail, "but in the last 36 races I've run, I've won 28!" At this point, they notice that a greyhound dog has been sitting there listening. "I don't mean to boast," says the greyhound, "but in my last 104 races, I've won 103 of them." The horses are clearly amazed. "Wow!" says one, after a hushed silence. "A talking dog!"

Why does an ostrich have such a long neck?
Because its head is so far from its body!

How can you tell when your dog is stupid?
He keeps barking up the wrong tree!

What do giraffes have that no other animal has?
Baby giraffes!

My dog likes to sit down each evening and surf the Internet.
Wow! What a smart animal!
Not really, it took the cat three weeks to teach him!

What do we get from naughty cows?
Bad milk!

Why did the dinosaur cross the road?
Because chickens weren't invented then!

What do you get if you cross a cow and a jogging machine?
A milk shake!

A Chihuahua, a Doberman and a Bulldog are in a doggie bar having a drink when a good-looking girl Poodle comes up to them and says, "Whoever can say 'liver and cheese' in the best sentence can go out on a date with me." So the Doberman says, "I love liver and cheese." The Poodle says, "That's not good enough!" The Bulldog says, "I hate liver and cheese." She says, "That's not good enough either!"
Finally, the Chihuahua says, "Liver alone... cheese mine!"

How do you stop an elephant from going through the eye of a needle?
Tie a knot in its tail!

Why did the ram run over the cliff?
He didn't see the ewe turn!

What's the loudest pet you can have?
A trumpet!

The Escaped Gorilla

A gorilla escapes from the zoo and after three weeks, the zoo keepers give up looking for him. Some time later, a man calls the zoo complaining of a gorilla in a tree in his back yard. The zoo keeper rushes right over. When he arrives, he has a net, a baseball bat, a shotgun, and a huge dog. The man asks what the items are for. He's told, "I'm gonna climb the tree and hit the gorilla in the head with the baseball bat. When he falls out of the tree, you throw the net over him. The dog will go straight for his bum and bite it really hard." The man asks, "But what's the shotgun for?" The zoo keeper answers, "If I miss the gorilla and fall out of the tree, you shoot the dog..."

What goes dot-dot-dash-dash-squeak?
Mouse code!

A guy went into a police station and put a dead cat on the counter. "Somebody threw this into my front garden!" he complained. "Alright, sir," said the officer.
"Come back in six months and if no-one's claimed it, it's yours!"

What did the giant canary say?
TWEET!

What do greedy fish eat?
Everyfin!

What has six legs and flies?
An airline pilot with a cat!

What does a cat go to sleep on?
A caterpillar!

Why was night cricket invented?
Because bats like to sleep in the daytime!

Why did the turkey cross the road?
It was the chicken's day off!

The Jungle Violinist

A famous violinist is canoeing up a river in Africa when he hits a rock and is forced to swim for shore. Soon he is surrounded by 40 hungry, snarling jungle beasts, from tigers and hyenas to huge man-eating snakes. The animals advance towards the musician, drooling. Thinking quickly, he whips out his violin and begins to play.
Sure enough, the animals are so bewitched by the music that they stop snarling and sit down to listen.
Presently an old crocodile emerges from the river, shuffles straight up to the violinist and eats him.

"Hey!" said a lion, "What are you doing? We were enjoying that!"
"PARDON?!" says the crocodile...

A woman is thinking about buying a mink coat. "Will it be all right in the rain?" she asked the shop assistant.
"Have you ever seen a mink with an umbrella?" he said.

Two sheep meet on a country lane. The first one says, "Baa!" The second one says, "Woof!" "What are you up to? Sheep don't go 'Woof'." said the first sheep.
"I'm sorry," said the second, "I'm new round here."

Why did the antelope?
Nobody gnu!

Why did the pelican refuse to pay for his meal?
His bill was too big!

What always goes to bed with shoes on?
A horse!

Tony, who lives in the city, asks a farmer: "Why doesn't this cow have any horns?"
Farmer: "There are many reasons: some cows are born without horns, some cows shed their horns, some cows have their horns taken out. But as for this cow here, the reason is simple. It's a horse."

What do you get if you cross a road with a safari park?
Double yellow lions!

A girl finds a frog in the woods. "Excuse me, young lady," says the frog, "I'm not really a frog, I'm a Prince! Kiss me and you will return me to my real form!"
"No thanks," said the girl.
"Princes are two a penny, but a talking frog? I'm going to make a packet!"

How do lobsters travel around?
Taxi crab!

How do you teach a dog to fetch?
Tie a cat to a stick!

What did the triceratops wear on its legs?
Tricerabottoms!

Why did the Tyrannosaurus stand in the corner?
Because he'd been naughty!

What lies on the ground 100 feet up in the air?
A dead caterpillar!

A bloke goes into a pub with a giraffe, they both get drunk and the giraffe collapses in a heap on the floor. The bloke goes to leave and the barman says, "Hey! You can't leave that lying on the floor!"
The bloke says:
"It's not a lion, it's a giraffe."

A Tasmanian wide-mouthed frog

This joke requires the teller to make two special faces!

The toad's speaking face.

The punch-line face.

Once, a Tasmanian wide-mouthed frog decided to leave Tasmania and see the world. After a long journey over land and sea, he found himself in Africa...

continued overleaf

Everything was new and exciting to him, and he was full of questions. He met a giraffe and said, "Wow! You're so tall, what are you?" "I'm a giraffe," said the giraffe. "Hello! I'm a Tasmanian wide-mouthed frog! What do giraffes eat?" said the Tasmanian wide-mouthed frog. "Oh, I eat leaves and fruit, mainly," said the giraffe. The frog said goodbye and hopped off. Next he came across a zebra. "Wow!" he said. "A stripey horse!" "No. I'm a zebra," said the zebra. "Hello! I'm a Tasmanian wide-mouthed frog! What do zebras eat?" said the Tasmanian wide-mouthed frog. "Oh, I eat grass, mainly," said the zebra. The frog said goodbye and hopped off. Soon, he came upon a great, big lion. "Wow!" said the Tasmanian wide-mouthed frog. "What are you?!" "I'm a lion," said the lion.

"Wow!" said the frog. "And what do lions eat?" The lion looked him right in the eye. "We eat Tasmanian wide-mouthed frogs," said the lion. "Oh..," said the frog,

"I don't suppose you get many of those round here, do you?"

Two guys are out hiking. All of a sudden, a bear starts chasing them. They climb a tree, but the bear starts climbing up the tree after them. The first guy gets his trainers out of his knapsack and starts putting them on. The second guy says, "What are you doing?" He says: "I figure when the bear gets close to us, we'll jump down and make a run for it." The second guy says: "Are you crazy? You can't run faster than a bear!" The first guy says: "I don't have to run faster than the bear. I only have to run faster than you!"

Baby skunk: Can I have a chemistry set for my birthday?
Mummy Skunk: No.
Baby Skunk: Why not?
Mummy Skunk: Because I don't want you stinking the house out!

What's grey, yellow, grey, yellow, grey, yellow, grey, yellow, grey, yellow, grey, yellow?
An elephant rolling down a hill with a daisy in its mouth.

What do you call it when a frog takes a shower?
Spring cleaning!

A horse, a monkey, a vicar, an Englishman, an Irishman, a Scotsman, a Rabbi, a hamster, a clown and a blonde all walk into a bar together.
The barman turns to them and says:
"Is this some kind of a joke?"

A naughty young chick is being told off by his angry Mum.
"If your father could see you now," said Mother Hen, "he'd turn over in his gravy!"

A fireman is working on the engine outside the station when he notices a little girl next door in a little red wagon with little ladders hung off the side and a garden hose tightly coiled in the middle. The girl is wearing a fireman's helmet and has the wagon tied to a dog and cat. The fireman walks over to take a closer look. "That's a nice fire engine," the fireman says with admiration. "Thanks," the girl says. The fireman looks a little closer and notices the girl has tied the wagon to the dog's collar and to the cat's tail. "Excuse me, Miss," the fire fighter says, "I don't want to tell you how to run your fire engine, but if you were to tie that rope around the cat's collar, I think you could go faster." The little girl replied, "You're probably right, but then I wouldn't have a siren."

What kind of ties do pigs wear?

Pig stys!

A man goes into a pet shop and tells the owner that he wants to buy a pet that can do everything. The shop owner suggests a faithful dog. The man replies, "Come on, a dog?" The owner says, "How about a cat?" The man replies, "No way! A cat certainly can't do everything. I want a pet that can do everything!" The shop owner thinks for a minute, then says, "I've got it! A centipede!" The man says, "A centipede? I can't imagine a centipede doing everything, but okay... I'll try a centipede." He gets the centipede home and says to the centipede, "Clean the kitchen." Thirty minutes later, he walks into the kitchen and... it's immaculate! All the dishes have been washed, dried, and put away; the counter-tops cleaned; the appliances sparkling; the floor waxed. He's amazed. He says to the centipede, "Clean the living room."

Twenty minutes later, he walks into the living room. The carpet has been vacuumed; the furniture cleaned and dusted; the pillows on the sofa plumped; the plants watered.

The man thinks to himself, "This is the most amazing thing I've ever seen. This really is a pet that can do everything!" Next he says to the centipede, "Run down to the corner and get me a newspaper." The centipede walks out the door. Ten minutes later... no centipede. Twenty minutes later... no centipede. Thirty minutes later... no centipede. By this point the man is wondering what's going on. The centipede should have been back in a couple of minutes. Forty-five minutes later... still no centipede! So he goes to the front door, opens it ... and there's the centipede sitting right outside. The man says, "Hey! I sent you down to the corner shop 45 minutes ago to get me a newspaper. What's the matter?!"

The centipede says, "I'm goin'! I'm goin'! I'm just puttin' on my shoes!"

What would you get if Batman and Robin were run over by a herd of stampeding elephants?
Flatman and Ribbon!

What does it mean when the Easter Bunny arrives one day late with melted chocolate?
He probably had a bad hare day.

Why do hens lay eggs?
If they dropped them, they'd break!

A leopard went to see an optician because he thought he needed an eye exam. "Every time I look at my wife," he worriedly told the optician, **"I see spots before my eyes."** **"So what's to worry about?" replied the doctor. "You're a leopard, aren't you?"** "What's that got to do with anything?" replied the patient. "My wife is a zebra!"

**Two fish were in a tank.
One says to the other,**
"So, how do you drive this thing?"

It's a sunny morning in the Big Forest and the Bear family are just waking up. Baby Bear goes downstairs and sits in his small chair at the table. He looks into his small bowl. It is empty! "Who's been eating my porridge?!" he squeaks. Daddy Bear arrives at the table and sits in his big chair. He looks into his big bowl. It is also empty! "Who's been eating my porridge?!" he roars. Mummy Bear puts her head through the serving hatch from the kitchen and screams,

"For Pete's sake, how many times do we have to go through this? I haven't made the stupid porridge yet!"

How does a rabbit make gold soup?
He begins with 24 carrots.

What did the frog order at McDonald's?
French flies and a diet Croak!

A mother and baby camel are talking one day when the baby camel asks, "Mum, why have I got these huge three-toed feet?" The mother replies, "Well son, when we trek across the desert your toes will help you to stay on top of the soft sand." "OK," said the son. A few minutes later the son asks, "Mum, why have I got these great long eyelashes?" "They are there to keep the sand out of your eyes on the trips through the desert." "I see," replies the son. After a short while, the son returns and asks, "Mum, why have I got these great big humps on my back?" The mother, now a little impatient with the boy replies, "They are there to help us store water for our long treks across the desert, so we can survive without eating and drinking for long periods of time!" "That's great, Mum, so we have huge feet to stop us sinking, and long eyelashes to keep the sand from our eyes and these humps to store water, but Mum..." "What now!?"

"Why are we in London Zoo?"

How does a frog feel when he has a broken leg?
Very unhoppy!

How do you hide an elephant in a box of Smarties?
Paint his toenails all different colours!

**Hank heard a shot, followed by howling and another shot.
He ran next door and found his friend Tony crying.
"Say, what's wrong?" Hank asked.
Tony sobbed, "I had to shoot my dog."
Hank said, "My God! Was he mad?"**
Tony replied,
"Well, he wasn't too happy about it."

A country dog, coming to the city and seeing his first parking meter, thinks,
"How do you like that? Pay toilets!"

What did the duck say when he'd finished shopping?

Put it on my bill please!

How do you keep an elephant from stampeding?
Take his stampeder away!

One night, two vampire bats were hanging upside down in a cave. One says, "Hey, you wanna go and get some blood?" and the other bat says, "Where are we going to get blood at two in the morning?"
So the other bat says, "You don't want to go? Fine, I'll go by myself!"
And off he flapped. About 30 minutes later, the first bat came back with fresh blood dripping out of his mouth and all over his body.
The second bat says,
"Hey, where did you get all that blood?"
The first bat says,
"See that tree over there?"
"Yeah," says the second bat..
"Well I didn't," said the first bat.

PART TWO
SCHOOL JOKES

Teacher: Tommy, put some more water in the fish tank...
Pupil: Why, Miss? I put some in only yesterday and he hasn't drunk that yet!

Billy: Do you think it's right to punish people for things they haven't done?
Teacher: No, Billy, of course not.
Billy: Good. I haven't done my homework!

Mum, I got 100 in an arithmetic test and still didn't pass!
Why not, for goodness sake?
Because the answer was 200!

Our teacher talks to herself. Does yours?
Yes, but she doesn't realise it, she thinks we're actually listening!

Teacher: You missed school yesterday didn't you?
Pupil: Not very much, no!

Mother: How was school today?
Lisa: OK, but our teacher doesn't really know what she's doing.
Mother: What makes you think that?
Lisa: Well, today she told us that four and four makes eight.
Mother: That's right!
Lisa: But yesterday she said that six and two makes eight!

Teacher: What are the small rivers that run into the Nile?
Pupil: The juve-niles!

Jono: My grandad is still living at 103.
Teacher: Amazing, 103 years old!
Jono: No, 103 Station Road!

Teacher: If you add 3452 and 3096, then divide the answer by 4 and multiply by 6, what would you get?
Tony: The wrong answer!

What's purple and ruled the world?
Alexander the Grape!

"Bobby, I have read your essay about your house," said the teacher, **"and it's word for word exactly the same as your brother's from last year!"**
"Of course it is," says Bobby.
"It's exactly the same house!"

Why did the student eat his homework?
The teacher told him it was a piece of cake!

Why did the germ cross the microscope?
To get to the other slide!

Pupil: If a person's brain stops working, does he die?
Teacher: You're alive, aren't you?

How can you tell a Geomet Tree?
It has square roots!

When does five and five make eleven?
When you're stupid!

Teacher: What are you writing?
Pupil: A letter to myself.
Teacher: What does it say?
Pupil: I don't know. I won't get it till tomorrow.

Why isn't whispering permitted in class?
Because it's not aloud!

Teacher: Why do they say the pen is mightier than the sword?
Pupil: Because no one's invented a ballpoint sword yet!

Teacher: Dorothy, what did you write your report on?
Dorothy: A piece of paper!

Mother: How was your first day at school?
Son: It was all right except for some man called "Teacher" who kept spoiling all our fun!

What are you going to be when you get out of school?
An old man!

Pupil: My teacher was mad with me because I didn't know where the Lake District was.
Mother: Well, next time, remember where you put things!

Jack: I'm not going back to school ever again.
Jim: Why ever not?
Jack: The teacher doesn't know a thing, all she does is ask questions!

Fred came home from his first day at school. "Nothing exciting happened," **he told his mother,**
"except the teacher didn't know how to spell 'cat', so I had to tell her."

I'm really glad you called me Fred, Dad.
Why is that?
Because when I got to school that's what everybody else called me!

Teacher: If you had five apples on your desk and the boy next to you took three what would you have?

Pupil: A fight!

Dad, can you help me find the lowest common denominator in this problem please?
Don't tell me that they haven't found it yet: I remember looking for it when I was a boy!

The teacher was doing counting with her first year class. "Jackie," she asked, "can you count to 10 without mistakes?" "Yes," said Jackie, and she did. "Now, Fred," said the teacher, "can you count from 10 to 20?"
"That depends," said Fred, "with or without mistakes?"

Teacher: The word 'politics' - can you give me an example of how to use it?
Pupil: My parrot swallowed a watch and now Polly ticks!

My teacher reminds me of history.
She's always repeating herself!

A nursery school teacher was observing her classroom of children while they drew pictures. She would occasionally walk around to see each child's artwork. As she got to one little girl who was working quietly, she asked what the drawing was of. The girl replied, "I'm drawing God." The teacher paused and said, "But no one knows what God looks like." Without looking up from her drawing the girl replied,
"They will in a minute."

Teacher: Class, we will have only half a day of school this morning.
Class: Hooray!
Teacher: We will have the other half this afternoon!

Pupil (on phone): My son has a bad cold and won't be able to come to school today.
School Secretary: Who is this?
Pupil: This is my father speaking!

Teacher: Why were you late?
Henry: Sorry, Miss, I overslept.
Teacher: You mean you sleep at home too?

**Teacher: That's quite a cough you have
there, what are you taking for it?**
Jules: I don't know Miss.
What do you think it's worth?

Father: How do you like going to school?
Son: The going bit is fine, and the
coming home bit too, but I'm not too
keen on the time in between!

**Teacher : Fred, your ideas are
like diamonds.**
Fred: You mean they're so valuable?
Teacher: No, I mean they're so rare!

Teacher: "You're pretty dirty, Helen."
Helen: "You should see me when
I'm clean. I'm even prettier!"

**Teacher:
When do
astronauts eat?**
Pupil: At launch time!

The Spanish explorers went round the world in a galleon.
Really? How many galleons did they get to the mile?

What did King Henry V say when he got on his horse at the battle of Agincourt?
Giddy up!

Teacher: What is migration?
Tim: A headache birds get when they fly south for the winter!

Why aren't you doing very well in history?
Because the teacher keeps asking about things that happened before I was born!

Dad: How did you do in your tests?
Son: I did what Winston Churchill did.
Dad: What was that?
Son: I went down in history!

"Is ink very expensive, Dad?"
"No, son, what makes you ask that?"
"Well, I spilt some on the Headmaster's carpet, and he went bananas!"

Teacher: Is Lapland heavily populated?
Class: No, there are not many Lapps to the mile!

The mathematics teacher saw that Johnny wasn't paying attention in class.
She called on him and said,
"Johnny! what are 6, 9, 28 and 44?"
Johnny quickly replied:
"Sky One, The Disney Channel, Granada Breeze and Cartoon Network!"

Dean: I didn't do my homework because I lost my memory.
Teacher: Goodness! When did this start?
Dean: When did what start?

Teacher: What are you reading?
Pupil: I dunno!
Teacher: But you're reading aloud!
Pupil: But I'm not listening!

Fred: I've added these figures ten times.
Teacher: Good work!
Fred: And here are my ten answers!

Father: What did you learn in school today?
Son: That three and three are seven.
Father: Three and three are six!
Son: In that case I didn't learn anything today!

Teacher: Why was George Washington buried at Mount Vernon?
Pupil: Because he was dead!

Teacher: What comes before 7?
Frank: The postman?

Teacher: Why do animals have fur coats?
Caroline: Because they would look stupid in denim jackets?

Teacher: Name three famous poles?
Mary: North, south and tad!

Father: I hear you skipped school to play football.
Son: No I didn't, and I have the fish to prove it!

Teacher: I'd like to go through one whole day without having to tell you off.
Pupil: You have my permission!

Teacher: Julie, take 932 from 1,439. What is the difference?
Julie: That's what I say, what's the difference?

Teacher: Why are you the only one in class today?
Pupil: Because I missed school dinner yesterday?

**Why does your geography exam
have a big zero over it?**
It's not a zero, the teacher ran out of stars,
so she gave me a moon instead!

**If I had five coconuts and I gave you
three, how many would I have left?**
I don't know.
Why not?
In our school we do all our
arithmetic in apples and oranges!

What did you learn in school today?
Not enough, they want me to go
back tomorrow!

**Teacher: If I lay one egg here and
another there, how many eggs will there be?**
Fred: None!
Teacher (surprised): Why not?
Fred: I don't think you can lay eggs!

Teacher: What is an island?
Kev: A piece of land surrounded by
water except on one side.
Teacher: On one side?
Kev: Yes, the topside!

"It's perfectly clear," said the teacher,
"that you haven't studied your
geography. What's your excuse?"
"Well, my dad says the world is
changing every day. So I decided
to wait until it settles down!"

Teacher: I said to draw a cow eating
some grass but you've only
drawn the cow?
Pupil: Yes, the cow ate it all!

Mother: Does your teacher like you?
Son: Like me, she loves me! Look at all
those X's she put on my homework!

Teacher: If I had seven apples in one hand and eight apples in the other, what would I have?
Student: Massive hands!

Teacher: What can you tell me about the Dead Sea?
Pupil: Dead? I didn't even know it was sick!

Teacher: What birds are found in Portugal?
Pupil: Portu-geese!

What animal is best at mathematics?
Rabbits, they multiply the quickest!

"Our teacher has a bad memory. For three days she asked us how much is two and two. We told her it was four. But she still hasn't got it.
Today she asked us again!"

Name an animal that lives in Lapland -
A reindeer.
Good, now name another.
Another reindeer!

Teacher: What's 2 and 2?
Pupil: 4
Teacher: That's good.
Pupil: Good? That's perfect!

The class had settled down to its colouring books. Stevie came up to the teacher's desk and said, "Miss Brownin', I ain't got no crayons." "Stevie," Miss Browning said, "you mean, 'I don't have any crayons. You don't have any crayons. We don't have any crayons. They don't have any crayons.' Do you see what I'm getting at?"
"You're jokin'!" Stevie said, "Who's 'ad all the crayons?"

Teacher: How can you prove the world is round?
Pupil: I didn't say it was!

Do you ever get straight A's?
No, but I sometimes get dodgy B's!

Teacher: This note from your father looks like your handwriting.
Pupil: Well, yes, he borrowed my pen!

Teacher: Would you at the back of the room stop passing notes?
Pupil: We're not passing notes. We're playing poker!

Are you in the top half of your class?
No, I'm one of the students who make the top half possible!

Elena's teacher was quizzing them on the alphabet. "Elena," she says, "what comes after 'O'?"
Elena says, "Yeah!"

Teacher: Spell "bet".
Ronan: B-e-t-t.
Teacher: Leave one of the t's.
Ronan: Which one?

What computer comes with the best chips?
A big Mac!

Jeff: My Gran knitted me three socks for my birthday...
Belinda: Why three socks?
Jeff: Because I wrote to her that I'd grown another foot!

Police arrested two children, one for drinking battery acid and the other one for eating fireworks.
They charged one and let the other one off!

What happens to a hamburger that misses a lot of school?
He has a lot of ketchup time!

What do elves do after school?
Gnomework!

Teacher: What's the biggest thing ever made from fruit?
Jill: The grape wall of China!

What was Camelot?
It's the place where people
used to park their camels!

Grandad: When I was your age, I could name all the kings and queens of England...
Grandson: Yes, but there hadn't been so many of them then!

Why were the teacher's eyes crossed?
She couldn't control her pupils!

Why don't cannibals like mathematics?
Because when you add four and four you get ate!

Dad: Come on, son, finish your homework, a little hard work never killed anyone...
Son: Well, I don't want to be the first!

Teacher: What family does the Antelope belong to?
Dawn: I don't know, nobody in our street's got one!

What would happen if you took the school bus home?
The police would make you bring it back!

Teacher: Simon, can you spell your name backwards?
Simon: No Mis!
Teacher: Tony, can you spell your name backwards?
Tony: Yes, Y not!

One day, Ella says to her Mum, "I've been banned from cooking classes." Mum asks why. "Because I burnt something."
"And what did you burn?" said Mum.
"The school."

What did the pencil say to the rubber?
Take me to your ruler!

Why do people go to night school?
So they can learn to read in the dark!

One day during cooking class, the teacher, Mrs. Jones, was telling the class her secrets for making perfect sauces. When she ordered them to the cookers to start cooking, she said, "And don't forget to use wooden spoons." As Donna stirred her sauce, she thought about the physics behind the mystery of the wooden spoon and decided it must have something to do with heat conduction. She approached Mrs. Jones to test her theory. "Why do we use wooden spoons, Miss?" she asked. "Because," she replied, "if I had to sit here listening to all your metal spoons banging against the metal pots all afternoon, I'd go mental."

Teacher: What did Julius Caesar say to Brutus when Brutus stabbed him?
Emma: Ow!

Teacher: Name four members of the cat family.

Pupil: Daddy cat, mummy cat and two kittens!

Teacher: If I bought a hundred currant buns for a pound, what would each bun be?
Pupil: Stale!

Son: I'm not going back to school tomorrow!
Father: Why not?
Son: Well, I've been there a whole day, I can't read, I can't write and they won't let me talk, so what's the point?

Mother: How do you like your new teacher?
Son: I don't. She told me to sit up the front for the present and then she didn't give me one!

Mother: What was the first thing you learned in class?
Daughter: How to talk without moving my lips!

One day a college professor of Psychology was greeting his new college class. He stood up in front of the class and said, "Would everyone who thinks hc or she is stupid please stand up?" After a minute or so of silence, a young man stood up. "Well, hello there. So you actually think you're an idiot?" the professor asked. The kid replied, "No sir, I just didn't want to see you standing there all by yourself."

Teacher: Where are you from, Pascal?
Pascal: I am from France, Miss.
Teacher: That's nice, which part exactly?
Pascal: All of me is from France.

Teacher: What's Fred's other name?
Jack: Fred who?

Teacher: If I cut two oranges into seven pieces, what have I got?
Francine: Sticky fingers!

Teacher: In 1940, what were the Poles doing in Russia?
Pupil: Holding up the telephone wires!

**Lee comes home from school one day with a huge black eye.
His Mum is suitably annoyed.
"Not again!" she says.
"How many times have I got to tell you, if you think you're going to lose your temper, stop and count to ten before you get into some silly fight!"
"I did!" said Lee.**
"But Jack Thomson's Mum told him to count only to five…"

Teacher: Why did Stone Age man draw cave pictures of rhinoceroses and hippopotamuses?
Tony: Because he didn't know how to spell them!

Mother: Son, what do you think of your new teacher?
Son: He's okay, but a bit strict.
Mother: What do you mean strict?
Son: Well, he thinks that words can be spelt only one way!

Teacher: How can you make so many mistakes in just one day?
Pupil: I get up early!

Teacher: What time do you wake up in the morning?
Pupil: About an hour and a half after I get to school!

Father: Well, Son, how are your exam results?
Son: They're under water.
Father: What do you mean?
Son: Below "C" level!

Son: Dad, can you write with your eyes shut?
Dad: Course I can.
Son: Good. Can you sign my report card?

Teacher: Why are you so late?
Tony: Well, I was obeying the sign that says 'School Ahead, Go Slow'.

Bobby: The brain is a wonderful thing.
Sam: Why do you say that?
Bobby: Because it starts working the second you get up in the morning and never stops until you get asked a question in class!

Playing truant from school is like a credit card:
Fun now, pay later!

Teacher: Be sure that you go straight home.
Will: I can't, I live round the corner!

Dinner Lady: What's the matter with your lunch?
Pupil: Can you tell me what it is in case I need to tell my doctor later what I've eaten?

Little Cannibal: I hate my teacher.
Mother Cannibal: Well just eat your salad up then, dear!

Mother: Why did you just swallow the money I gave you?
Son: Well you did say it was for my lunch!

What tables don't you have to learn?
Dinner tables!

Teacher: Can anyone tell me what sort of animal a slug is?
Pupil: It's a snail with a housing problem!

What did the zero say to the eight?
Nice belt!

Why did the cyclops stop teaching?
It had only one pupil!

A group of school students were on a field trip to the local police station. Several of the children were fascinated by the "Wanted" posters on the wall. Little Billy raised his hand and asked the policeman giving them the tour who the people on the wall were.
"Those are pictures of criminals we are looking for," answered the policeman. "We call those 'Wanted' posters."
Little Billy looked puzzled.
His hand went back up into the air.
"Why didn't you just keep hold of them when you took their picture?"

What fur do we get from a tiger?
As fur as possible!

Teacher: Give me three reasons why the world is round.
Pupil: Well my dad says so, my mum says so, and you say so!

Teacher: Are you good at mathematics?
Pupil: Yes and no.
Teacher: What do you mean?
Pupil: Yes, I'm no good at mathematics!

Jason: I got 100% in school today.
Mother: Wonderful. What did you get 100 in?
Jason: Two things: I got 50% in Spelling
and 50% in History!

What kind of pliers do you use in arithmetic?
Multipliers!

Teacher: If you had one pound and you asked your father for another, how many pounds would you have?
Jake: One pound.
Teacher: You don't know your arithmetic.
Jake: You don't know my Dad!

Teacher: Sam, what's an autobiography?
Sam: The story of a car, of course!

Teacher: What shape is the planet we live in?
Pupil: Terrible!

Teacher: When you yawn, you're supposed to put your hand to your mouth!
Pupil: What, and get bitten?!

Mother: What did you learn in school today?
Son: How to write.
Mother: Great! What did you write?
Son: I don't know, they haven't taught us how to read yet!

When I was your age I thought nothing of walking 5 miles to school.
I agree, I don't think much of it myself!

What do we do with crude oil?
Teach it some manners!

My dog is great at mathematics.
Really?
Ask him how much is two minus two...
But two minus two is nothing!
That's what he'll say, nothing!

My Geography Teacher is so Stupid he Thinks...

...the English Channel is on satellite TV

...Ben Nevis has a brother named Bill

...New York is 5 hours behind London because London was discovered first

...the Cheddar Gorge is a big cheese sandwich

...the language in Cuba is cubic

...birds fly South for the winter because they can't afford the train fare

...a volcano is a mountain with hiccups

...Germany is where germs come from

...A fjord is a Norwegian car

...The Rocky Mountains are named after Sylvester Stallone

Dinner Lady: Eat up your greens, they are good for your skin.
Pupil: But I don't want green skin!

I failed every subject except for algebra. How did you keep from failing that?
I didn't take algebra!

Teacher: If 1+1=2 and 2+2=4, what is 4+4?
Pupil: That's not fair! You answered the easy ones and leave us with the hard one!

Finding one of her students making faces at others in the playground, Mrs. Smith stopped to gently correct the girl. Smiling sweetly, the teacher said, "When I was a child, I was told if I made ugly faces I would stay like that." The girl looked up and replied,
"Well you can't say you weren't warned!"

Where is the best place to have the sickroom at school?
Next to the canteen!

How did the dinner lady get an electric shock?
She stepped on a bun and a current went up her leg!

What's a mushroom?
The place they store the school food!

Teacher: Can you count to 10?
Billy: Yes, Miss. One, two, three, four, five, six, seven, eight, nine, ten.
Teacher: Good. Now can you count any higher?
Billy: Sure. Do you want me to stand on a chair?

Teacher: Do you file your nails Billy?
Billy: No, I just throw them away!

Pupil: I thought we got a choice for dinner, but there is only burnt sausages and soggy chips!
Dinner Lady: That's the choice, take it or leave it!

"Darling," said Mrs Beldon, "Tim's teacher says he ought to have an encyclopedia."
"Encyclopedia, my eye!" said Mr Beldon.
"He can walk to school like I had to!"

Teacher: Can you count to 10?
Brooklyn: Yes, Miss. One, two, three, four, five, six, seven, eight, nine, ten.
Teacher: Now go on from there...
Brooklyn: Jack, Queen, King...

Teacher: I told you to stand at the end of the queue.
Pupil: I tried, but there was someone already there!

Why don't you see giraffes in college?
Because they're all in High School!

Teacher: Why does the Statue of Liberty stand in New York harbour?
Pupil: Because it can't sit down!

Pupil: I don't like cheese with holes.
Dinner Lady: Well, just eat the cheese and leave the holes on the side of your plate!

Early one morning, a Mum went in to wake up her son. "Get up, it's time to go to school!" "But why, Mum? I don't want to go!" "Give me two reasons why you don't want to go." "Well, the kids hate me for one, and the teachers hate me, too!" "Oh, that's no reason not to go to school. Come on now and get ready." "Give me two reasons why I should go to school." "Well, for one, you're 52 years old. And for another, you're the Headmaster!"

Teacher: Where was the Queen crowned?
Gary: On her head?

Pupil: I don't think I deserved the 0% you gave me for that test.
Teacher: Neither do I, but it's the lowest I could give!

Teacher: Daniela, would you rather have ten ice creams, or six times three ice creams?
Daniela: Ten.
Teacher: No, six times three is eighteen!
Daniela: I know, I don't like ice cream.

It's important to wear glasses during mathematics because it improves de-vision...

Teacher: Are you chewing gum?
Anthony: No, I'm Anthony Johnstone, Miss!

Teacher: You're talking again, James! Do you think you are the teacher of this class?
James: No, Miss.
Teacher: Then stop behaving like a idiot!

A sixth grade class is doing some spelling drills. The teacher asks Tommy if he can spell 'before'. He stands up and says, "B-E-P-H-O-R."
The teacher says, "No, that's wrong. Can anyone else spell 'before'?" Another little boy stands up and says, "B-E-F-O-O-R." Again the teacher says, "No, that's wrong." The teacher asks, "Jethro, can you spell 'before'?" Jethro stands up and says, "B-E-F-O-R-E." "Excellent Jethro, now can you use it in a sentence?"
Jethro says, "That's easy. Two plus two be fore..."

Teacher: How much is half of 8?
Pupil: Up and down or across?
Teacher: What do you mean?
Pupil: Well, up and down makes a 3 or across the middle leaves a 0!

Pupil: Do hams grow on plants?
Teacher: No, it's a meat.
Pupil: So what's an ambush?

Mother: What courses are you taking again, Penelope?
Penelope: Algebra and French.
Mother: How do you say "Hello" in Algebra?

Teacher: How did they divide the Roman Empire?
Sarah: With a pair of Caesars!

Teacher: If you got £10 from 20 people, what would you have?
Mikey: A Playstation!

Biology Teacher: What do we call the outermost layer of a tree?
Ryan: Don't know, Miss!
Biology Teacher: Bark, you idiot!
Ryan: Woof, woof!

Teacher: I wish you would pay a little attention!
Pupil: I'm paying as little as I can!

Julie: What's that mark on your shoulder, Miss?
Teacher: It's a birth mark, Julie.
Julie: Oh, have you had it long?

A teacher asked one of the boys in her class, "Can people predict the future with cards?" The boy said, "My Mum can." The teacher replied, "Really?"
The boy said, "Yes, she takes one look at my report card and tells me what will happen when my Dad gets home!"

Pupil: Is it true that people from Hong Kong are really thick?
Teacher: Why do you say that?
Pupil: My book says they have the densest population!

Mother: How did you find school today?
Daughter: I just got off the bus and there it was!

Where did the pilgrims land when they came to America?
On their feet!

Why does history keep repeating itself?
Because we weren't listening the first time!

Who succeeded the first President of the USA?
The second one!

What did Noah do while spending time on the Ark?
Fished, but he didn't catch much. He had only two worms!

Did you hear about the kid that was named after his father?
They called him Dad!

What do you do to a troublesome chick?
Eggspell him!

Who invented fractions?
Henry the Eighth!

What was the first thing Queen Elizabeth did on reaching the throne?
She sat down!

Teacher: When was Rome built?
Pupil: At night.
Teacher: Why did you say that?
Pupil: Because my Dad always says that Rome wasn't built in a day!

Why were the early days of history called the dark ages?
Because there were so many knights!

When a knight in armour was killed in battle, what sign did they put on his grave?
Rust in peace!

What was Camelot famous for?
The knight life!

Tony: I got an "A" in spelling, Dad!
Dad: You idiot! There's no "A" in "spelling"!

What did the Sheriff of Nottingham say when Robin fired at him?
That was an arrow escape!

Who can tell me where Hadrian's Wall is?
I expect it's around Hadrian's garden!

Teacher: Why are you picking your nose in class?
Pupil: My mothcr won't let me do it at home!

Teacher: Does anyone know who broke the sound barrier?
Pupil: I never touched it!

Teacher: How would the world be different if Edison hadn't invented the light bulb?
Bobby: We'd all be playing Nintendo by candlelight!

Aliens Ate My Homework
and some other brilliant excuses...

Some aliens from outer space ate it

I lost it fighting this kid who
said you weren't the best
teacher in the school

My pet gerbil's had babies,
and they used it to make a nest

Some other aliens from outer space
borrowed it so they could study
how the human brain worked

I put it in a safe,
but lost the combination

I left it in my shirt and my mother
put it in the washing machine

I didn't do it because I didn't want to add to your already heavy workload

A sudden gust of wind blew it out of my hand and I never saw it again

Teacher: You seem very well read: have you read Shakespeare?
Pupil: No.
Teacher: What have you read, then?
Pupil: Um... I've red hair!

Mum: "Did you enjoy the school outing?"
Donna: "Yes, and we're going back tomorrow."
Mum: "What for?"
Donna: "To look for the children who got left behind."

Ron: What's the weather whas-name thingy like around Mount Everest, Sir?
Teacher: Climate, Ron.
Ron: "Blimey, I don't want to know that badly!"

Teacher: Jenny, why are you late?
Jenny: There are eight of us in my family and the alarm was only set for seven!

The class was on a field study trip to the countryside. "That's a nice cow," said Julia. "That's a Jersey," said the teacher. "Oh," said Julie, "I thought that was its skin!"

Teacher: If this class doesn't stop making so much noise, I'll go crazy!
Pupil: I think it's too late. We haven't made a sound for an hour!

Pupil: This egg is bad.
Dinner Lady: Don't blame me, I only laid the table!

Teacher: Lee, I hope I didn't see you copying from David's work!
Lee: So do I!

Well, here's my report, Dad.
Well, there is one thing in your favour, son. With grades like this, you can't be cheating!

Teacher: What is the plural of mouse?
Pupil: Mice.
Teacher: Good, now what's the plural of baby?
Pupil: Twins!

Father: You've got 4 F's and a D on your report!
Son: Maybe I concentrated too much on the one subject...

Teacher: Can't you keep anything in your head for longer than five minutes?
Pupil: Of course, I've had this cold in my head for nearly a week!

Teacher: Jane, why do you have such a problem with decimals?
Jane: I just can't see the point, Miss!

"An abstract noun," the teacher said, "is something you can think of, but you can't touch it. Can you give me an example of one?"
"Yes," a teenage boy replied.
"My Dad's new car."

Teacher: You're new here aren't you?
What's your name?
Pupil: Dicky Mickey Smith.
Teacher: I'll call you Dicky Smith then.
Pupil: My dad won't like that.
Teacher: Why is that?
Pupil: He doesn't like people taking the
Mickey out of my name!

Joanne was looking miserable.
She says to her teacher,
"I hate school! I can't believe I have to
stay here until I'm sixteen!"
"I know the feeling," said the teacher,
"I have to stay here till I'm sixty-five..."

Teacher: Johnny, give me a
sentence starting with "I".
Elisa: I is...
Teacher: No, Elisa. Always say, "I am."
Elisa: All right. "I am the ninth letter
of the alphabet."

Teacher: What are you doing, hopping into school ten minutes late?
Pupil: Well, you told me never to stroll into school ten minutes late!

Teacher: "If I cut a potato in two, then in two again, then once more, what do I have?"
Jack: "Chips!"

Teacher: What's the difference between an African and an Indian elephant?
Theresa: About three thousand miles!

What did the French book say to the Maths book?
Let me 'elp you wiz your problems!

George: Look, I just found a lost football.
Louis: How do you know it's lost?
George: Because the kids down the street are still looking for it!

Teacher: I see you've got your Easter shirt on, Martin.
Martin: Why do you call it that, Miss?
Teacher: Because it's got egg on it.

A lady began a job as a school counsellor, and she was eager to help. One day during break she noticed a boy standing by himself on the side of a playing field while the rest of the kids enjoyed a game of football. She approached and asked if he was alright.
The boy said he was fine, thank you.
A little while later, however, she noticed the boy was in the same spot, still by himself.
Approaching again, the lady said,
"Would you like me to be your friend?" The boy hesitated, then said, "OK," looking at the woman suspiciously. Feeling she was making progress, she then asked, "Why are you standing here all alone? Why don't you go and join those boys playing football over there?"
"Because," the little boy said,
"I'm the goalkeeper."

Teacher: Don't you cut your hair any longer?
Fred: No, sir, I cut it shorter!

Sarah: Why were you late for school?
Jan: I had to say goodbye to my pets.
Sarah: But you were 2 hours late!
Jan: I have an ant farm!

Teacher: Charles, please use "discount"
in a sentence.
Charles: Yes, ma'am.
Does discount as a sentence?

Pupils: Can we go outside and watch the
solar eclipse?
Teacher: All right, but don't stand too close!

Danny: I can't solve this problem.
Teacher: What? Any five-year-old should
be able to solve this one!
Danny: No wonder I can't do it then,
I'm nearly ten!

Teacher: What's a wombat?
Frank: Something you play Wom with?

Can you tell me where elephants are found?
You don't have to find elephants, they're so big, they never get lost!

A policeman sees a small boy in a pub drinking a pint of beer and smoking. "Hey! Why aren't you at school?" he says. "I don't have to go to school," says the kid, "I'm only four."

Teacher: Didn't you promise to behave?
Sean: Yes, sir.
Teacher: And didn't I promise to punish you if you didn't?
Sean: Yes, sir, but since I broke my promise, you didn't have to keep yours!

What is the difference between a school teacher and a train?
The teacher says 'Spit your gum out' and the train says 'chew chew chew'!

Teacher: Frank, if you had £8 in one pocket and £11 in the other, what would you have?
Frank: Someone else's trousers on!

Biology Teacher: Why do whales have waterproof skin?
Pupil: To keep their insides from falling out!

Dad, we're collecting for the new swimming pool at school.
Hang on, I'll get you a glass of water!

Cookery Teacher: Fred, there were two chocolate cakes in the stock room before break, and now there's only one. Why?
Fred: I don't know. It must have been so dark I didn't see the other one!

Do you think there should be a club for kids who like Maths?
No, you don't have to beat them, just ignore them!

Teacher: What's the capital of France, Jenny?
Jenny: F?

Teacher: Sean, if you had £2, and eggs were a 50p a dozen, how many would you buy?
Sean: "None, Miss."
Teacher: "None?"
Sean: "No, if I had £2, I'd get a Big Mac and fries!"

Billy: I failed everything except biology.
Mum: How did you keep from failing that?
Billy: I overslept!

Teacher: What did the pencil say to the rubber?
Jim: Take me to your ruler!

In what school do you learn how to greet people?
Hi school!

Teacher: Say, you can't sleep in my class.
Student: I could if you didn't talk so loud!

Dinner Lady: It's very rude to reach over the table for the salt, haven't you got a tongue in your head?

Pupil: Yes, but my arms are longer!

Billy phones his Mum one day. "Mum, I fell off the bike shed roof today and broke four ribs." "Gracious!" says his Mum. "Which hospital did they take you to?" "I didn't go to hospital," says Billy. "What? You've got four broken ribs and they didn't take you to hospital?" his Mum screams. "Oh they weren't my ribs," says Billy, "I landed on Sally Jameson!"

Tony is having an eye test at school. "Can you read the top line of letters on the chart, Tony?" said the nurse. "No," said Tony. "How about the second line, can you read that?" said the nurse. "Nope," said Tony. "Can you read the bottom line, then?" said the nurse. "No," said Tony, "I can't read at all, yet."

Teacher: Matthew, what is the climate like in New Zealand?
Matthew: Really, really cold.
Teacher: It's not that cold, actually.
Matthew: You're joking, when they send us lamb, it's frozen solid!

Teacher: What noise does a squirrel make?
Kelly: Woof Woof?
Teacher: Squirrels don't go "Woof Woof"!
Kelly: It says in this book that squirrels eat acorns and bark!

Teacher: Sara, if you had 16 chocolates, and Vernon asked you for 10, how many would you have left?
Sara: Sixteen. I hate Vernon.

Teacher: Dean, if I say "I have went," is that right or wrong?
Dean: Wrong. You ain't gone nowhere. You're still 'ere innit?

Teacher: Did you parents help you with these homework problems?
Pupil: No I got them wrong all by myself!

Why did the pioneers cross the country in covered wagons?
Because they didn't want to wait 40 years for a train!

Teacher: Can anyone tell me how many seconds there are in a year?
Pupil: Twelve, Miss - 2nd January, 2nd February, 2nd March...!

Teacher: Simon. Give me a sentence with the words defence, defeat and detail in it.
Simon: When a horse jumps over defence, defeat go before detail!

Teacher: What can we do to stop polluting our waters?
Pupil: Stop taking baths?

What kind of lighting did Noah use for the Ark?

Floodlights!

Little Johnny was having problems in school. He was always bringing home bad grades and was especially bad in reading. When receiving his report card one day he got all excited and ran home to show his father. He handed his father the report card and proudly says, "Look dad, I got a 'B' in Reading." His dad looks at the report card and gets furious. He looks down at Johnny and says, "You idiot, that's a 'D'!"

Teacher: You aren't paying attention to me. Are you having trouble hearing?
Pupil: No, I'm having trouble listening!

Teacher: Spell "Aardvark".
Student: I don't know how.
Teacher: Well, look it up in the dictionary!
Student: How can I look up a word to spell in the dictionary if I don't know how to spell the word in the first place?

Why did the teacher put the lights on?
Because the class was so dim!

Teacher: Now class, whatever I ask, I want you to all answer at once. How much is 6 plus 4?
Class: At once!

Teacher: What's happens to gold when it is exposed to the air?
Barry: Someone nicks it!

Teacher: Nicky? Didn't you hear me call you?
Nicky: Yes, but you told us not to answer back!

Teacher: Billy, please don't whistle while you're working.
Billy: Oh, I'm not working - just whistling!

Teacher: If I had ten flies on my desk and I swatted one, how many would be left?
Pupil: One - the others would have flown off!

Teacher: What does the 1286BC written on the mummy's tomb indicate?
Student: The registration of the car that ran him over!

Teacher: Does anyone know which month has 28 days?
Gary: All of them!

Sally was hungry, so she went into a baker's shop. "How much are a couple of buns?" she said. "Two for 25p," said the shopkeeper. "How much for one?" Sally asked. "One is 13p," said the shopkeeper.
Sally thought for a second.
"I'll take the other one!"

Teacher: What's your name?
Pupil: Jason.
Teacher: You should say "Sir".
Pupil: OK, Sir Jason!

Barney: My grandad was a hunter in Scotland. He used to go hunting lions! Kev: You liar! There aren't any lions in Scotland!
Barney: There aren't any now — my grandad shot them all!

Why do teachers use a bamboo cane?
Because when the cane goes "bam" the child goes "boo"!

Teacher: William, please use the word "window" in a sentence.
William: OK. I entered a competition, but I didn't "window!"

Teacher: Simon, can you give me a good example of how heat expands things and cold contracts them?
Simon: Well, I've noticed that the days tend to be longer in the summer and shorter in the winter!

How do you know carrots are good for your eyesight?
Did you ever see a rabbit wearing glasses?

Teacher: What is a comet?
Pupil: A star with a tail.
Teacher: Can you name one?
Pupil: Mickey Mouse?

Teacher: Where does your mother come from?
Pupil: Alaska!
Teacher: Don't worry, I'll ask her myself!

Teacher: What is the most common phrase used in school?
Pupil: Dunno, Miss.
Teacher: Correct!

Pupil: What's for lunch today, Rose?
Dinner Lady: The specials today are shepherd's pie and apple crumble.
Pupil: I see... Which one is this?

Teacher: What's a Grecian Urn?
Kate: About 50 Drachmas a week!

Woodwork teacher: You're just like lightning with that hammer, Tony.
Tony: Because I'm so quick, sir?
Woodwork teacher: No, because you never strike in the same place twice!

Teacher: Why do mermaids wear seashells?
Sarah: Because B shells are too small and D shells are too big!

Teacher: What's the difference between roast beef and pea soup?
Danny: Anyone can roast beef, Miss!

Billy: The new Geography teacher's got a wig made out of cat fur!
Emma: Really? How do you know?
Billy: Because every time he scratches his head, his bottom shoots up in the air!

Teacher: Why shouldn't you eat uranium?
Pupil: Because you'll get atomic ache!

Teacher: Fred, I'm glad to see your writing has improved.
Fred: Thank you.
Teacher: Unfortunately, now I can see how bad your spelling is!

Pupil: The art teacher doesn't like what I'm making...
Dad: Why is that? What are you making?
Pupil: A mess!

Teacher: Which one burns longer, a black one or a white one?
Pupil: Neither, they both burn shorter!

Teacher: Belinda. Can you find me Australia on the map please?
Belinda: There it is.
Teacher: Well done! Louise, who discovered Australia?
Louise: Belinda did!

Why did Robin Hood rob only the rich?
Because the poor didn't
have anything
worth stealing!

Teacher: Do you want to borrow a pocket calculator?
Pupil: No thanks, I know how many pockets I've got!

Teacher: Karen, stop your day dreaming!
Karen: I wasn't day dreaming, I was taking a nap!

Teacher: What is "can't" short for?
Pupil: Cannot?
Teacher: Right! And what is "don't" short for?
Pupil: Doughnut?

Art Teacher: Michele, what colour are you going to paint the sun and the wind?
Michele: The sun rose, and the wind blue!

Teacher: OK, Bill. In this exam you will be allowed 30 minutes for each question.
Bill: How long do we get for the answers?

Teacher: What is further away, Australia or the Moon?
Pupil: Australia, because you can see the Moon at night!

Tom had this problem of getting up late in the morning and was always late for school. His teacher was angry with him and threatened to expel him if he didn't do something about it. So Tom went to a doctor who gave him a pill and told him to take it before he went to bed to help him sleep. Tom slept well and in fact beat the alarm in the morning. He had breakfast and got the bus to school. He said to the teacher: "I made it, and I slept really well and I feel great!"
"That's all fine," said the teacher, "But where were you yesterday?"

Teacher: Do we all know what adding is?
Susie: It's the noise my doorbell makes!

Teacher: Mark, I told you to write this poem out 10 times to improve your handwriting and you've only done it 7 times...
Mark: That's because my maths is rubbish as well!

Teacher: This is the third time I've had to tell you off this week: what have you got to say about that?
Pupil: I'm glad it's Friday!

Teacher: Why can't you ever answer any of my questions?
Pupil: Well if I could, there wouldn't be much point in my being here!

Teacher: Why weren't you in school yesterday?
Damien: I was sick.
Teacher: Sick of what?
Damien: Sick of school!

Troy: Mum, I got sent home because the boy next to me in class was smoking!

Mum: The boy next to you? Why didn't they send him home, then?

Troy: Cos it was me that set him on fire!

Donny: How do I measure this ladder?
Teacher: Lay it on the ground and pace it out.
Donny: But I want to know how tall it is, not how long!

Teacher: Samantha, you copied these answers from Monica, didn't you?
Samantha: What makes you say that?
Teacher: Because her answer to question 5 is "I don't know," and yours is "Me neither".

Biology Teacher: Barney, what do you get hanging from Horse Chestnut trees?
Barney: Sore arms!

Teacher: Good grief, Darren. R-O-X doesn't spell rocks!
Darren: Really? What does it spell then?

Teacher : Were you copying his sums?
Pupil : No! Just seeing if he got mine right!

"What's your father's occupation?"
asked the school secretary on the
first day of the new school year.
"He's a magician, Miss," said the new boy.
"How interesting. What's his favourite trick?"
"He saws people in half."
"Gosh! Now, next question: do you have any
brothers or sisters?"
"Yes, one half brother and two half sisters."

Teacher: How many bones do we
have in our body?
Harry: I have a couple of
thousand, I should think.
Teacher: How do you make that out?
Harry: I had sardines for lunch!

Which Queen was the longest on the throne?
The one that was the tallest standing up!

Teacher 1: My, hasn't Emma Jones grown?
Teacher 2: Yes, she's certainly gruesome!

Teacher: Where were you yesterday, Daisy?
Daisy: At the dentist, Miss. I had a bad tooth.
Teacher: Oh, I'm sorry to hear that. Is it better today?
Daisy: I don't know Miss, the dentist kept it!

Teacher: Sam, why are you spinning on your head?
Sam: I like to do a good turn every day!

Do you know a teacher with one eye called Mr Hargreaves?
No, what's his other eye called?

Headmaster: Smith, come here! I'll teach you to throw stones at the school minibus!
Smith: I wish you would, Sir. I keep missing it!

What kind of food do maths teachers eat?

Square meals!

Biology Teacher: What's an indication of iron deficiency?
Fiona: Wrinkly clothes, Miss!

Why was 6 afraid of 7?
Because 789!

Jerry: I'm worried about the exams, Miss. I bumped my head and now I can't remember anything!
Teacher: When did this happen?
Jerry: When did what happen?

Why is Alabama the cleverest state in the USA?
Because it has 4 A's and one B!

Teacher: Where is the English Channel?
Sid: I don't know, we haven't got cable!

What do you measure farm vehicles with?
A protractor!

Teacher: What came after the stone age and the bronze age?

Pupil: The sausage?

What do Mallards keep their schoolbooks in?
A ducksack!

Why does the school brass band march while they play?
They're trying to get away from the noise!

Geography Teacher: How many balls of string would it take to reach the moon?
Pupil: Just one if it's long enough!

Arthur: There is definitely a connection between television and violence.
Martha: What makes you think that?
Arthur: Because I told my Mum I had watched television instead of doing my homework, and she hit me!

Teacher: Did you sister help you with your homework, David?
David: No, she did it all!

Physics Teacher: Tim, who might use microwaves?
Tim: Very small surfers?

Where do children learn their ABC's?
At LMN-tary school!

What do ghosts write their homework in?
Exorcise books!

Science Teacher: What is the centre of gravity?
Pupil: The letter V!

English Teacher: Which is the longest word you can think of?
Pupil: "Smiles", because there is a mile between each "s"!

Why did the Tyrannosaurus stand in the corner?
Because he'd been naughty!

My History Teacher is so stupid, he thinks...

...Joan of Arc was Noah's wife!

... and Noah was an Ark-itect!

...That "Gladiator" was how a cannibal felt after lunch!

... That the Romans built straight roads so their soldiers didn't go around the bend!

... That a Roman forum is two-um plus two-um!

... That a saxophone was a Saxon telephone!

... That King Arthur's round table was made by Sir Circumference!

... That the Vikings send secret messages by Norse code!

... That King Alfred the Grate invented the fireplace!

... That the Black Prince was the son of Old King Cole!

Biology Teacher: Bobby, can you give me an example of a Fungi?
Pupil: Someone with a Playstation who knows lots of dirty jokes?

A small boy went up to a teacher in the playground on his first day of school. "I've lost my brother!" he said. The teacher said, "Don't worry, we'll find him. What's he like?"
The little boy replied, "Crisps and Lego!"

Teacher: What a glum face, what would you say if I came to school with a face like yours?
Pupil: I'd be too polite to mention it!

Maths Teacher: What do you get when you divide the diameter of a pumpkin by its circumference?
Pupil: Pumpkin Pi!

Father: Why did you get such a low score in that maths test?
Son: Absence.
Father: What, you were absent on the day of the maths test?
Son: No but the boy who usually sits next to me was!

I wish I had been born 1,000 years ago. Why is that?
Just think of all the history that I wouldn't have to learn!

A boy comes into class with a carrot up his nose and a sausage in each ear. "I'm not feeling very well, Miss," he says. "I'm not surprised," says the teacher.
"You obviously aren't eating properly!"

Mother: Let me see your report, son.
Son: Here it is, Mum, but don't show it to Dad. He's been helping me!

Chemistry Teacher: What is copper nitrate?
Pupil: Overtime for policemen!

A teacher catches an older girl in school whom she doesn't recognise. "Who are you, young lady?" she says. "Maddy Jones, Miss," says the girl. "I don't know you, can you identify yourself?" says the teacher. The girl gets a mirror out of her bag and looks into it...
"Yes," she says, "that's definitely me!"

Geography Teacher: What would happen if the Thames Flood Barrier broke?
Pupil: It would be a dam shame, sir!

Why should fish be clever?
Because they hang around in schools!

What do small music students sit at?
Compact Desks!

"Sara, can you name two living things that don't have any teeth?" asked the science teacher.

Sara: "Yes. Granny and Grandpa."

Mr Hubbins, the deputy headmaster, needed to use a pay phone, but didn't have change for a pound. He saw Billy Wiggins in the corridor, and asked him, "Wiggins, do you have change for a pound coin?"
Billy shrugged and replied, "Yes, Mate."
Mr Hubbins turned red.
"Wiggins, that's no way to address a teacher! What's the matter with you? Are you worthless AND stupid? Now let's try it again... Wiggins, do you have change for a pound coin?"
Billy replied, "No, SIR!"

Why wasn't Cinderella picked for the school hockey team?
She kept running away from the ball!

And why did Cinderella never get good at netball?
Because her coach was a pumpkin!

A school party to the Natural History Museum are looking at the dinosaur bones. One of the students asks the guard, "Can you tell me how old the dinosaur bones are?" The guard replies, "They are 3 million, four years, and six months old." "Wow!" says the student, "How do you know their age so exactly?" The guard answers,
"Well, the dinosaur bones were three million years old when I started working here, and that was four and a half years ago."

Donald: Sorry I'm late, my canary died of flu. Teacher: I didn't know canaries could die of flu...
Donald: Mine did, it flew into a bus!

Bobby was a very clever little boy. Whenever he got an 'A' at school, his Dad would give him ten pence and a pat on the head.
By the time he was sixteen he had two hundred pounds and a flat head!

Wrong! Some definitely daft definitions:

Abundance - A baker's disco

Arcade - A lemonade-type drink served on Noah's Ark

Avoidable - What a bullfighter tries to do

Contents - Where con men sleep while camping

Cowhide - Game played by cows

Eclipse - What a barber does for a living

Eyedropper - A clumsy ophthalmologist

Fan Club - A weapon used by a celebrity

Fire Escape - A way for a fire to go out

Handicap - A hat cover that is easy to find and wear

Hardship - A ship protected by tough cover

Hatchet - What a hen does to an egg

Hence - An enclosure around a hen yard

Heroes - What a guy in a boat does

Himalaya - A rooster that makes an egg

Holy Smoke - The church is on fire

Illegal - A sick bird
Life Jacket - A special long-lasting coat
Matchbook - A book about matches
Misty - How golfers create divots

Cowhide

Wrong! More definitely daft definitions:

Mohair - What bald-headed men need
Network - The process of making nets
Paradox - Two Doctors
Pharmacist - A helper on the farm
Piggyback - A lost pig is back home
Polarise - What penguins see with
Polite - A light on a pole
Polygon - A parrot that got away
Protest - Testing a professional person
Relief - What trees do in the spring
Remind - A brain transplant
Showoff - The show has been cancelled
Selfish - What the owner of a
fish shop does
Subdued - A dude who works on
a submarine
Weekend - A book with a rubbish ending
Whether - Unpredictable weather
Writer - One who corrects a wrong

PART THREE
DISGUSTING JOKES

Mummy! I keep running in circles.
Shut up or I'll nail your other foot to the floor!

The first time Esmerelda met the Hunchback of Notre Dame she was shopping with her friend; she saw the hideous hunchback and was aghast - she had to speak to him... "Goodness! How did you get so ugly?" she said. Quasimodo replied: "Well, when I was younger and I couldn't reach the bell rope, I'd climb up to the belfry and ring the bell by bashing my head against it." "I see!" said Esmerelda, and she went back to her friend. "Who was that?" her friend asked.
"I don't know," said Esmerelda.
"But his face rings a bell..."

When do cannibals leave the table?
When everyone's eaten!

What do you call a cow with no legs?
Ground Beef!

There was a farmer who grew watermelons. He was doing pretty well, but he was plagued by local children who would sneak into his patch at night and steal his watermelons. After some careful thought he comes up with a brilliantly clever idea that he thinks will scare the kids away for sure. So he makes up a sign and sticks it in the field. The sign says, "Warning, one of the watermelons in this field has been poisoned." The farmer goes to inspect his field the next morning and finds a new sign that says:

"Warning, now two of the watermelons in this field have been poisoned."

Where does an Eskimo pig live?
In a Pigloo!

Why was the sand wet?
Because the sea-weed!

A man goes to the doctor with a problem. "You have to help me, Doc. I think I'm a kleptomaniac: I can't stop myself stealing things!" "Take these pills," says the Doctor. "They might help." "But what if they don't?" says the man. "See if you can get me a DVD player, will you?"

Mummy! What happens to all that dog food Patch doesn't eat? Shut up and eat your meatloaf!

What do you call a bad lion tamer? Claude Bottom!

Cannibal husband: What's for lunch, Dear? Cannibal Wife: Salad. Cannibal Husband: Can't we open a tin of someone?

A three-legged dog walks into a saloon in the Old West.
He sidles up to the bar and announces:
"I'm looking for the man who shot my paw!"

One day a pirate and a bartender were talking to each other in a pub. The bartender asked the pirate, "Where did you get that wooden leg from?" "Arr," the pirate said, "we were sailing the seven seas when a big old shark came up to me while I was swimmin' and bit off me leg."
The bartender then asked, "And how did you get that hook?" "Arr," the pirate said, "me crew and I were in a mighty battle and it got cut through the bone wi' a cutlass." The bartender then asked, "Then where did ya get the eye patch from?" The pirate said, "In a harbour I looked at a gull flying overhead and it took a dump right in me eye." The bartender was puzzled and asked the pirate, "How would that make you get an eye patch?"
The pirate looked sad. "Arr," he said, "twas me first day with me new hook."

What has four legs and an arm?
A happy Rottweiler!

"My girlfriend is one of identical twins."
"Really? How do you tell them apart?"
"Her brother's got a beard."

What is the last thing to go through a
bug's mind before
he hits the windscreen?
His bum!

How do you keep flies out of
the kitchen?
Put a big pile of manure in the living room!

A stone-age hunter walking through the
jungle found a huge dead dinosaur with a
little pygmy standing beside it. Amazed,
he asked: "Did you kill that?"
The pygmy said, "Yes."
The hunter asked, "How could a little
bloke like you kill a huge dinosaur like
that?" The pygmy said:
"I killed it with my club."

The astonished hunter asked:
"How big is your club?"
The pygmy replied: "There's about 60 of us."

Teacher: Where was Joan of Arc burned?
Dan: All over her body!

Two cannibals sat beside a large fire, after eating the best meal they'd had in ages. "Your wife sure makes a good roast," said the first cannibal.
"Yeah," replied the second, "I'm really going to miss her..."

What do you call a dog with no legs?
Doesn't matter... he won't come to you anyway!

Why didn't the skeleton go to the party?
He had no body to go with!

What happened to the kid who drank eight Cokes?
He burped Seven-up!

How can you tell if a corpse is angry?
It flips its lid!

Waiter, I've got a maggot in my salad!
Well, it's better than half a maggot!

How can you tell which end is which on a worm?
Put it in a bowl of flour and wait till it farts!

What happened at the cannibal's wedding party?
They toasted the bride and groom!

Superman bumped into the Incredible Hulk. "Are you still seeing that girl Helen?" he said. "Nah, she bled to death from the flu," the Hulk said. Superman said, "You don't bleed to death from the flu!"
The Hulk said, "You do if you give it to me!"

The best cannibal's cookbook is called 'How to Better Serve your Fellow Man'.
It was written by a man who had a wife and ate kids!

I have five eyes, three green ears and a yellow nose, what am I?
Really ugly!

What is the height of stupidity?
I don't know, how tall are you?

Three missionaries in Africa were captured by a tribe of very hostile cannibals who put them in a large pot of water, built a huge fire under it, and left them there. A few minutes later, one of the missionaries started to laugh uncontrollably. The other missionaries were appalled, and one said, "What's wrong with you? We're being boiled alive! They're going to eat us! What could possibly be funny at a time like this?" The laughing missionary said,
"I just weed in the soup!"

The Dead Dog

A man runs into a vet's office carrying his dog, screaming for help. The vet has him put his dog down on the table. The vet examines the still, limp body and tells the man that his dog, unfortunately, is dead. The man, clearly upset, demands a second opinion. The vet goes into the back room and brings in a black labrador. The lab sniffs the body, walks from head to tail, and finally looks at the vet and barks. The vet looks at the man and says, "I'm sorry, but the labrador thinks your dog is dead too." The man, finally accepting the diagnosis, thanks the vet and asks how much he owes. The vet answers, "£650." "£650 to tell me my dog is dead?" exclaimed the man. "Well," the vet replies, "I would have charged you only £50 for my initial diagnosis. The additional £600 was for the lab tests."

"I've got a chicken that lays square eggs,"
said the farmer.
"Really, that's amazing," his friend said.
"Yep, and not only that, it talks as well!"
said the farmer.
"No! What does it say?" said his mate.
"It says 'OUCH!'"

Did you hear the joke about the fart?
You don't want to, it stinks!

What do cannibals eat on toast?
Baked Beings!

**"Doctor, my tummy hurts! I've just eaten four
red snooker balls, two blue snooker balls
and a pink snooker ball."**
"No wonder you're not feeling well, you aren't
eating enough greens!"

Did you hear about the Indian chief who drank 15 cups of tea before bed-time?
That night he drowned in his tea-pee!

Why does the boy monster kiss the girl monster on the back of her neck?
That's where her lips are!

Why did the toilet paper roll down the hill?
Because it wanted to get to the bottom!

What's disgusting and visits Earth once every 80 years?
Halley's Vomit!

An Apache is lying in the road with his ear to the ground when a cowboy comes by. The Apache says, "Stagecoach went by here half an hour ago."

**The cowboy says,
"Wow, how do you know that?"**
The Apache says, "Broke my damn neck."

**Why did the chewing gum
cross the road?**
It was stuck to the leg of a chicken!

What do you call a man with no legs?
Neil!

**What do you get when you toss a hand
grenade into a French kitchen?**
Linoleum blownapart!

Why did the monkey fall out of the tree?
Because it was dead!

**Why did the bald man put rabbits
on his head?**
Someone said that from a distance they
looked like hares!

**What do you call a man with cow
droppings all over his feet?**
An incowpoop!

A man wakes up from an operation and the doctor tells him,
"I've got good news and bad news for you."
So the man says,
"OK, give me the bad news first."
And the doctor says,
"We've made a mistake and cut off the wrong leg." After a while the man pulls himself together and says,
"So what's the good news?"
and the doctor replies,
"We ran a second check and decided we didn't need to cut your leg off at all!"

Why did the zombie fail his driving test?
He left his foot on the clutch!

Why did Henry VIII have so many wives?
He liked to chop and change!

What do vegetarian cannibals eat?
Swedes!

**Two flies are sitting on a dog doodoo, and one of them burps...
"Do you mind?" says one,**
"I'm trying to eat here!"

What's red, has wheels and lies on its back?
A dead bus!

Who looks after sick dwarves?
The national elf service!

Tim was in the garden filling a hole when his neighbour peered over the fence. Interested in what the cheeky-faced youngster was up to, he politely asked, 'What are you up to there, Tim?' 'My goldfish died,' replied Tim tearfully, without looking up, 'and I've just buried him.' The neighbour said, 'That's an awfully big hole for a goldfish isn't it, Tim?'

Tim patted down the last heap of earth, and then replied,
'That's because he's still inside your stupid cat.'

A man goes to the optician to have his glass eye cleaned. The optician says, "I can't do it now, but leave it with me and I'll deliver it to you this afternoon. Where do you live?"
"Just round the corner, in Station Road," says the man. "Righto, I'll be round about 4 o'clock," says the optician.
"Great," says the man.
"I'll keep an eye out for you!"

Mummy! When are we going to have Aunt Edna for dinner?
Shut up, we haven't even finished Gran yet!

A man and his friend were travelling on a train and they decided to eat a banana. Just as the first man took a bite of his, the train entered a tunnel and everything went dark. The man said to his friend:
"Don't eat your banana! I took one bite and I went blind!"

What's a skeleton?
Bones with the person off!

This man decides to start up a chicken farm, so he buys a hundred chickens to get up and running. A month later he returns to the dealer to get another hundred chickens because the first lot had died. Another month passes and he's back at the dealers for another hundred chickens, "I don't know what's wrong," he tells the dealer,
"Do you think I'm planting them too deep?"

Did you hear about the lumberjack that lost his left arm and leg in a chainsaw accident?
He's all right now!

Did you hear about the cannibal's daughter?
She was ate before she was seven!

How do you make a shepherd's pie?
First peel two shepherds...

A woman walked up to a little old man rocking in a chair on his porch. "I couldn't help noticing how happy you look," she said. "What's your secret for a long happy life?" "I smoke three packs of cigarettes a day," he said, "I also drink a case of whisky a week, eat fatty foods, and never exercise!"
"That's amazing," the woman said, "how old are you?'
He thought for a moment, and replied, "Twenty-six."

Why are monsters huge and hairy and ugly?
Because if they were small and round and smooth they'd be M&M's!

How about the bear that was hit by an 18-wheeler and splattered all over the place?
They said it was a grizzly accident.

What do you get if you cross a Rottweiler with a Saint Bernard?
A dog that bites your arm off and goes for help!

What is a polygon?
A dead parrot!

How do you know that owls are cleverer than chickens?
Have you ever heard of Kentucky-fried owl?

What goes "Ha, ha, ha, plop"?
A man laughing his head off!

A man goes to the doctor with terrible wind. "It's funny, Doc. I pass wind every two minutes, but it has no smell and makes no noise." The Doctor gives him some pills and the next day the man is back. "Doc, I'm still passing wind, and they still make no noise, but now they smell awful!" The Doctor says, "Good, we've cured your blocked nose, now let's do something about your hearing!"

A teacher was asking her class what their grandfathers did. When she asked young Johnny, he said, "My grandfather's dead, Miss." "Oh, I am sorry, Johnny. In that case, what did he do before he died?" "He went blue and fell over, Miss."

Barber: Sir, were you wearing a red scarf when you came in? Customer: No... Barber: Oh dear, I think I've cut your throat!

Dentist: Good grief! You've got the biggest cavity I've ever seen! The biggest cavity I've ever seen! Patient: You don't have to say it twice. Dentist: I didn't, that was an echo!

What do you call a man with no arms and legs in a swimming pool? Bob!

Your Dad is so Stupid...

When your Mum said it was chilly outside, he ran outside with a spoon!

He could trip over a cordless phone!

He sold his car for petrol money!

He bought a solar-powered torch!

He took a ruler to bed to see how long he slept!

When he went to take the 44 bus, he took the 22 twice instead!

He jumped out the window and went up!

He sent me a fax with a stamp on it!

Continued...

I told him Christmas was just round the corner and he went looking for it!

If brains were dynamite, he wouldn't have enough to blow his nose!

He went to the airport and saw a sign saying "Airport Left," so he turned around and went home!

He got fired from the M&M factory for throwing away all the W's!

He ordered a cheeseburger from McDonalds and said, "Hold the cheese!"

When he worked at McDonalds and someone ordered small fries, he said, "Hey Boss, all the small ones have gone!"

He tried to throw a bird off a cliff!

He couldn't tell which way a lift was going if I
gave him two guesses!

At the bottom of a form where
it says Sign Here -
He put "Scorpio!"

He sits on the TV, and
watches the sofa!

What's the difference between Mozart and a dead body?
One composes, the other decomposes!

Do you think there should be a club for kids who like Robbie Williams?
No, you don't have to beat them, just ignore them!

What do Dutch pet shop owners have on toast?
Hamster jam!

How do you make a Maltese Cross?
Poke him with a stick!

How many pigs does it take to really smell?
A phew!

Cannibal 1: I'm on a diet.
Cannibal 2: Alright, just have a pygmy!

Two Old Ladies

Two old ladies, Millie and Pam, were out driving and they came to some traffic lights. The lights were red but they just went on through. Millie thought to herself, "I could have sworn Pam just drove us through a red light." After a few more minutes they came to another set of lights. The light was red again, and again they went straight through. This time Millie was almost sure that the light had been red... She was getting nervous and decided to pay very close attention to the road and the next set of lights to see what was going on. At the next junction, sure enough, the light was definitely red and they went right through. She turned to Pam and said, "Pam! Did you know we just went through three red lights in a row! You could have killed us!"
Pam turned to her and said, "Oh, am I driving?"

The Three-Legged Mule

What do you call a mule with three legs?
A wonky donkey!

What do you call a short mule with three legs?
A dinky wonky donkey!

What do you call a short mule with three legs and one eye?
A winky dinky wonky donkey!

What do you call a short mule with three legs and one eye breaking wind?
A stinky winky dinky wonky donkey!

What do you call a short mule with three legs and one eye breaking wind and playing the piano ?
A plinky plonky stinky winky dinky wonky donkey!

What do you call a short mule with three legs and one eye, breaking wind, playing the piano and driving a tractor?

Very clever!

Harry was trying to smuggle a skunk out of America to sell it abroad. He asks his friend the best way to do it. "Just stick it down your trousers," his friend said. "He won't bite unless you sit on him." "But what about the terrible smell?" said Harry. His friend thought for a moment...
"If he dies, he dies!"

Why do cyclists wear lycra shorts?
Because if they didn't, they'd be arrested!

Why shouldn't you put a cat in the washing machine?
In case you get a sock in the puss!

Why do strawberries cry?
Because their mum is in a jam!

What did the monkey say when he cut off his tail?
It won't be long now!

Mummy! Are you sure this is the way to make gingerbread men?
Shut up and get back in the oven!

What's the difference between roast beef and pea soup?
Anyone can roast beef!

Where do you find a no-legged dog?
Wherever you left him.

An artist asked the gallery owner if there had been any interest in his paintings on display at that time. "I have good news and bad news," the owner replied. "The good news is that a man asked about your work and wondered if it would be worth more after your death. I said it would, and he bought all 15 of your paintings."
"That's brilliant!" the artist said.
"What's the bad news?"
"He was your doctor."

Mummy! Why do I have to hop everywhere?
Shut up or I'll chop the other leg off!

A man in the cinema left his seat to go and buy an ice cream. When he came back, he asked an old lady sitting on the aisle. "Excuse me, but did I step on your foot and elbow you in the nose just now?"
"Yes, you did!" said the lady indignantly.
"Oh good," said the man, "this is my row then."

Is it good manners to eat fried chicken with your fingers?
No, you should eat your fingers separately!

What is pig swill?
It's what pigs write before they die so their piglets can have their money!

Did you hear about the man that got the sack from the zoo for feeding the penguins?

He fed them to the tigers!

A man goes to see his doctor feeling a bit unwell. The doctor checks him over and eventually finds a couple of bags of money stuck up his bottom. He pulls them out and can't resist totalling up the value of the coins. "Well," says the doctor, "I've found £1,999 up your bottom."
"Hmmm," replies the patient, "that would explain why I haven't been feeling too grand!"

What happened when the ghost asked for a whisky at his local bar?
The bartender said, "Sorry sir, we don't serve spirits here!"

Why did the cannibal live on his own?
He was fed up with other people!

What does a vampire fear most?
Tooth decay!

Two hunters, not the sharpest tools in the box, went duck hunting one morning with their dogs. After four hours with no success, Bobby says,
"I know what we're doing wrong, Terry: We're not throwing the dogs high enough..."

What's pink and grey and wrinkly and old and belongs to Grandpa monster?
Grandma monster!

What do you get when you cross Bambi with a ghost?
Bamboo!

What's small and cuddly and bright purple?
A koala holding his breath!

Did you hear about the cannibal who loved fast food?
He ordered a pizza with everybody on it!

A woman went to see a psychiatrist and complained, "Doctor, my husband thinks he's a magician." "What's so bad about that?" the Doctor asked. "We're being sued. A week ago my husband shoved a girl into a trunk and sawed it in half." "The girl's family is suing you?" the psychiatrist asked. "No, the circus," the woman replied. "The elephant bled to death."

Doctor, I'm having trouble breathing!
Don't worry, we'll soon put a stop to that!

Do you know a bloke with one eye called Frank Jones?
No, what's his other eye called?

What do you get when you drop a piano down a mineshaft?
A flat miner!

A boy goes to a Doctor with an elephant on his head. "My word, you look like you need my help!" said the Doctor.
"You're telling me, Doc!" said the elephant.
"Can you get this kid off my foot?"

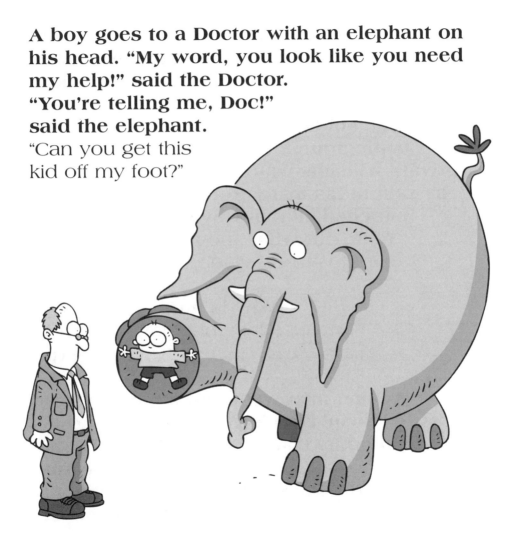

Doctor, I have an awful lot of wind, can you give me anything for it?
Yes, you can borrow my kite!

The soldiers marched 50 miles to the battleground. As soon as they arrived, private Williams was shot. As he lay dying, he said to his mate, Bob, "I can't believe I marched all this way just to get shot!" "Yeah, but what about me?" said Bob,
"I've got to march all the way back again!"

Why is a tree like a dog?
Because they both lose their bark when they die!

A blind man went into a gift shop and started swinging his guide dog around his head on its lead. "Can I help you?" said the assistant.
"No thank you," said the blind man, "I'm just browsing."

An actor sawed off his own leg so he could play Long John Silver in a new movie. He didn't get the part though... it was the wrong leg!

Some Cannibal Munchies

Am I too late for dinner?
Yes, I'm afraid everyone's eaten!

Waiter: How many people for lunch?
Cannibal: Two each, please.

One cannibal to another:
I never met a man I didn't like!

What did the cannibal get when he was late for dinner?
The cold shoulder.

Did you hear about the cannibal who was expelled from school for buttering up his teacher?

Two cannibals were sitting by a fire. The first says, "Gee, I hate my mother-in-law."
The 2nd replies, "So, try the potatoes!"

A cannibal and his son are wandering through the desert and have not eaten in days. They come upon an oasis and decide to camp in the bushes till someone comes. The next morning they awake to see a beautiful woman bathing in the waterfall. As the father watches the lovely woman bathing, he is aware of his son at his side. The boy says, "I'm hungry dad, let's eat." The father replies,
"We can't eat her, she's gorgeous!" The boy grumbles that they have not eaten for days and he is really hungry. The father says he has a plan. The boy is overjoyed that he will soon eat, so he asks what the plan is...
The father says:
"We sneak up to the edge of the clearing, and when she comes out of the water, we kidnap her, take her home and eat your mother..."

What is a cannibal's favourite game?
Swallow the leader!

A tourist goes to Africa and asks his tourist guide, while walking in the jungle, "Are we safe here? Aren't there cannibals around?" And the tourist guide says, "You're completely safe. There are no cannibals in Africa." The tourist says, "How can you be sure?" And the tourist guide says: "We ate the last one on Monday!"

A cannibal goes into a restaurant. "How much for the set menu?" he asks. "Ten pounds a head," says the waiter. "Fine," says the cannibal, "I'll have a couple of arms and a foot as well."

Air Steward: Would you like to see the menu, Sir?
Cannibal: No, just bring me the passenger list!

What do cats have for a breakfast?
Mice Krispies!

Tony's brother and his girlfriend shared the same birthday. He got his brother, a keen hunter, a new shotgun, and for his girlfriend a bottle of nice perfume. He wrote his girlfriend a sweet note saying "Use this on yourself and think of me." Unfortunately he put the note in with the wrong present...

Why did the mummy call the doctor?
Because he was coffin!

Where did the vampire open his savings account?
At a blood bank!

A man walks into a doctor's office. He has a cucumber up his nose, a carrot in his left ear and a banana in his right ear. "What's the matter with me?" he asks the doctor. The doctor replies, "You're not eating properly."

The Titanic is beginning to sink and everyone is abandoning ship. "Excuse me, Steward. Are there any sharks in the ocean here?" asks a little old lady, terrified.

"Yes, I'm afraid there are. But not to worry, we have a special gel in the bottle in your cabin especially for emergencies like this. Just rub the gel onto your arms and legs."

"And if I do this, the sharks won't eat me?" asks the little lady.

"Oh, they'll eat you all right, but they won't enjoy it nearly as much."

What did the skunk say when the wind changed direction?

"It's all coming back to me now!"

A boy is sitting on a train chewing gum and staring into space when the old lady opposite him says,

"It's no good talking to me, young man, I'm stone deaf!"

A young man from the city went to visit his farmer uncle. For the first few days, the uncle showed him the usual things - chickens, cows, crops, etc. After three days, however, it was obvious that the nephew was getting bored, and the uncle was running out of things to amuse him with. Finally, the uncle had an idea. "Why don't you grab a gun, take the dogs, and go hunting?" This seemed to cheer the nephew up, and with enthusiasm, off he went with the dogs. After a few hours, the nephew returned.
"How did you enjoy that?" asked the uncle.
"It was great!" exclaimed the nephew. "Got any more dogs?"

My wife and I tour theatres with our animal impressions act.
She does the sounds, I do the smells...

How does a monster count to 13?
On his fingers!

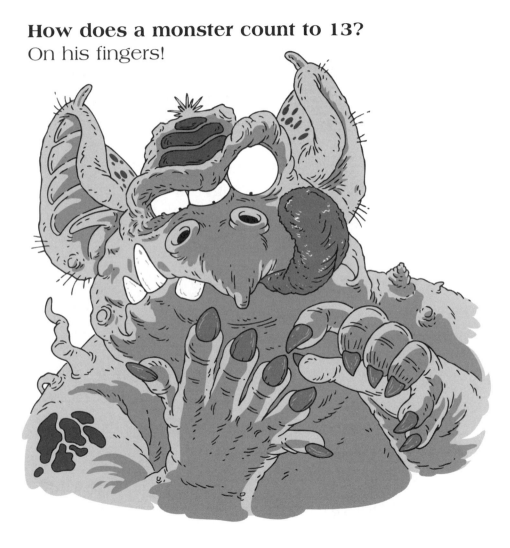

A tough old cowboy told his grandson that if he wanted to live a long life, the secret was to sprinkle a little gunpowder on his cornflakes every morning. The grandson did this every day and he lived to the age of 93. When he died, he left 14 children, 28 grandchildren, 35 great grandchildren and a 15-foot hole in the wall of the crematorium...

What do you call a man with a spade in his head?
Doug!

What do you call a man without a spade in his head?
Douglas!

Mummy! Why are we pushing the car off the cliff?
Shut up, you'll wake your little brother!

No Dogs Allowed

A guy walking his Alsatian says to a guy walking his little Chihuahua, "Let's go over to that restaurant and get something to eat." The guy with the Chihuahua says, "We can't go in there. We've got dogs with us." The guy with the Alsatian says, "Just leave it to me." They go over to the restaurant, and the guy with the Alsatian puts on a pair of dark glasses, and walks in. A waiter says, "Sorry, sir, no pets allowed." The guy with the Alsatian says, "You don't understand, I'm blind, this is my guide dog!" The waiter says, "I'm terribly sorry, Sir. Come on in." The guy with the Chihuahua puts on a pair of dark glasses, and walks in. The waiter says, "I'm sorry, Sir. No pets allowed." "You don't understand," says the guy. "I'm blind, this is my guide dog!" The waiter says, "What, a Chihuahua?" Thinking quickly, the guy says, "Don't tell me they've given me a Chihuahua?!"

What do your call two robbers?
A pair of nickers!

What do you get if you cross a bear with a skunk?
Winnie-the-Pooh!

A man goes skydiving for the first time. After listening to the instructor for what seems like days, he is ready to go. Excited, he jumps out of the plane. About five seconds later, he pulls the ripcord. Nothing happens. He tries again. Still nothing. He starts to panic, but remembers his reserve chute. He pulls that cord. Nothing happens. He frantically begins pulling both cords, but to no avail. Suddenly, he looks down and he can't believe his eyes. Another man is in the air with him, but this guy is going up! Just as the other guy passes by, the skydiver yells,

"Hey! Do you know anything about skydiving?"
The other man shouts back,
"No! Do you know anything about gas cookers?"

Your Mum is so fat...

I ran around her twice and got lost!

I saw a picture of her in a magazine on page 4, 5, 6, 7, and 8!

Instead of Levi's 501 jeans, she wears Levi's 1002's!

She fell in the Grand Canyon and got wedged in!

She goes to a restaurant, looks at the menu, and says "Okay"!

She has to grease her hands to get into her pockets!

She has to put her belt on with a boomerang!

After she got off the Merry-Go-Round, the horse limped for a week!

When she was diagnosed with the flesh-eating disease the doctor gave her 13 years to live!

She puts mayonnaise on aspirins!

Her bottom has its own Member of Parliament!

Her cereal bowl came with a lifeguard!

When she goes to the zoo the elephants throw her peanuts!

Her school picture was an aerial photograph!

Her driving licence says, "Picture continued on the other side!"

They had to change "One size fits all"
to "One size fits most!"

When she gets in a lift, it HAS to go down!

People jog around her for exercise!

When she goes to a restaurant,
she doesn't get a menu,
she gets an estimate!

When they used her underwear
elastic for bungee jumping,
they hit the ground!

When I tried to drive around her,
I ran out of petrol!

All the restaurants in town have signs that
say: MAXIMUM OCCUPANCY: 240
PATRONS or YOUR MUM!

A picture of her fell off the wall!

She jumped up in the air and got stuck!

She was floating in the ocean and Spain claimed her as a New World!

She sat on a rowing machine and it sank!

A man gets pulled over by the police.
The officer walks up to car and says,
"Excuse me, Sir, but do you realise your
wife fell out of the car two miles back?"
"Thank Goodness for that," says the man,
"I thought I'd gone deaf!"

Ah, Doctor Watson.
You're wearing your winter underwear!
Good Lord, Holmes! How on Earth did
you deduce that?
You've forgotten to put
your trousers on again!

How do you get a zombie out of bed?
With a Hoover!

A guy is going on an ocean cruise,
and he tells his doctor that
he's worried about getting seasick.
The doctor says,
"Just eat two pounds of stewed tomatoes
before you leave the dock."

The guy says, "Will that keep me from getting sick, Doc?"
The doctor says,
"No, but it'll look very pretty in the water."

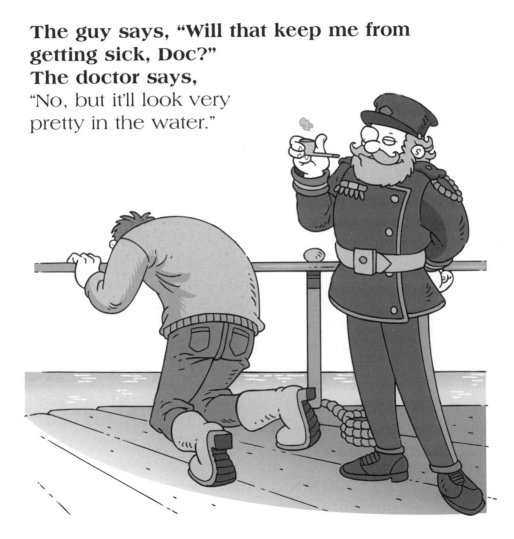

How did you burn your face?
At the Hallowe'en party,
I was bobbing for chips!

Little Darren refused to eat. So his mother took him to the Doctor. The Doctor asked, "What would you like to eat?" "A worm," Darren said. Reluctantly, the Doc sent his nurse out for a worm. Placing it on a plate, the Doc said, "Here it is." "I want it fried," said the boy. The nurse took it out and fried it. When she brought it back, the Doc said, "Now eat it." "I only want half and you eat the other half," said Darren. The Doctor swallowed one half and gave the other to the boy. Just then little Darren began to cry. The doctor asked what was wrong. Darren said, "You ate my half!"

Little Johnny was in church with his mom for Sunday service when he suddenly felt sick. "Mum, I think I'm going to throw up!"
She told him, "I want you to run outside as fast as you can. Run across the lawn and go behind the bushes. You can throw up behind the bushes and nobody will see you." So Johnny ran for the door. Less than a minute later, he returned to his seat next to his mom. He had the look of obvious relief on his young face. "Did you make it all the way to the bushes, Johnny?"
"I didn't have to go that far, Mum. Just as I got to the front door, I found a box that had a sign on it that said 'FOR THE SICK'."

What do you call a deer with no eyes?
No idea!

What do you call a deer with no eyes and no legs?
Still no idea!

What do you get if you cross an owl with a skunk?
A bird that smells but doesn't give a hoot!

Why do worms taste like chewing gum?
Because they're Wrigleys!

What do you call a man with no arms and no legs who lives in a bush?
Russell!

A worried woman goes to the Doctor and asks him:
"Doctor, what can I do? My husband was asleep with his mouth open, and he's swallowed a mouse!"
"Calm down," said the Doctor. "It's quite simple, you must tie a piece of cheese to some string and dangle it over your husband's mouth. As soon as the mouse takes a bite, whip him out!"
"Right-ho Doctor, thank you. I'll just nip

round to the fishmonger for a cod's head," said the woman. "What?" said the Doc, "What on Earth do you need a cod's head for?"

"Oh, I forgot to tell you, I've got to get the cat out first!"

Where do you find giant snails?
At the end of giants' fingers!

A man is feeling very ill, so he goes to see his doctor and is immediately rushed to hospital to undergo tests. The man wakes up after the tests in a private room at the hospital, and the phone by his bed rings. "This is your doctor. We've had the results back from your tests and we've found you have a really nasty disease, and it's very catching."
"Oh my God, doctor! What are you going to do?"
"We're going to put you on a diet of pizzas, pancakes and pitta bread."
"Will that cure me?" said the man.
"Well no, but it's the only food we can get under the door!"

Doctor, I think I'm going to die!
Nonsense, that's the last thing you'll do!

The Speedy Turtle

A guy comes walking into a bar with a little turtle in his hand. The turtle's one eye is black and blue, two of his legs are bandaged, and his whole shell is taped together with sticky tape. The bartender asks the man, "What's wrong with your turtle?" "Nothing," the man responds. "This turtle is super fast! Take your dog and let him stand at the end of the bar. Then go and stand at the other end of the room and call your dog. I'll bet you £50 that before your dog reaches you, my turtle will be there." So the bartender, thinking it's an easy £50, agrees. He goes to the other side of the bar, and on the count of three calls his dog. Suddenly the guy picks up his turtle and throws it across the room, narrowly missing the bartender, and smashing into the wall.

"Fifty pounds, please."

What do you call a man who was born in Manchester, married in London, and died in Glasgow?
Dead!

This man took his two-year-old daughter, Madison, to the DIY superstore. Madison got tired of walking, so he let her ride on his shoulders. As he walked, Madison began pulling his hair. Although he asked her to stop several times, she kept on. Getting annoyed, he scolded, "Madison! Stop that!"
"But, Daddy," she replied, "I'm just trying to get my chewing gum back!"

It was the last day of school and children brought gifts for the teachers. The flower shop owner's son brought a big bouquet of flowers for Miss Jones. The candy store owner's daughter

brought her a big box of chocolates. The off-licence owner's son brought a big heavy box. The teacher lifted the box and noticed it was leaking. She tasted one of the drops.
"Oo, is it wine?" she guessed.
"Nooo..," said the little boy.
She tasted another drop.
"Is it Champagne?" she guessed.
"Nooo..," said the little boy.
"I give up." she said,
"What is it?"
"It's a puppy, Miss!"

A man is sitting at home one night. Suddenly, there's a loud knock at the door. The man opens the door to find a six-foot beetle standing at the doorstep. "What in the world is this?" he asks. The beetle responds by attacking the man viciously, with a flurry of kicks and punches. Then the beetle leaves. The man crawls into his house and calls an ambulance. At the hospital, the nurse asks him how it happened. The guy tells her about the beetle and what happened. "Yes," the nurse says, with an understanding nod,
"there is a nasty bug going around at the moment..."

What's green, hairy and takes Aspirin?
A gooseberry with a hangover!

What's the best time to pick apples?
When the farmer's not looking!

In a hospital, a man wakes up from surgery.

Man: How did it go, Doctor?

Doctor: Well, the bad news is we've had to amputate both your legs...

Man: Oh no! What's the good news?

Doctor: The man in the next bed wants to buy your slippers!

How did the dentist become a brain surgeon?

When his drill slipped!

"Look at the speed of that thing!" said one hawk to another as a jet flew past.

"Not really surprising," said the second.

"You'd fly that fast if your bum was on fire!"

Teacher: Sara, if you had 16 chocolates, and Charlie asked you for ten, how many would you have left?

Sara: Sixteen, I hate Charlie.

Why did the basketball floor get wet?
The players dribbled on it!

There was a bloke on a motorcycle driving down the road on a cold and windy day. After a while he decided to put his leather jacket on backwards to protect him better against the wind. Five minutes later he took a corner too fast, hit a patch of oil on the road and crashed the bike. A passer-by found him, called the police and told them what happened. The police asked him, "Is he showing any signs of life?" The passer-by then said, "Well, he was till I turned his head around the right way."

The first cannibal asked the second cannibal, "Aren't you done eating yet?" The second cannibal replied, "I'm on my last leg now!"

1st man: Every day I go for a tramp in the woods with my dog.

2nd man: I bet the dog enjoys that!

1st man: He does: the tramp's getting a bit fed up, though!

The Speed Cop

A farmer got pulled over by a policeman for speeding. The cop gave the farmer a big lecture about how stupid he was. Finally, he wrote out the ticket, and as he was doing that he kept swatting at some flies buzzing around his head. The farmer said, "Having some problems with circle flies there?" The cop stopped and said, "Circle flies? Never heard of them!" So the farmer says, "Well, they're called circle flies because they circle around the back end of a horse." The cop says, "Oh," and goes back to writing the ticket. After a minute he stops and says, "Hey...wait a minute, are you trying to call me a horse's arse?" The farmer says, "Oh no, officer. I wouldn't even think that!" The cop says, "Well, alright then," and goes back to writing the ticket. After a pause, the farmer says:

"Can't fool those flies though."

A blind beggar says to a passing woman, "Excuse me, love. Can you spare a pound for a blind man?" The woman looks at him suspiciously. "Wait a minute, I'm sure you can see out of that eye!"
"Alright," he says, "Give me 50 pence, then."

Joe comes home to his wife very upset. "The Doctor told me I've got to take these pills for the rest of my life," he tells her. "So, what's the problem?" she asks.
"He only gave me six!"

What's the difference between Tony Blair and a dog?
Tony Blair usually wears a suit, a dog just pants!

Mother: Mrs Jokes next door has a new baby.
Daughter: What will she do with her old one?

A salesman is getting the sack from his boss for being useless at his job.
"Give me one more chance," he pleads, "I'll sell anything!"
His boss gives him a hundred toothbrushes and tells him if he sells them all in an hour, he can keep his job.
In an hour's time, the salesman is back with a bundle of money.
His boss is amazed...
"How on Earth did you manage to sell all those toothbrushes?" The man says, "Well, I stood on a street corner with a plate of toast and spread, and gave pieces away free. People would try a bite of toast and say "Yuck! That tastes like dog poo!"
And I'd say, "It is! Do you want to buy a toothbrush?"

What is green and has four legs and two trunks?
Two seasick tourists!

How do you tidy up a murder scene?
With a victim cleaner!

A woman got on a bus holding a baby. The bus driver said: "Blimey! that's the ugliest baby I've ever seen!" In a huff, the woman slammed her fare into the tray and took a seat near the back of the bus. The man sitting next to her sensed that she was upset and asked her what was wrong. "The bus driver completely insulted me!" she fumed. The man said, "He can't do that, he's a public servant. He's not allowed to say things to insult passengers!"

"You're right," she said. "I think I'll go back up there and give him a piece of my mind."

"That's a good idea," the man said. "Here, let me hold your monkey..."

What happened to the man who couldn't keep up payments to his exorcist?
He was repossessed!

A young woman smashes her car into a lamp post, and the police are gathering details about the accident.

Policeman: Can you tell me what gear you were in, Miss?

Young Lady: Yes, I was wearing white jeans and a cut-off T-shirt...

Did you hear about the two peanuts that were walking down the street and one got beaten up?
Yes, he was a salted!

A little boy watched, fascinated, as his mother gently rubbed cold cream on her face. "Why are you rubbing cold cream on you face, mommy?" he asked. "To make myself beautiful," said his mother. A few minutes later, she began removing the cream with a tissue.
"What's the matter?" he asked.
"Are you giving up?

A bear and a rabbit are taking a dump in the woods. The bear turns to the rabbit and says, "Hey, do have a problem with it, you know, sticking to your fur?" The rabbit says, "Nope, never."
So the bear wipes his bum with the rabbit...

What's better than a drip dry vampire?
A wash and werewolf!

A man walks into a restaurant with a shark. "Do you serve children in here?" he askes the barman. "Certainly, Sir," the barman replies.
"Good. A pizza for me, then, please, and two children for the shark..."

How do you make holy water?
Boil the hell out of it!

Why was the Egyptian girl worried?
Because her daddy was a mummy!

Postman 1: A dog bit me on the leg this morning.
Postman 2: Did you put anything on it?
Postman 1: No, he seemed to like it plain!

How do you keep a skunk from smelling?
Hold his nose!

What's a haunted chicken?
A poultry-geist!

A circus owner walked into a bar to see everyone crowded about a table watching a little show. On the table was an upside-down pot and a duck dancing on it. The circus owner was so impressed that he offered to buy the duck from its owner. After some wheeling and dealing they settled for $10,000 for the duck and the pot. Three days later the circus owner runs back to the bar in anger: "Your duck is a rip-off! I put him on the pot before a whole audience and he didn't dance a single step!" "Well," said the duck's former owner, "did you remember to light a candle under the pot?"

Where do mummies go for a swim?
To the Dead Sea!

Why do witches fly around on broomsticks?
Because Hoovers don't have long
enough cords!!

A man finds he hasn't been able to go to the toilet for three days and he goes to the Doctor to do something about it. The Doc gives him a laxative and sends him home, telling him to take it at midnight. Next day, the man calls the Doctor on the phone: "Doc, that laxative you gave me really did the trick, I took it at midnight and I went at 8 o' clock this morning!" "Yep," says the Doc, "works in 8 hours, guaranteed!" "That's the problem," says the man, "I didn't wake up till half past nine..."

"Doctor, will this ointment clear up my itchy spots?" "I'm not making any rash promises!"

A guy goes in to see a psychiatrist. He says, "Doc, I can't seem to make any friends. Can you help me, you fat slob?"

The Almond Bowl

A vicar decides one day to visit one of his elderly parishoners, Mrs Smith. He rings the door bell and Mrs Smith appears. "Good Day Mrs Smith. I just thought I would drop by and see how you're getting on." The woman says, "Oh I'm fine, Vicar, come on in and we'll have some tea." While sitting at the coffee table, the vicar notices a bowl of almonds on the table. "Mind if I have one?" the vicar says. "Not at all, have as many as you like." After a few hours the vicar looks at his watch and, alarmed at how long he has been visiting, says to Mrs Smith, "Oh my goodness, look at the time! I must be going. Oh but, dear me, I have eaten all your almonds. I'll have to replace them next time I visit!" To which Mrs Smith replied,
"Oh don't bother Father.
Ever since I lost all my teeth, it's all I can do just to lick the chocolate off them."

"Mommy, my turtle is dead," wailed the little boy to his mother, holding the turtle out to her in his hand. His Mum said, "That's all right. We'll wrap him in tissue paper, put him in a little box, then have a lovely burial ceremony in the back yard. After that, we'll go out for a yummy big ice cream, and then get you a great new pet, like a puppy! Just then, she noticed the turtle move. "Look! Your turtle isn't dead after all!" "Oh," said the boy, "can we kill it?"

Bobby says to the gardener:
"What are you doing with that manure?"
The gardener says:
"I'm putting it on my rhubarb."
"Really?" says Bobby.
"We usually have custard on ours!"

How do you teach a dog to fetch?
Tie a cat to a stick!

Mum, Can I have a dog for Christmas?
No, you can have turkey like everyone else!

The Children's Party

A lady is giving a party for her grand-daughter, and has hired a clown. Just before the party starts, two tramps turn up at the door. The woman tells them that she'll pay them to chop some wood for her. Gratefully, they head to the back of the house... All is going well, with the kids having a wonderful time, but the clown phones to cancel! The woman is very disappointed; she happens to look out the window and sees one of the tramps doing cartwheels across the lawn and yodelling. She watches amazed as he swings from branches, does mid-air flips, and leaps in the air. She says to the other tramp, "Do you think your friend would do that again for the children? I would pay him £50!" The tramp says, "I dunno. I'll ask him...

Hey, Willie, for fifty quid, would you chop off another toe?"

What do you call a person who puts poison in a person's corn flakes?
A cereal killer!

What do you call four drowning bullfighters?
Quattro sinko!

How did the carpenter break his teeth?
He chewed his nails!

Jack: Did you hear about the giant that threw up?
Jill: No, how'd you know?
Jack: It's all over town!

A man takes his Rottweiler to the vet. "My dog's cross-eyed, is there anything you can do for him?" "Alright," says the vet, "let's have a look at him." So he picks the dog up and has a good look at its eyes. "Well," says the vet, "I'm afraid I'm going to have to put him down." "Why? Because he's cross-eyed?"
"No, because he's extremely heavy..."

A family of moles had been hibernating all winter. One beautiful spring morning, they woke up. The father mole stuck his head out of the hole and looked around. "Mother Mole!" he called back down the hole. "Come up here! I smell honey, freshly-made honey!"
The mother mole ran up and squeezed in next to him. "That's not honey, that's maple syrup! I smell maple syrup!" The baby mole, still down in the hole, was sulking.
"I can't smell anything down here but molasses...."

Mummy. I hate my sister's guts!
You'll eat what's put in front of you!

Diner: Waiter? I can't eat this chicken. Call the manager.
Waiter: It's no use.
He can't eat it either!

Did you hear about the cannibal policeman who was arrested?
He was caught grilling his suspects!

Bigger in Texas

This man decided to visit Texas. When he arrived on the plane, he saw the seats and said, "Wow, these seats are big!" The person next to him said, "Everything is big in Texas." When he got to Texas, he decided to visit a bar. He ordered a beer and got a mug placed in his hand. He exclaimed, "Wow these mugs are big!" The barman said, "Everything is big in Texas." After ten more beers, the man asked the barman where the toilets were.. The barman replied, "Second door to the right." The man staggered to his feet and headed for the loo, but accidentally tripped over and skipped the second door. Instead, he entered the third door, which lead to the swimming pool. He crashed through it and fell into the pool by accident. Scared to death, the man started shouting, "Don't flush, don't flush!"

Your Sister is so Ugly...

When she joined an ugly contest, they said "Sorry, no professionals!"

She looked out the window and got arrested for mooning!

When she was born, your Mum said, "What a treasure!" and your Dad said, "Yes, let's bury it!"

When she goes to the bank, they turn off the surveillance cameras!

You have to tie a sausage around her neck to get the dog to play with her!

The government moved Hallowe'en to her birthday!

She threw a boomerang and it wouldn't even come back!

When she sits in the sand on the beach, cats try to bury her!

Your Dad takes her to work with him so that he doesn't have to kiss her goodbye!

Her dentist treats her by mail-order!

Her pillow cries at night!

If she was a scarecrow, the potatoes would run away!

People hang her picture in their cars so their radios don't get stolen!

She looks like her face caught fire and they put it out with a fork!

She tried to take a bath and the water jumped out!

When she was born, the doctor smacked the wrong end!

When she was a baby, her parents had to feed her with a catapault!

She made an onion cry!

An old chap and his little grandson Eddy were digging for fishing bait in the garden. Uncovering a many-legged creature, Eddy proudly dangled it before his Grandad. "No, Ed, he won't do for bait," his Grandad said. "He's not an earthworm."
"He's not?" Eddy asked.
"What planet is he from?"

Why did the lion throw up after he'd eaten the priest?
Because it's hard to keep a good man down!

A man is standing at a bus stop eating sausage and chips when a woman turns up with a dog. The dog is very excited at the smell of sausage and starts barking like crazy. "Shall I throw him a bit?" says the man. "If you like," says the woman.
So he chucked the dog over a wall...

What did one zombie ask the other?
Can you lend me a hand?

The Rude Parrot

A lady goes to a pet shop one day and buys a talking parrot. As soon as she gets it home, the parrot says "What a dump! This place sucks! You should get the hoover out once in a while, you lazy old bat!" The lady is shocked. "How dare you be so rude!" she says, and she puts the parrot in a cupboard to teach it a lesson. An hour later, she takes it out. "Are you going to behave?" she asks. "Get stuffed you old crow!" says the parrot. "How dare you be so rude!" says the lady, and she stuffs the parrot into a saucepan, to teach it a lesson. An hour later, she takes it out again. "Well, are you going to be nice now?" she asks it. "Go and boil your head, you wrinkly old cow!" said the parrot. "How dare you be so rude!" says the lady, and she sticks the parrot in the freezer, to teach it a lesson once and for

all. An hour later she takes it out.
"Are you going to behave?" she asks.
The parrot shivers, "Y-Yes, Miss, I'm
going to be g-good from now on, th-thank
you very m-much." Sure enough, he is
good as gold all afternoon.
That evening, the lady is putting the cover
over the cage for the night when the parrot
says in a little voice,
"By the way, just how rude was that chicken?"

**Did you hear about the constipated
Maths teacher?**
He worked it out with a pencil!

**The farmer says to his wife, "Two of our
hens have stopped laying." "How do you
know?" says his wife.**
"Because I've just run them over with a tractor."

What does the Queen do when she burps?
Issues a royal pardon!

Pam: Is it OK to eat hotdogs with hands?
Sam: No, hotdogs aren't supposed to have hands!

What's big and green and slimy, and hangs from tall trees?
Elephant bogies!

What did one zombie say to another?
Get a life!

Why do monkeys scratch themselves?
Because they're the only ones who know where the itch is!

Farmer John: That pig is like one of the family.
Farmer Bob: Really? Which one?

What happened when a cannibal went on a self-catering holiday?
He ate himself!

Why are Giraffes' necks so long?
Because their feet stink!

A very old man is sitting on a bench in tears. A lady goes up to him and asks "Excuse me. But is something wrong?" "It's my 100th birthday today," said the old man. "I've got lots of friends coming round to my house with champagne and cake. There'll be a band playing music and they've hired dancing girls to entertain me, and everyone's bought me lots of wonderful gifts." "Well, that sounds marvellous," said the lady. "Why are you upset, then?"
The old chap looked up and wailed:
"I can't remember where I live!"

Why do ghouls and demons hang out together?
Because demons are a ghoul's best friend!

What do you call a man with rabbits in his trousers?
Warren!

Young Marie went to visit her cousin Sophie in France. She was most excited about learning French. When she arrived, she was even more thrilled because Sophie's cat had just had a kitten, and Sophie gave it to Marie to raise as her very own. Because Marie was beginning to learn French, she named her new kitten Un Deux Trois. One day, Marie and Sophie were playing beside the river. Marie put her kitten in a small toy boat and pulled it along the river. Unfortunately, a large boat sped by, and the wake tipped Marie's toy boat and the kitten spilled overboard. Seeing Marie in tears, Sophie rushed up and asked what had happened.

Marie said, "Un Deux Trois cat sank!"

Why did the Mexican throw his wife out of the window?

He wanted tequila!

**How do you catch an elephant?
Dig a hole, fill it with ashes,
surround it by peas.**
When he comes to take a pea, kick
him in the ash hole!

Why do surgeons wear masks?
If somebody makes a mistake nobody
will know who did it!

**Which hand do you use to clean the
toilet? My right hand.**
Really! I'd use a brush!

How do you make a cat go "woof"?
Set him on fire!

**Two men meet on a train.
One asks after the other's wife.
"Oh, she's dead..," says the friend.
"She was chopping french beans and
accidentally cut her own head clean off."**

**"Good Lord!" says the other chap.
"What did you do?"**
"What else could I do?
I opencd a tin of peas..."

Strangers in a Bar

A couple of strangers were drinking at a cliffside bar overlooking the ocean. Both of them are a little drunk, when one says to the other: "Hey, look at the wind whipping up the side of that cliff. I'll bet I could jump off of the ledge, catch the wind in my coat, and get lifted right back up to the bar!" "No way," says the other guy, "you'd fall to your death." "Well, I'm going to try it!" says the first, and at that he walks over, stands on the ledge, and leaps off in a dive. Sure enough, he comes sailing back up, and lands on his feet in front of the bar. "I can't believe it!" says the second guy, "That's impossible." So the first drunk does it again: he jumps off the cliff, catches the wind in his coat, and comes sailing back to the bar. "Go ahead," he says, "try it, it's great!" "Well, OK, I'm just drunk enough to give it a go," says the second fellow.

So he climbs the ledge and leaps off the cliff, only to fall screaming to his death on the rocks below.
The first guy walks back to the bar and sits down to his drink.
The bartender steps over, looks him in the eye, and says to him:
"You know, you can be really mean sometimes when you've been drinking, Superman."

Grandad: Look at my fantastic new hearing aid, it's made with the very latest technology developed from the US Space programme.
Grandson: Wow! How does it work?
Grandad: Half past seven!

Why did the lady miss her husband?
Because she never shot a gun before!

What happens if you upset a cannibal?
You get into hot water!

Little Johnny is approached by the lifeguard at the public swimming pool. "You're not allowed to wee in the pool," said the lifeguard. "I'm going to report you." "But everyone wees in the pool," said Little Johnny.
"Possibly," said the lifeguard, "but not from the diving board!"

A man is walking by a children's playground and hears all the kids chanting, "Thirteen! Thirteen! Thirteen!" Quite curious about all this, he finds a hole in the fence, looks in and someone pokes him in the eye. Everyone in the playground starts chanting,
"Fourteen! Fourteen! Fourteen!"

What do you get if you cross a skeleton and a dog?
An animal that buries itself in the garden!

MUTE TESTIMONY

Hiram jerked awake, realizing that hours had passed. Sitting up, he reached for a water bottle—and saw the boy.

The boy shouldn't have been visible. With no moon, even a boy of flesh and bones should have been an invisible shadow, one more object in the sea of shadows swamping the bottom of the wash.

Instead, Hiram saw him clearly. The jacket, too big for him and frayed at the sleeves and collar, with one button missing, so probably a hand-me-down. Alive, his sun-pink skin might have had freckles. Dead, his pale flesh made those freckles look like mud spackle. His curly brown hair was long enough to make him look wild. The boot-laces were knotted and re-knotted to repair them.

"Hello," Hiram said.

The boy slowly raised his arms. The sleeves of the jacket fell down to his elbows and the front hung open, exposing his forearms and neck. All down his arms, Hiram saw bite marks. The indentations left by teeth were raw and red, bleeding slightly. The boy tipped his head back and Hiram saw more bite marks on his throat.

The jawline that had left those marks was circular, and the canines were understated.

They looked like bites left by human teeth.

The Jupiter Knife

D.J. Butler
Aaron Michael Ritchey

A Baen Books Original

Baen Publishing Enterprises
P.O. Box 1403
Riverdale, NY 10471
www.baen.com

ISBN: 978-1-9821-2599-8

Cover art by Dan dos Santos

First printing, February 2021
First mass market printing, March 2021

Distributed by Simon & Schuster
1230 Avenue of the Americas
New York, NY 10020

Library of Congress Control Number: 2020048133

Pages by Joy Freeman (www.pagesbyjoy.com)
Printed in the United States of America
10 9 8 7 6 5 4 3 2 1

For D. Michael Quinn

Big thanks are due to Jim Killen, and to the many booksellers at Barnes & Noble and in independent bookstores across the country, who helped the first Hiram Woolley novel, *The Cunning Man*, reach its audience.

"First, that one *Garner* in the shape of a woolfe killed a girle of the age of twelve yeares, and did eat up hir armes and legges, and carried the rest home to his wife. Item, that *Peter Burget* and *Michael Werdon*, having turned themselves with an ointment into woolves, killed, and finallie did eate up an infinite number of people."

—Reginald Scot, *The Discoverie of Witchcraft*, Booke V, Chapter I

"[T]hey were scattered on the west, and on the north, until they had reached the wilderness, which was called Hermounts; and it was that part of the wilderness which was infested by wild and ravenous beasts."

—*The Book of Mormon*, Alma 2:37

Chapter One

"I'LL TELL YOU THE TRUTH, MR. WOOLLEY," REX
Whittle said. The farmer stood with his hands in the
pockets of his denim overalls, nut-brown face stream-
ing sweat under the late June sun. "I can't afford to
pay you anything."

"Don't give it a second thought, Mr. Whittle." Hiram
Woolley tossed aside the last peelings of hazel bark.
For finding water, he liked the twenty-third Psalm. A
well *should* have still waters, and he liked the idea of
a feast with God. He hummed a few notes experimentally, trying to find the old melody Grandma Hettie
had taught him for the Psalm. Hiram, his son, and
a knot of men stood on hard red earth, southeast of
Moab in Spanish Valley. The La Sal Mountains were
green with pine trees, but those pines drank the
melt-off and left everything below them yellowed by
summer. Stretches of gray slickrock broke up the red
dirt of the desolate place.

To the west of them and lower in elevation, the small
town of Moab lay stretched along the Colorado River

and the highway. Upriver, north and east of the town, the Colorado cut through the canyons, one branch of the highway following it while the other climbed through red rock north and west, toward Helper and Price, and beyond that, Provo and Lehi, Hiram's home. Due north of Moab, between the two arms of the highway, lay the strange badlands of the Monument, full of stone arches and spires and surreal canyons.

Like Whittle, Hiram wore battered denim overalls and a long-sleeved shirt that had once been white, but had been washed into a mottled gray. The long sleeves meant he didn't feel the infrequent breezes with as much pleasure, but it also kept him from getting sunburned. His high-crowned fedora had a brim wide enough to help keep the sun off Hiram's neck, without fully preventing his skin from darkening into a color his dead wife Elmina had once described as "vermilion."

Whittle shifted from one foot to the other. "I heard about you from a cousin of mine that works the Latuda mine up in Helper. You're famous, least among the coal miners. The stories I heard about you..."

Ernie Smothers, a bug-eyed, unshaven man in a straw hat, knocked his friend, Don Pout, with an elbow. Pout had a tiny nose, a freckled little button that would have looked more at home in the face of a child, and unusually long eyelashes. "Told you."

Pout grinned, his eyelashes fluttering.

Uh oh. The last thing Hiram wanted was fame. Fame might interfere with his work as a cunning man, and it would definitely get him in trouble with the church. His friend John Wells could only run interference for him so much. "Don't give it a third thought, either." He carved several crosses into the hazel with his clasp knife.

Hiram's son Michael stood in the small group surrounding Hiram. This was the first time Michael had watched Hiram dowse for a client, and he was paying close attention, eyes drinking in every detail of what Hiram did and said, but also closely observing the others present. Michael wore jeans and a long-sleeved shirt, too, but his sleeves were pushed up and he wore no hat. The complexion he'd inherited from his Navajo blood parents offered him a potent protection against the sun that baked Hiram like a fish on hot coals.

"To tell you the truth," Rex Whittle said, "my cousin told me you refused payment. He said you did what you did up there for free, to help the poor. So I thought I could afford you. But I feel bad, seeing as you drove all the way down here from Lehi." The farmer chuckled uneasily. "To tell you the truth, I might have gone to the widow Artemis, but she charges too much."

Gudmund Gudmundson clapped a hand on Whittle's shoulder. Gudmundson was a handyman, and had the big muscles, callused hands, and patched pants to show it. He also had a broad face with a strong chin, and seemed to be perpetually smiling. As he raised his hand to touch Whittle, Hiram saw a knife hilt and sheath hanging from his belt. It was a brief flash, but the metal of the knife looked like silver, and had Hiram seen Hebrew letters on the crosspiece? Was that some kind of Masonic dagger? "As your bishop, Rex," Gudmundson said, "I'm going to ask you to stop telling the truth right now."

That drew a chuckle from the others standing and watching: Pout and Smothers, Lloyd Preece the rancher, who was Gudmundson's counselor, and the burnt-faced ranch hand whose only name, apparently, was Clem.

"Why?" Rex asked. "Because she's a fallen woman? I wasn't saying I'd pay her for *that*."

"It's Brother Woolley's calling," Gudmundson said, "isn't it? He's an assistant to the Presiding Bishopric. He travels around the state, helping out. Sometimes he helps with his truck...sometimes he helps with his Mosaical Rod."

"That's basically it," Hiram said, "only it's not that official. I just...try to help out, is all."

Whittle shrugged. "I bet the widow could dowse, though. Told my Cherellen's horoscope pretty clear, and I hear she cured Orville Peterson's falling sickness."

Hiram's ears perked up. "Falling sickness?"

Whittle nodded. "The widow gave him what looked like a silver cross, and from the moment he started carrying it in his pocket, the seizures stopped."

Hiram suffered from the falling sickness; from time to time, it caused him to pass out completely. That was one of the reasons he had Michael along—his son drove, so Hiram didn't risk falling asleep at the wheel. Hiram had a verbal charm against the malady that was reasonably effective. If he could reinforce that, or even replace his chant about Rupert and Giles with the passive craft of an amulet, it would make his life easier. Even better would be a permanent cure.

He resolved to find this widow Artemis, once he'd dowsed Mr. Whittle's water.

"Now, Rex," Lloyd Preece said. He was tall and portly, and stood with a lodgepole-straight spine. He wore a flannel shirt buttoned to the wrists despite the heat, and a broad-brimmed hat. "Diana might not want you telling stories out of school about her."

Michael snickered, but then caught himself. "*Diana Artemis.* Really?"

Rex wrinkled his nose. "I figured it was just her business, you know, like what Mr. Woolley does."

"Maybe," Preece countered, "but some folks aren't as open-minded as you and I. We don't know if Mr. Woolley believes in all that hocus pocus."

"They *are* here *dowsing*," Gudmundson pointed out.

"We both are firm believers in the hocus part," Michael said instantly, "but I'm only fifty-fifty on the pocus."

Preece snorted. "And I'm partial to the pocus myself." He gave Michael a wink. Then to Rex, "Let's not talk about Mr. Woolley's competition. If you want him to place your well, you're going to have to give him time. And don't you worry about Mr. Woolley's driving, we paid for his gasoline."

Preece had given Hiram forty dollars, enough for gas and food and two days in a hotel and still some to spare. Hiram had resisted, but eventually yielded when Preece had threatened to slip sixty dollars into Hiram's truck if Hiram wouldn't take forty from his hand. The truth was that Hiram could always use the extra cash.

Forty dollars was a lot of money.

Rather than spend any of the cash on a hotel room, Hiram had asked if he and Michael could camp on Preece's land, just up the river from Moab. The rancher had allowed it with a nod and a firm shake of the hand.

"Lucky you," Rex Whittle said. "I wish I'd been the one to find that stolen silver."

Lloyd Preece chuckled and shook his head. "That's a good one."

"You been listening too much to them vagrants you hire." Clem spat tobacco onto the crumbling red earth. "Weren't no silver."

"I was here in 1923," Whittle said defensively. "The bank was robbed. *Someone* found that silver."

"The *bank* found it." Preece smiled. "What *I* found was good watering holes for my cattle, in canyons the coyotes can't get to."

"Lucky either way, I guess," Whittle said. Gudmundson clapped him across the shoulders again. "Since you got a cunning man out here, maybe you could get him to deal with that ghost on your land."

"It's not on my land," Preece said. "It's on the Monument. Up in the wash right underneath the Schoolmarm's Bloomers, is what I heard. That might be the Wolfe Ranch, I guess."

"Nobody calls it that no more." Clem grunted. "Turnbows live there now."

"Ghost?" Hiram asked.

Preece nodded. "Moab is a small town in a big wilderness, Mr. Woolley. Of course, we have our ghosts."

Hiram nodded and began to sing.

> *The Lord is my shepherd; I shall not want.*
> *He maketh me to lie down in green pastures:*
> *he leadeth me beside the still waters.*

He finished out the short Psalm with Grandma Hettie's melody, making eye contact with Michael as he did so. Later, he'd remind his son of the melody and they'd practice together. Michael might not need the practice, in any case—not only was he much smarter than Hiram, he was also musical.

Of course, what Michael usually sang was boisterous blues songs, and not the ancient modal tunes by which Grandma Hettie had turned the Psalms into incantations.

Then Hiram began to swing the rod.

The four men from Moab stepped back. They didn't need to give Hiram room for the charm to succeed, but many people liked to keep a distance between themselves and a hex being worked. Michael, by contrast, stepped closer. He was staring at Hiram's hands. Hiram held the forked end of the rod loosely with his palms, so that he could feel its action when it moved.

A Mosaical Rod could do many things. If Hiram were dowsing to find a person or a specific object, he'd have had to prepare the rod to that end, carving into it signs identifying the person or thing sought, and maybe even wrapping objects around the rod that were connected to the object. The rod would dip whenever Hiram swung it in the direction he needed to go. A rod was also a divination tool that could answer yes or no questions, in which case the tip of the rod dipped to signify yes.

But today, Hiram was looking for water. The rod would dip when it passed over an underground water source.

Hiram paced across the property. This was poor land, not close enough to the Colorado River to water by means of irrigation ditches, and not possessing any obvious springs. Rex Whittle wouldn't get enough water out of any well that Hiram placed to farm big acreage, but he might get enough to keep himself, his family, some small livestock, and an acre or two watered. Which was what Whittle said he wanted.

"I ain't sure there's a ghost at all," Hiram heard Clem say to Rex Whittle as the men watched Hiram work. "Might just be that crazy feller."

Lloyd Preece laughed. "Which one? The one digging for moon rocks, or the hobo who thinks the end of the world is coming?"

Clem spat. "It ain't moon rocks. It's Uranus."

"Uranium," Gudmundson said.

Clem nodded. "And he might be crazy, but you can sell that stuff. Howard Balsley used to ship a box of rocks off to Germany once a month, and he got paid."

"France, I heard," the bishop said. "But speaking of the Reverend Majestic Earl Bill Clay...you're not churching in that dugout he has, are you, Rex?"

Hiram felt a tug on the rod and stopped. He swung the rod back and forth several times experimentally, and felt a pull each time.

But the tug was weak, suggesting little water, or water that was far away.

"Did you find it, Pap?" Michael asked.

Hiram tracked an X in the dry earth with the toe of his Redwing Harvester. "There's water there. Might not be much. I'll see if I can find better. You want to try?"

Michael shook his head. "Maybe not this time."

"Ain't exactly a dugout," Clem observed. "More of a hole in the rock."

"I church with *you*, bishop," Whittle said. "If you haven't seen me as much as you'd like, it's just that I've been putting up fenceposts."

"My son-in-law has time to help, if you're looking for a hand," Preece offered.

Clem chuckled and spat.

"To tell the truth," Whittle said, "I don't think I have any more time for Guy Tunstall than you do, Mr. Preece. But Addy's a hard worker, and if she had time to dig postholes, I'd be grateful for the help."

"My daughter's busy with her three children." Preece's response sounded mechanical, and a little distant.

"Did you find water there, Mr. Woolley?" Gudmundson asked.

"Maybe." Hiram continued his pacing, swinging the Mosaical Rod back and forth.

"There might be a scientific explanation," Michael said softly, walking at Hiram's shoulder. Hiram would have sworn Michael had grown an inch so far this year—at seventeen, he was already taller than his adopted father, and might have years left to grow. Michael's biological father, Yas Yazzie, had been a big, strong man.

"For the dowsing rod?"

Michael nodded. "You know, some plants turn toward the sun as the sun moves. Maybe some plants sense and turn toward water, too. So they know where to send their roots. Didn't you tell me that the hazel rod has to be fresh?"

"As fresh as possible," Hiram agreed. "But what does your scientific explanation say about why I have to sing a Psalm before I dowse?"

"I guess in my scientific *hypothesis*, you wouldn't have to sing a Psalm. Or cut crosses." Michael pondered, and for a brief time all Hiram heard was the crunch of their boots on the earth and the distant whistle of wind coming down from the La Sals. "I could devise a scientific experiment to test that."

"Hmm." Hiram had dowsed far too many impossible answers out of Mosaical Rods, and far too many secret doors and buried treasure, to give any credence to Michael's hypothesis. But he also didn't want to discourage Michael's interest in science—for all that Michael had learned about Hiram's traditional practices and was starting to master them, they both still expected that the day would come, and soon, when Michael would go to college to study chemistry or geology.

Other than driving, Michael was with Hiram to learn Grandma Hettie's lore. This was a recent development. Until February of that year, Hiram had kept secret from his son the fact that he used the same charms, hexes, and lore that his grandma had. But in order to defeat a demon in a cavern beneath a coal mine, Hiram had had to reveal his craft to his son. Michael had accepted the news surprisingly well, and asked to learn it himself.

But the young man still struggled to believe that it was real.

"You worried about coyotes, Rex?" Pout asked. The men from Moab drifted slowly behind Hiram, and within earshot. "That why you're putting up fence?"

"I'm going to have goats," Whittle answered. "I don't want them to run off, so I want a fence. And yeah, coyotes or wolves or whatever. You know some hunters up in the La Sals saw tracks of Three Toe as recently as just this spring. Jeff Webb was with them, he told me himself Three Toe had taken down an elk. Alone."

"That's one way you know Three Toe ain't real," Clem said. "Wolves hunt in packs. There's no solitary ghost wolf missing a toe who runs around killing bears and elk. And didn't folks already kill him?"

"Maybe, maybe not," Smothers said. "But there have been reports of his tracks in Colorado and Wyoming and Montana, so if he's not real, he sure leaves his mark."

"*I* worry about Three Toe," Preece said, "as well as about normal wolves. But predators are one of the risks you run when you take on ranching."

Hiram felt a second tug on the rod. This one was stronger, but still not as distinct as he'd like. He wasn't doing Rex Whittle much of a service if he placed a weak well for the man. Hiram looked around and realized, also, that he had drifted far from the plank cabin and its low chicken coop. Ideally, a well would be right beside the house.

He didn't bother marking the ground, but turned his course toward the house.

"I thought I saw the rod dip," Michael said.

"Yeah," Hiram agreed. "But remember, we're not out here looking for water like . . . scientists, I guess. We're not disinterested researchers. We're not just making a map. We're looking for water that's good for that man's family. That means we need to find enough, and in a good location."

"Ah," Michael said. "This water is too far from the house."

They walked a few moments in silence, drawing closer to the cabin as they pivoted around the watching men.

"I like being out here with you," Michael said. "I

like that we help the poor and the unfortunate. A lot of people have opinions galore, but we actually provide a service."

Hiram cracked a grin. "You're saying you're not quite as excited about planting sugar beets?"

As he said the word *beets*, the rod dipped again. This time the dip was abrupt and violent, and the tip of the rod slammed into the earth. It was dramatic enough that the watching men could see it. Clem cursed.

Hiram looked up—he was within an easy stone's throw of the cabin. He swung the rod several more times, and each time the tip of the hazel branch plunged, striking the earth in the same location each time.

Hiram marked out the spot with his foot. "Come feel this," he said to his son.

With a deep breath, Michael took the rod in his hands.

"Don't *grip* the rod," Hiram suggested. "Curl your fingers, and let it lie loose in there. You want it to be able to move. Take a step away and swing the rod gently back and forth. Yeah, just like that. Now step toward the spot I marked, still letting the rod swing. Good job."

The rod swung over Hiram's X, and the tip plunged right into the letter's center.

"Holy . . ." Michael said. "Sh . . . cr . . ."

Hiram patted his son on the back. "Good job not cussing."

"You hit water?" Rex Whittle called.

"This will make a good well," Hiram told him. "We'll walk the property and see if we can find any

that are even better, but in the meantime, why don't
you mark this spot with a rock cairn?" A summer
rain or even a strong wind might obliterate Hiram's X.

"Good work," Gudmund Gudmundson said cheer-
fully. "Rex, I've got six men lined up to come back
on Monday and dig her out for you."

Rex Whittle looked suddenly bashful. "To tell you
the truth, I . . . thanks, Bishop."

The men from Moab piled up rocks on the spot
Hiram indicated. Hiram and Michael quickly paced out
the circle of land that was closer to the cabin. The rod
tugged twice more, but they were faint motions, and
Hiram didn't bother to mention them to Rex Whittle.

When they had finished, Hiram put the rod into
the cab of his Model AA Ford truck. A dowsing rod
wasn't a sacred thing, exactly, but it was close to being
sacred. Hiram preferred to burn a used rod rather
than merely cast it aside.

Rex Whittle thanked Hiram and Michael both.
"You won't take money, but I'd be pleased if you'd
take some pie."

"It's good to be married to a woman who can
bake." Hiram smiled.

Whittle snorted. "My wife can't cook for sweet
goddamn. That woman would burn water. But *I* bake
the best peach pie in Grand County."

"We'd love pie," Michael said.

Whittle jogged up to the cabin. Gudmundson waved
goodbye and Clem spat affably, and then both men
climbed into the bishop's blue-green Buick Series 40
and rattled away toward town. Smothers and Pout
drove away in a Model T that seemed to lean sideways
at a forty-five-degree angle.

Lloyd Preece shook Hiram's and Michael's hands.

"You looked interested when you heard mention of the ghost," the rancher said.

Hiram shrugged. "I guess. A ghost is generally someone who died with unfinished business, maybe betrayed or terrified. A ghost is someone who needs help."

The rancher raised his eyebrows. "You planning to help the *ghost*?"

"Maybe," Hiram allowed.

"That seems a little bit out of the purview of the Presiding Bishop."

Hiram chuckled. "Jesus helps everyone. I guess I can try to do the same."

Preece nodded. "Well, if you do, come by the house and tell me how it went."

"You connected with that ghost?" Hiram asked.

Preece nodded. "It's on my land! Or rather, it's close. If you take the cable car near where you're camped across the river, there's a path that cuts into the Monument and eventually connects with the road. That road takes you to the Schoolmarm's Bloomers, and that's where people say they saw the ghost. The wash beneath the arch. You can drive, but it'll take you longer—you have to go in on the west side of the Monument."

"This ghost been around a long time?" Hiram asked.

"I only heard of it recently."

"Do you know a name?" Hiram continued.

The rancher shrugged.

"And the bloomers," Michael said, "just how racy are they? My Pap here is awkward around women, and I'd hate for him to feel uncomfortable."

Lloyd Preece laughed. "Lonely cowboys. They get out away from women, and every rock formation they see is named *nipple* or *crotch*."

"And who can blame them?" Michael said.

Hiram chuckled, feeling slightly uneasy.

"If you don't find me at home," Preece said, "come into town and try the Maxwell House Hotel. I'm a widower, you know, and sometimes I go out. There's a group of us—an informal gathering, ranchers, bankers, good people—who like to meet at the watering hole there on evenings. Especially at the weekend."

"Share tips on branding?" Michael asked. "Compare balance sheets?"

"Yes." Preece smiled, and he reached down to roll up the cuff of one pant leg. From the top of a tall boot, he pulled a knife in its sheath. The hilt was definitely silver, and there was writing on the cross-piece. Hiram wished he knew Hebrew—or anything beyond mere English—but in the moment in which he saw the letters, before Preece wrapped his hand around the hilt, he wouldn't have been able to read anything. That dagger seemed to be a twin to the one Gudmund wore on his hip. Were they some kind of lodge brothers? "We discuss business. And also, we are vain, and like to be seen as successful. You'd be surprised how much time a man like me spends looking into the mirror."

Preece laughed at his own joke, then climbed into his truck, a newer and shinier Model AA, and drove away.

"It wasn't just the ghost that got your attention," Michael said. "You perked right up at the mention of that woman who can cure the falling sickness."

"I did," Hiram agreed. "But that's me being selfish."

"So we'll go see her *after* we see to the ghost?"

"You're learning."

Rex Whittle returned with a peach pie and two forks. Hiram and Michael ate it in the truck; Hiram managed two of the six thick wedges before he felt he would burst. Michael ate the rest.

Chapter Two

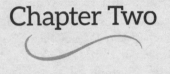

THE DIRT ROAD DRIFTING DOWN SPANISH VALLEY toward the highway was rippled and hard like a washboard. Hiram gritted his teeth and smiled to avoid telling Michael how to drive, but the pie swung around in his stomach like a baseball in a sock. The constant rattle of the Model AA nearly made him throw up.

"How old were you when Grandma Hettie first taught you to dowse?" Michael asked.

"I don't remember a first time." Hiram was grateful for the distraction. "I suppose that means I must have seen her do it when I was very young. She taught me . . . well, I was a little younger than you are now."

"What about your mother and father?" Michael asked. "Did you ever watch either of them dowse a well? Or, you know, open a locked door, or heal cowpox, or do anything else with . . . with lore like Grandma Hettie's?"

Michael didn't say "magic."

"No." Hiram had rarely seen his father doing anything at all; Abner Woolley was a polygamist, and he had neglected Hiram and his mother in favor of his other families, even before he had finally lit out for Mexico. The closest he'd ever come to performing an act of craft in Hiram's presence was a blessing of comfort he had once offered Hiram, at the end of a brief visit. Hands heavy on his son's head, Abner had sternly enjoined Hiram to obedience and patience, promising that all suffering would be repaid in the fullness of time. Hiram's neck had hurt for an hour after his father had left. "My mother...sang the Psalms. She knew Grandma Hettie's melodies, but she didn't use them to do anything. She just liked to sing."

Michael cleared his throat. "And after she, uh, disappeared...did you ever dowse to find out where she went? What happened to her? The Mosaical Rod can answer yes and no questions, can't it?"

The light reflecting off the white and orange rock was intense. Hiram rubbed both his eyes with his knuckles. His mother had vanished one night after his father had abandoned them. Hiram had tried various divination techniques to discover her fate, and had yet to learn anything. The mystery made him feel ill at ease.

"It's like twenty questions, right?" Michael pressed. "Is my mother alive? Is she in the United States? Is she in Utah? If the rod works, you ought to get answers."

"You know the rod works." Hiram's voice was suddenly hoarse. "You saw it work today."

"I know you miss your mom, Pap. You *must* have asked these questions. And if you didn't get answers... maybe the rod doesn't work, after all. Maybe I was fooling myself, back there on Whittle's farm. Or did you get answers you don't want to share with me?"

"I asked." Hiram's eyes stung, and he squeezed

them shut. "I never got any real answers. Never could figure it out."

"Damn," Michael said.

Hiram nodded. He had skirted a lie. He had divined after his mother's fate more than once, and never been able to make any sense of the answers. *Is my mother alive? No. Is my mother dead? No.*

The dirt road poured down onto the highway at a steep angle, cutting through a knotted grove of juniper trees. As Michael shifted down and the Double-A groaned into compliance, Hiram saw a flash of blue-green metal through the foliage.

"Cars!" he snapped.

Michael brought the truck careening over to the side of the road faster than Hiram would have done. His son also braked more abruptly than Hiram liked, but he put the Model AA right behind a blue-green Buick Series 40 that sat at the mouth of the gravel road: Bishop Gudmundson's car. Beyond the Buick, a Model AA Ford truck sat parked on the highway; it was an older version of Hiram's own vehicle, dark blue and dusty. Gray men in overalls stood around it, slapping their hats on their knees. The ranch hand Clem stood with them. Beyond that, on the highway's shoulder, sat Lloyd Preece's much newer truck.

"Maybe get a bottle of water from the back," Hiram suggested.

Michael turned off the truck and climbed into the back to get water. Hiram descended to join the other men. As he got closer, he could see that the hood of the truck was raised, and both Lloyd Preece and Bishop Gudmundson were poking around beneath it.

"Woolley!" Gudmundson called. "Perfect, I was

hoping you hadn't taken that turn south back there. Do you have a crescent wrench? Stupid me, I was in the middle of fixing a sink before I had to get up to Rex's place, and I left all my tools back in town!"

Lloyd raised a hand. "Glad you stopped, Hiram."

Hiram put a finger to the brim of his hat.

"I'll get the wrench, Pap!" Michael called from the back of Hiram's truck.

Hiram joined the men around the Model AA, looking both ways up the highway. "Five men and a truck. You fellows work for one of the ranchers around here?"

As he asked the question, he thought he knew the answer. Battered trunks and suitcases sat in the back of the vehicle, and the men's clothing was frayed at every edge, sweater elbows unraveling and soiled collars flapping loose.

"We would," one of the men answered. He was deeply tanned, short, and unshaven, and he smelled like cigarette smoke. "You know anyone who's got work?"

"You aren't from Grand County, are you, brother?" Bishop Gudmundson asked.

The short man shook his head. "I've come from Colorado looking for work. Some of these boys have come a lot farther than that."

"We'll get this started, no problem." Preece pointed along the highway. "Moab is that way. It's the only town of any size within fifty miles. Go to the Maxwell House Hotel, tell them you're looking for work, and that you're friends with Lloyd Preece and Gudmund Gudmundson. Leon should be able to set you up."

"I don't know about hotel work," the short man said. "But I'm handy enough, and I'm up for any kind of manual labor."

Clem spat. "There's work. You come to the right place."

Preece scratched his head. "Maybe Don Pout has something for them."

Gudmundson shrugged. "Maybe. You know what I'd do, Lloyd?"

Preece grinned. "I expect you'll tell me."

"All the town's ranchers meet at the Maxwell House for drinks," Gudmundson said. "The hotel staff know who's hiring. They should try there."

Preece laughed long and hard. "That's a great idea, Bishop. I'm so glad you thought of it."

Gudmundson smiled. "And if Gudmundson is too strange a name to remember, these fellows can tell Leon the bishop sent them."

The short man chuckled. "What's that? A nickname?"

Gudmundson laughed, too. "You could say that."

Hiram found himself smiling.

Michael arrived with the crescent wrench and two bottles of water. He handed the wrench to Bishop Gudmundson and one bottle to the short man. He handed the second bottle to another of the migrants. They were glass bottles, with cork stoppers wired to their mouths, full of well water pumped in Lehi. "Sorry it isn't cold," he told them. "We've been out in the desert all day."

"Sorry it isn't a *woman*," a tall migrant with a sharp nose shot back, "but I'll take what I can get!"

A raucous round of laughter petered out quickly as the men passed the bottles around. Gudmundson emerged from the engine and closed the truck's hood. He was covered in grease up to his elbows and had a big smear of grease on one cheek, but he was smiling. "Should start now."

The hawk-nosed migrant climbed into the truck and started it. The engine rumbled smoothly into life and Gudmundson patted the hood. "You shouldn't need a replacement part," he called to the men as they climbed into the back of the Model AA. "I guess you'll get ten thousand more miles out of it."

"I can't pay you gentlemen," the short migrant said. "Maybe if I get a job in town I can find you."

Lloyd waved a hand. "Not at all. When I'm down on my luck, someday, you'll be the one helping me." He reached into his working coat and pulled out a calf-skin wallet. He peeled off a hundred dollars in twenties, right there. "Or someone else will."

Michael gasped.

Lloyd pressed a twenty-dollar bill into each vagrant's hand.

The tall man with the sharp nose stood blinking. "Why, I'd fight you not to take charity, but I reckon you'd fight me back. You sure?"

"We're sure." Gudmundson marched forward and slapped the tall man on the back. "Lloyd's set for money," the bishop said. "Me, I work for other reasons than money. And this fellow here," he jerked a thumb at Hiram, "he's even worse than I am. Don't be like him. He turns money down left and right."

Hiram smiled. "I have what I need."

"Can't argue with that. I reckon with this depression going, God is busier than a one-armed paper hanger giving folks what they need. Like he brought you here for us today. And we appreciate it." The short man collected the two glass bottles and handed them to Michael. He bowed before Preece. "Mister, we needed this windfall bad. But we won't just drink it away. We're gonna go on to that hotel and find work. We have families. We'll send the money." He climbed into the back of the truck with his fellows, and they drove up the road toward Moab.

"Well done, Woolley," the bishop said.

"I didn't do anything." Hiram clapped Michael on the shoulder. "Well done, Michael, getting two bottles out when I suggested one."

"I just thought they looked thirsty," Michael said, "and I asked myself how much water I would want someone to offer me, if *I* was that thirsty."

"That is the most profound sermon I am going to hear today," Bishop Gudmundson said. "Now if you brethren will excuse me, I better get back to that sink, or Ida Mae Stokes will never let me hear the end of it."

Preece nodded at Hiram. "You and your boy take care, now."

The rancher drove off first. The bishop and Clem climbed into the Buick and Hiram and Michael returned to the Double-A. "Are we really going to go help this ghost?" Michael asked.

"At least we'll go look for it," Hiram said. "If we *can* help it, we will."

Michael shut his eyes and sighed. "Helping men in need makes perfect sense to me. Helping ghosts forces me to question your sanity, Pap." His eyes popped open, and he grinned at Hiram to show he was kidding.

Hiram laughed. "Sometimes, I question it myself."

They got into the truck and pulled back onto the road.

He didn't say what he was thinking—he could barely

admit it to himself. Not entirely consciously, Hiram believed that if he worked hard enough, if he was good enough, if he helped enough people, then maybe... just maybe... Hiram might be able to reconnect with some of what he'd lost in his life.

Maybe he'd be able to find his mother.

Someday.

Chapter Three

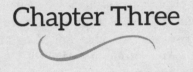

HIRAM AND MICHAEL HAD SET UP CAMP IN A FOREST of juniper trees alongside the Colorado River. The canyon was wide enough to allow the river a little room to meander. The wide flow of water was fenced in on the southeast and the northwest by high, red rock walls. They'd found a ring of scorched stones around old charcoal beside a small patch of bare sand, indicating a prior camper's use, and they'd pitched their tent on the sand. The junipers in the area were sparse enough that Michael could drive from the road to the campsite, but thick enough to hide the Double-A from the view of casual passersby.

The Preece house—a surprisingly modest cabin—was visible farther from the river, against the south-eastern cliff and near where the road cut through the canyon.

Fifteen minutes of exploring the riverbank found the cable car Lloyd Preece had told them about. An iron cable stretched across the river, bolted into a cliff on the northwest side, and on the southeast into a boulder larger than a house. The big stone had once been part of the cliff, but had been carved out and then left behind by the millennially-slow action of the river. A rusty iron bucket hung suspended from a track of wheels that gripped the cable; the bucket was shaped like a bathtub, but was large enough to hold two cushioned seats, one at each end, both facing the center and riveted to the floor. A long, thick spring coiled around the cable kept the car from touching the boulder. A second cable ran alongside the first, but slightly lower. Hiram and Michael set their knapsacks on the floor and climbed into the seats, Hiram facing forward while Michael faced back. They hauled themselves across the river, hand over hand along the second line.

"We're pulling uphill." Michael grunted.

Hiram nodded. "The cliff on the other side is much taller than the boulder on this side. Don't let go or we'll slide back."

Michael grinned. "Crossing the other way will be tons more fun."

The ride ended on a red-rock ledge high over the river. Rock cairns marked their trail onward, up a narrow defile. Hiram improvised a brake for the cable car by shoving a dried-out bit of juniper wood into the wheels above the car.

"What if that breaks while we're gone?" Michael asked. "The car will cross the river without us."

"Good thing we know how to swim."

"As a mode of transportation," Michael said, "this cable car has some limitations."

They shouldered their knapsacks and started up the trail. The bags held food but especially water in the wire-topped glass bottles. They also brought along wool blankets, as well as a few select items from Hiram's toolbox of accouterments that he thought they might need. Hiram, in particular, carried a kerosene lantern.

They hiked up the trail plotted out by cairns. The Schoolmarm's Bloomers were marked on Hiram's map—the Bloomers were a rock formation with multiple names, one of the many red-rock arches that had caused President Hoover to declare the area a national monument. Hiram had seen arches before, but never the Bloomers. Apparently, this arch was one of the most striking, and that fact, together with the area's new status as a national monument, had some people anxious to find an official name for the formation, something a bit more reserved.

Hiram had also heard the stones called the Cowboy Chaps and the Devil's Crotch. He found himself looking forward to actually seeing it.

Once through the defile, they found themselves hiking across a broken tableland. Sagebrush, juniper, and thin clumps of tall grass decorated a landscape that seemed to have no water and a large surplus of red stone sculpted into improbable shapes. Red goblins haunted the turns, and orange trolls with long noses leaned forward out of the rock overhangs. The neat stacks of rock continued to lead them, but otherwise, there was little to indicate a trail. From time to time, the fading print of a boot suggested prior human passage.

An hour's walk brought them to their first tire-rutted road. They rested there briefly and drank water. Hiram's fedora was so full of sweat he nearly twisted it to wring the moisture out.

The next time they came, they'd bring the truck and drive the long way around.

From this point, their trail paralleled the road.

After sunset, with the light waning, they passed a campsite, a hundred feet from their trail and right at the edge of the ruts. A large tent stood beside crates, suggesting that the camper had come in by automobile, but there was no car in sight, and when Hiram hailed the camp, no answer came back.

"What do you think?" Hiram asked his son. "Does that look like a preacher's tent to you? Or a prospector's?"

"I don't see stacks of Bibles lying around," Michael said, "*or* pickaxes."

They kept hiking.

Later still, they passed a dugout house, built into the side of a tawny yellow landslide, the walls stacked like rock pancakes. A black tarpaulin-reinforced roof stuck out of the side of the hill. A wax-paper window showed a yellow light inside. Woodsmoke and bacon perfumed the night air. A silhouette near the window might be a Plymouth Model 30U, though without a moon there wasn't enough light to be certain.

Hiram's stomach rumbled, but they had work to do.

The night sky was moonless, so they found their way with flashlights.

"I'm not complaining," Michael said, "but this is somewhat farther than I had appreciated."

"I'm glad you're not complaining."

An hour later, they were tramping up a wooded wash fenced in by steep-sloping stone walls, and Hiram consulted his map. "We should be able to see the Bloomers any moment."

"I looked at your map earlier," Michael said. "I believe you mean we should be able to see Pants Crotch."

"I'm sorry I couldn't protect you from that knowledge." Hiram chuckled.

"I almost had to use the smelling salts on myself."

Hiram looked up and saw the arch, and it took his breath away.

Some arches were hard to see, clinging tightly to canyon walls. Others stood overhead and a person could follow the river that had formed them and walk right underneath. The Schoolmarm's Bloomers stood alone on a promontory of rock above the head of the wash, as if in defiance of all geological probabilities. If a river had carved the arch, it had also wiped out everything around it, and then disappeared. The arch was tall, majestic, and irregular, but also perfect; it did look like someone's long legs and hips, cocked slightly to one side, and Hiram wasn't even seeing it very clearly—with no sun and also no moon, he saw the Bloomers mostly as the starless darkness of the rock's silhouette, with a faint silver-orange icing around the edge where the light struck it.

"She could kick me to the Gulf of Mexico," Michael said. "If that were my schoolmarm, I'd be on my very best behavior."

"If that were your teacher," Hiram said, "so would I."

"Do we climb?" Michael pointed out the slope leading up to the Bloomers. A man might have to lean forward and steady himself with his hands at several points, but the rock wasn't a sheer cliff, and could be ascended.

Hiram looked about. The yellow grass shivered in a faint breeze. The presence of a pair of cottonwoods and a grove of aspens suggested that there was water near the surface. Maybe a rock seep Hiram couldn't see in the darkness, though he didn't smell moisture, either. "I don't think so. We're in the wash below the Bloomers now."

Michael took one step closer to Hiram. "I'm not going to tell you what science says about ghosts."

"I guess I don't think you need to." Hiram set down his pack and took the lantern in hand. He shook it gently to be sure its fuel tank was full, then turned the wick knob to get a suitable amount of cotton available.

"What are you going to do?" Michael asked.

"Talk to the ghost," Hiram said. "If there is one."

He found a raised bar of sand and set the lantern down. With a long match, he lit the wick and then replaced the glass chimney.

"Where should I stand?" Michael asked.

"Just take a step or two back," Hiram suggested. "Maybe here with me."

Michael quickly found his place at Hiram's side. "I don't suppose ghosts have vocal cords, even if they do exist. So how do they talk?"

"Various ways," Hiram said. "But they can all manipulate flame. Fire and light are highly refined matter—everything is matter, even spirit. Spirit is just the most highly refined matter there is, that's what Brother Joseph taught. Almost sounds scientific, doesn't it?"

"It's not like any science I've ever heard of."

That made Hiram laugh. "We'll ask the ghost to manipulate the flame."

Michael reached his hand inside his jacket. He was touching his chi-rho medallion, the iron amulet that both men wore that protected them from enemies.

When Michael was younger, Hiram had hidden the metal disk in the heel of his son's boot, but now that the youngster knew his father was a cunning man, he wore the amulet on his chest.

Hiram resisted the urge to touch his own talisman. He cleared his throat.

"My name is Hiram Woolley," he said in a loud voice. "I've been told there's someone here." Silence. Then a distant hoot. "Maybe someone in distress."

"Would it help if we knew the ghost's name?" Michael whispered.

"It probably would." Hiram raised his voice again. "If there's anyone here, I've brought a light so we can communicate. Maybe you can see it. It's an oil lantern, and I've set it on the ground. I just want to talk."

Silence. The air was still, and the flame of the lantern stood straight upright.

"If you can hear me," Hiram said, speaking slowly and loudly, "make the flame of my lantern dance."

The lantern's flame bent sharply sideways, once.

Michael sucked in a sudden breath. "Impossible."

Hiram nodded. "I want to help you," he called out to the ghost.

The night was still and cold.

"I'm going to ask you some questions," Hiram continued. "If the answer to any of my questions is yes, make the flame dance again, just as you did a moment ago." He considered his questions. "Are you an adult?"

The flame stood still. *No.*

"Are you a child?"

The flame danced. *Yes.*

"Are you from Moab? Did you live near here somewhere? Did you live on the Monument?"

No. Yes. Yes.

"Do you know what killed you?"

Yes.

"Was it an accident? Were you killed by disease? Were you murdered by a family member?"

No. No. No.

"Were you killed by wild animals?"

Yes.

"That's a bit odd," Hiram murmured.

"No," Michael said. "It's *really* odd. Not only is there no wind, but the lantern has the glass chimney over it. That flame should be still as a stone, but it's snapping sideways. Pap, I...it..." Michael struggled to find words.

"It's answering my questions," Hiram said.

"Unless there's some other explanation." Michael chuckled nervously. "But if you're talking to a ghost, Pap...is it really an *it*?"

Hiram addressed the ghost again. "Are you a boy?"

Yes.

"He, then." Michael was trembling, just a bit.

"What's slightly odd," Hiram said, "is that he was killed by animals. Usually a ghost has unfinished business, like revenge. So ghosts tend to result from murders and suicides, or strange supernatural deaths."

"Huh."

"Did you die in the last year?" Hiram asked. "Less than nine months ago? Less than six months ago? About eight months ago?"

Yes. Yes. No. Yes.

"This is getting eerily precise," Michael said.

"What else should we ask?"

"It might take some time," Michael suggested,

"but we could get him to spell out his name. Twenty questions again."

"Do you know how to spell your name?" Hiram called out to the ghost.

No.

"Oh," Michael said.

"Were you less than twelve years old when you died?" Hiram pressed. "Eleven? Ten?"

Yes. Yes. No.

"He was ten," Michael said. "Ten's kind of old to not be able to spell your own name."

"Is your family poor?" Hiram asked the spirit.

Yes.

"There can't be that many families living on the Monument," Michael said.

"No," Hiram agreed. "For starters, I'd like to talk to the people in that dugout we passed, not to mention whoever is staying in the campsite."

"What do we do when we find out who the ghost is?" Michael asked. "And what he wants?"

"We lay him to rest."

"How do we do that?" Michael asked.

"That depends," Hiram said.

"On what?"

"Whether he resists," Hiram said. "Whether we can get him the justice he feels he needs."

"Could you just, I don't know, exorcise him right now? Cast him out and be done with him?"

"I could try," Hiram said. "But that might be a wicked act. Wouldn't you rather see justice done, if possible?"

"If possible," Michael agreed. "But if justice means we're hunting some three-toed ghost wolf that ranges all over the Rocky Mountains eating bears and ten-year-old children, I think I might be willing to just go straight for an exorcism now."

"There's probably no three-toed ghost wolf."

"You said 'probably,' Pap."

"Well, there are strange things in the world."

Hiram could think of no more questions to ask the spirit, and neither could Michael. Hiram thanked the ghost boy and then blew out the lantern, plunging them into darkness relieved only by a few stars.

They bedded down among the aspens, wrapping themselves in their wool blankets. Michael made his bed closer to Hiram than he usually would have, as if he was nervous, but his breathing fell immediately into the rhythms of sleep.

Hiram lay awake, watching the stars. Hercules and the Summer Triangle stared down at him with no answers. He touched the ring on his left hand with the fingers of his right, evoking Saturn and the power of visionary dreams it possessed. With his crop in the ground, Hiram didn't need to be back at the farm immediately, but still, he didn't want to linger too long in Moab. He wanted to help this ghost, but he also wanted to do it quickly.

Who was the boy and why had he died?

Hiram jerked awake. Overhead, Hercules and the Summer Triangle were gone, replaced by...Andromeda? Perseus? He wasn't sure. In any case, hours had passed.

Michael's breathing was deep and regular.

Hiram's mouth was dry, and he had a kink in his neck. Sitting up, he reached for a water bottle—

and saw the boy.

The boy, however refined the matter that comprised

him, shouldn't have been visible. With no moon, even a boy of flesh and bones should have been an invisible shadow, one more object in the sea of shadows swamping the bottom of the wash.

Instead, Hiram saw him clearly. The jacket, too big for him and frayed at the sleeves and collar, with one button missing, so probably a hand-me-down. Alive, his sun-pink skin might have had freckles. Dead, his pale flesh made those freckles look like mud spackle. His curly brown hair was long enough to make him look wild. The boot-laces were knotted and re-knotted to repair them.

"Hello," Hiram said.

The boy slowly raised his arms. The sleeves of the jacket fell down to his elbows and the front hung open, exposing his forearms and neck. All down his arms, Hiram saw bite marks. The indentations left by teeth were raw and red, bleeding slightly. The boy tipped his head back and Hiram saw more bite marks on his throat.

The jawline that had left those marks was circular, and the canines were understated.

They looked like bites left by human teeth.

Hiram sat up suddenly.

Morning light filled the wash, revealing explosions of golden grass and pale green weeds near the dusty red of the stone walls. Above, pink in the bright early sunshine, the Schoolmarm's Bloomers presided in a calm and stately fashion.

Michael snored deeply beside him.

Hiram rubbed sleep from his eyes. He didn't need to consult his dream dictionary to know what he'd seen; the ghost had appeared to him.

But bite marks from human teeth? Hiram dug the dream dictionary from his knapsack and thumbed through his handwritten notes, looking for any explanation. He found none.

He jostled Michael gently. "Come on, son. Time to get a move on."

"Why?"

"Because I wanted to see the widow Artemis."

Michael rose, groggy, his black hair dusty from their night out under the sky. "That's right. From ghosts to widows. I almost forgot about the so-called Diana Artemis. We wouldn't want you miss your hot date."

"I wouldn't call it a date. But yeah, let's go see what she might know." She might know something about the ghost. Or, if Hiram could get a permanent solution to his sleeping sickness, then Michael would be free to go on to college. Hiram could then drive himself around to do his work.

As he watched Michael fold up his blanket and strap it to his knapsack, Hiram found the idea lonesome. But Michael deserved a better life than to be a beet farmer and a village cunning man.

Hiram rose and began rolling up his bedding.

Chapter Four

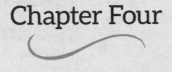

COULD GHOSTS REALLY EXIST?

Michael wanted so much to doubt even the possibility. He *did* doubt the possibility. From all the science he had ever learned, it seemed to him impossible that ghosts could exist. Heaven and hell...okay, *maybe*. But ghosts? No way.

And yet the flame had moved.

The image of that flame leaping sideways at his pap's questions was the first thing on Michael's mind when he had awoken. He couldn't quite shake the thought that there was an enormous world beyond his grasp, a world of which he was only just beginning to learn the rules, a world whose very existence made him uncomfortable. Part of him wanted to retreat, pull back from that larger universe.

But there was also power in that world. Power that could bring down fire from heaven, and see through lies, and stop bullets. And Michael had his pap for a guide.

And that was why he was still going along with his pap. To the ghost wash last night, and now to see the widow Artemis. He was undecided what to think about her, too, but she seemed to be part of this large, untamed new world, so maybe she could help his pap. On the other hand, the name *Diana Artemis* was simply ridiculous. If she'd come in on a circus train, it would make sense. As it was, the name just didn't fit a widow living in the dusty end of a Utah desert town, five hundred miles away from anything interesting.

Diana and Artemis were both the same goddess, weren't they? The Roman and the Greek versions of the goddess of the hunt?

If it wasn't a fake name, the widow Artemis's mother had played a cruel joke on her.

They hiked away from the Schoolmarm's Bloomers and made their way down the wash. They knocked on the dugout's leather-hinged door, but unlike the previous night, nobody was home. Towels and dish-cloths, long dried, flapped on the line.

The campsite beside the road was similarly deserted.

Michael had a brief vision of himself and his pap with the lantern out, trying to talk to more ghosts at the campsite and at the dugout. He shivered, despite the heat, and hoped the inhabitants were simply away from home. One ghost—if there were such things—was enough.

They reached the cable car at midday, finding it still wedged into place with the bit of juniper. They climbed in, gasping as the bucket swung wildly with each new addition of weight, and then Pap yanked the brake out and they began to roll.

Riding down wasn't as thrilling as Michael had expected. He'd expected a chute-the-chute experience, like he'd had at the county fair up in Lehi. Instead, the wheels squealed as they slowly slid over the brown waters of the river below.

Back at their camp proper, they were eating cold biscuits when the bishop's blue-green Series 40 pulled up. He slowed down as he approached, and parked a short distance from their camp; it was a polite way to drive up, that didn't throw dust over Michael and his pap.

Gudmundson got out and approached on foot. He wore a dirty work shirt and blue jeans, and had grease on his knuckles.

"One thing I will say about you Mormons," Michael said. "You have the most unbishoply bishops imaginable."

Gudmundson grinned. "'You Mormons'? You're not a Mormon yourself, then?"

"Formally, I suppose," Michael conceded, "but I'm more of a free thinker."

"Then I'll take your observation on bishops as a compliment."

Michael nodded solemnly. "That's how it was intended."

"I'm a free thinker myself," Gudmundson added.

"You look like you've come from work," Hiram said, swallowing the last of his biscuit.

Gudmundson laughed, holding up his hands to show dirty fingernails. "I only ever really have time to clean them on Sunday mornings. But yes, I was out working this morning. I got a call that Ernie Smothers needs help moving."

"Moving house?" Hiram asked. "What happened?"

"Tree fell over and crushed the roof," the bishop said. "Thank God no one was hurt. But Ernie's wife Bobette tracked me down and I found a few rooms they can rent, so I'm going over to help them move their beds and dressers now. My Buick's pretty good for carrying around people, but not as good as a truck for hauling furniture."

"We're happy to help," Hiram said. "Why don't you drive and we'll follow?"

"Pap," Michael said as they reached the road behind the bishop's blue-green car, "remind me. In the Bible, was it Moab that had all the fleshpots?" He wasn't really sure what fleshpots were, but it sure sounded decadent.

"Egypt," his pap said.

"Nuts."

It was hot, even with the windows rolled down, and Michael felt sweat slip down the side of his face. They left the greenery and murky, fertile scents of the Colorado River behind. He and his pap puttered through the odor of hot sandstone behind Bishop Gudmundson for what seemed like hours, finally passing a sign that said simply MOAB, and then immediately hitting the town's main road. Michael turned left.

A mile further on, they drove into Moab's downtown. It was a short downtown, with brick buildings and whitewashed wood along the main street. Like most towns in Utah, Moab was laid out in a grid system, blocks counted north, south, east, west, from a central point, which in this case was Main Street and Center. Beyond the stores, sheltered by sparse trees, Michael glimpsed adobe houses. Sunshine flashed off windshields of only a handful of parked cars. There were nearly as many horses, mules, and wagons as automobiles in sight.

Friday at noon, Moab wasn't exactly hopping.

Could its Friday nights be much better?

The town's main street was made of packed red dirt with irrigation ditches dug on either side. A wooden walkway lined the street along the storefronts, and hitching posts still stood in front of some of the buildings. Michael shifted down and the Double-A muttered in protest. "Well, Pap, you're certainly showing me the grand metropolises of the world. First Helper, and now Moab. Eventually, I figure we'll just camp out in a ghost town. Oh, wait, is Moab a ghost town already?"

"That might be a little harsh."

"Are you worried I'm going to hurt Moab's feelings?" Michael sighed. "All I'm saying is, next time, let's get invited to a big city to dig a well. To Salt Lake, at least."

"I'll do my best."

"The streets are so wide," Michael said. "I bet it was to allow for the big horse teams, so you could park your wagons here, hitch up your horses, and go get a beer. Or buy hardtack and coffee from the Moab Co-Op, or maybe from the Banjo & Sons Mercantile back a ways. We should probably go to the co-op. The place looks like it's on its last legs, unlike the mercantile."

Pap made a sound of agreement in the back of his throat.

"Moab." Michael felt the word in his mouth. "It's not fleshpots, but it is biblical, right?"

"Ruth came from Moab," Hiram said. "And the Moabites worshipped idols."

"Ruth...the widow?" Michael pressed.

Hiram said nothing.

"Mr. Preece and Mr. Gudmundson are nice," Michael continued. "And hey, Bishop Gudmundson helps the needy, right? People with their roofs smashed in? Guys who need jobs? He's like us. And Preece practically *leaks* twenty-dollar bills on the poor. So maybe a little idol worship isn't so bad for the soul."

That brought sighs out of his father.

"So, I saw a movie theatre, the Ides, and a couple of dance halls, Woodmen of the West and the Star, but no brothels. Come on, Pap, where are the brothels?"

But his pap had stopped sighing and his mouth was getting small, his brow furrowed.

Michael decided to let up. "Okay, okay, if we need food, I bet the Williams Drugstore would have a soda fountain. Or we passed that hotel Mr. Preece and the bishop both mentioned, the Maxwell House Hotel, on 100 North, and that'll definitely have a kitchen. And beds. We could stay there, because however much I like sleeping on dirt, I'd much rather have a bed. And I like hotels."

"You'll want to take this next left." Pap pointed.

Michael didn't hide his annoyance. "Yeah, the old pioneers didn't take too many risks with their addresses. I could find 160 East 300 South Street with my eyes closed. Thank you, Nauvoo, Illinois. Did Mormons really try out this grid system there first?"

"First in the world? I doubt it." Pap rested his arm on the window ledge and ran his fingers through his hair. "But Joseph laid out his city on a grid in the 1840s, so that must have been pretty early for planned American cities, at least. You think of us as old-fashioned, but in some ways our church was pretty progressive."

"*Your* church."

"Yes." His pap nodded slowly. "You're very kind to attend services with me."

Michael regretted his immediate response, and found he wasn't sure what to say to make it better. He said nothing.

They parked behind the bishop in front of a wrecked house. An old cottonwood, hoary and enormous, half its limbs leafless despite the surrounding green of summer, had toppled over and fallen into the building. The house was a one-story wooden structure, and the tree was heavy enough that it had crashed straight through the roof and hit the floor without slowing down. Women swarmed the ruins, piling the small household objects—clothing and dishes and pictures and books and toys—into a row of boxes alongside the street.

"The Relief Society sure jumped in with both feet," Michael said. "I guess the Elders Quorum would be here too, but it's Friday and they're probably at work."

"See?" Hiram opened the door and climbed out. "We're good at some things."

A woman with abundant curly brown hair and a tearful smile was thanking Bishop Gudmundson profusely as Michael caught up to his father and the bishop. She must be Bobette Smothers. She was much better-looking than her husband.

"Show us all the heavy furniture, Bobette," Gudmundson said. To Pap, he said, "You got ties?"

"I have plenty of rope," Hiram told him.

Michael helped the two older men haul out two dressers, a wardrobe, and five beds. He was reminded that his father—former soldier and a man who worked the land—was surprisingly strong, but Gudmund Gudmundson was even stronger. When Michael's grip on the wardrobe slipped, coming down off the brick porch, the bishop was underneath. He didn't even grunt as he caught the entire weight of the heavy oak wardrobe himself and held it until Michael and Hiram could get into place again.

When the furniture was all tied to the truck, one of the women—not Bobette Smothers, but an older woman with silver hair and two moles like a pair of extra nostrils in the center of her forehead—gave Hiram and Michael two sandwiches wrapped in wax paper and two cold grape Nehis.

"Thank you," Hiram said.

The new rented house was only four blocks away. By the time the three men had unloaded the furniture, Bobette Smothers was there to direct them where to put it. On the porch, she thanked Gudmundson again and wrung Hiram's hand, but Pap demurred.

"When you buy a truck," he said, "I figure you take on a responsibility to use it properly."

Gudmundson walked Hiram and Michael back to the Double-A. The bishop took off his hat to wipe the sweat from his forehead before replacing it. He spoke to Michael and his pap through the window. "Thanks. I could have waited until this evening, and a bunch of men would have been able to help. Only I figured you'd be willing, and Bobette would get a roof over her head sooner. Seemed like the right thing."

Hiram nodded and shook the bishop's hand through the window of the Double-A. "Can you give us directions to where Diana Artemis lives?"

Michael had to shake his head again at that name. Gudmundson nodded. "She doesn't come to church, but it's a small town." He pointed. "Three blocks that way. She's in the little house behind the house with a vegetable patch in front."

Chapter Five

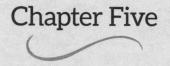

"WHAT'S WITH THE CRAZY NAMES?" MICHAEL ASKED as he drove.

"You've lived in Lehi as long as you can remember," Hiram said. "You're only asking this now?"

"I had to ask about the even crazier things first," Michael said. "I've worked my way down to names. What was Mrs. Whittle's name again...Cherapple?"

"Cherellen," Hiram said. "I think cherapple is a flavor of soda."

"And *Bobette*? As in, female Bob, I guess?"

"I guess when you live in a big empty place like Utah, you look for ways to entertain yourself," Hiram said. "For some folks, that must mean giving your kids invented names. Be grateful I named you 'Michael.'"

Michael snorted. At his pap's direction, he pulled over in front of a small bungalow. Michael set the hand brake, to the left and under the steering wheel.

The vegetable garden in front of the bungalow was leafy and full, and the cottonwood beside the street front wept white fuzz. Michael didn't have his father's skill with the dowsing rod, but he could smell running water—there must be a creek or a river nearby.

A path led down the side of the house. A small hand-written sign, nailed to a fence post, pointed to the back. On it was the name of the widow they were there to see, Diana Artemis. The name might be pure P.T. Barnum, but she was sticking to it. Surrounding the name were various symbols: an eye, a cross, an "H" with bowed sides, a crescent moon, and a five-pointed star.

Michael squinted in the harsh sunlight. "So, those symbols, it's kind of generic occult, don't you think? I mean, other than the crosses, it's not like on our lamens. It looks...fake as can be."

Fake as her fakey fake name. With this much obvious flimflam, could she possibly have any real magical lore?

"It's just advertising," Pap said quietly. "She needs customers. First rule of business is give the customer what he wants. Or what he thinks he wants, I suppose. Besides, a person who knows important things sometimes conceals them."

"You mean, like trade secrets?"

Hiram frowned. "No, I mean that some kinds of knowledge are progressive. You learn the first thing, and before the second thing will be told to you, you have to prove that you're using the earlier knowledge responsibly. That you're keeping secret things secret, that you're acting appropriately on your knowledge."

"That sounds like...is that...is that *magic* you're talking about, Pap, or *God*?"

Hiram nodded and stepped out of the truck. Michael banged out of the Double-A after him in time to see his pap's hand go to the chi-rho amulet under his heavy work shirt.

Michael had seen his father make that same gesture, thousands of times. For most of his life, he'd figured his father had some sort of nervous tic, or a lingering rash on his sternum. Now, he knew better. The chi-rho amulet supposedly had powerful protection magic.

According to his pap, the amulet that Michael wore was the reason he had survived their tussle with the coal-mine demon in Helper.

"You don't expect trouble, do you?" Michael managed to avoid touching his own chi-rho medallion.

Hiram shrugged. "I didn't expect Gus Dollar to be a witch. Here we have someone making *sure* people think she's one."

Michael felt a prickle at the back of his neck at the mere mention of the old shopkeeper. "You have your heliotropius in case she's lying, right?"

Another nod. "Probably ought to get you a stone, too." Hiram walked along the crushed gravel path and Michael followed, down a narrow passageway between the house and the neighbor's fence. The bungalow's tiny backyard had flowers and a path that connected the house to a privy and a second little house in the rear.

The sight of the outhouse made Michael feel immediate sympathy for Diana Artemis. Back on their farm in Lehi, the Woolleys had electricity, but no water closet yet. Hiram thought it was too much of a luxury and didn't like the idea spending that much money in a time where a lot of families couldn't eat. He might be right. So Michael suffered in solidarity with the poor, freezing his buttocks raw in the winter and choking on the thick stench in summertime.

Up brick stairs, next to the lace-filled windows of the door, hung another sign proclaiming the occupant to be Diana Artemis, though this sign didn't have any of the symbols. A string dangled behind the sign, connected to a bell.

Pap pulled the cord.

Michael stood behind him.

The door opened promptly, and in the doorway stood the most beautiful woman Michael had ever seen.

He couldn't look away. Pale skin, a perfect nose, and red lips. No hat covered her raven-dark hair, which tumbled down to the shoulders of her black dress, patterned with red roses. Her emerald-colored eyes were accentuated by the smoky make-up she wore. If all witches looked like her, Michael decided he would embrace the occult whole-heartedly.

Diana Artemis smiled. "Hello. Can I help you?"

Hiram Woolley whipped off his hat. Suddenly, Michael wished he'd bathed that morning, and wondered what his hair looked like; probably a mess, dusty, if not greasy. He felt like a backwoods hick standing in this woman's presence.

Pap wasn't saying anything. At the best of times, Hiram Woolley didn't say much—Michael drove for his father, and often talked for him as well. Like Moses talked for Elijah, as Hiram himself might say. Or whoever it was that did that in the Bible. But the thing that really knocked all the words out of Hiram Woolley's head was women. Michael would have to take it upon himself.

"Hello, ma'am. I'm Michael Woolley and this is my father, Hiram. We'd like to ask you a few questions."

Pap muttered something, nodding.

Diana stood in her doorway. Hiram was on the first step, Michael below him, and she was eye-level to them. She couldn't be more than five feet tall, and yet, she seemed to tower over them both.

Michael forced himself to look away.

Diana's laughter sounded like singing. "Questions? From *two* handsome men? Well, today has suddenly become far more interesting."

Michael laughed. Hiram said nothing.

Diana stepped back. "Please, come inside. The heat is getting worse, and I have an electric fan. We can talk. And I can answer your questions."

Hiram shuffled inside and Michael followed.

The room had furnishings that would have rendered it comfortable, if it had been twice the size. As it was, the round table, the wooden stools, the overstuffed easy chair, and the wide sofa were crammed inside, butting up against an overflowing bookcase. A fan with the General Electric logo on the front sat in the window, spinning. A silver wind-up clock sat beside the books on a shelf.

When the woman turned, Michael's eyes dropped to her shapely backside and the silk stockings she wore. Her shoes clacked across the wood until they found the plush carpet under her table. She walked with a limp. Something was wrong with her right leg.

She turned on it, pivoting with a bit of wobble in her balance. In another woman, that wobble might have looked ungainly. On the widow Artemis, it was a very gainly wobble indeed. Michael again had to look away. He hoped she hadn't caught him staring.

She sat in the easy chair. "Please, pull up a chair, or there's the sofa." Michael caught a slight accent in the word *sofa*, something European maybe, but when she spoke again, she sounded like any other American. "I must say, I am dying of curiosity."

Michael nudged his pap to take the sofa. He grabbed a stool and sat down on it. "Mrs. Artemis, me and my father were in town to help Lloyd Preece and his friend Gudmund Gudmundson dig a well for the Whittles up in Spanish Valley. We heard the local gossip, at least some of it, anyway, and there's the matter of a ghost."

"I know Lloyd," the widow said, "and the bishop. What's the gossip you heard?"

"Falling sickness." Hiram's face was pale. "I suffer from the falling sickness. Mr. Preece said you might be able to help."

The woman's eyes went from Hiram to Michael and back. "I've heard about you, Mr. Woolley. I could have helped Rex Whittle find his well, so you've cost me a nice little piece of business. It's hard to beat free."

"I'm sorry, Ma'am," Hiram murmured. "I didn't know."

She waved a hand. "That's not really my line of work. I appreciate the stars and planets more than the dirt and what men do in it."

"You write horoscopes?" Hiram asked.

"I *cast* them, yes. For all the best men in town, I assure you. Erasmus Green, the banker, Lloyd Preece, the rancher."

"Bishop Gudmundson?"

She shook her head. "He's a little too church-y, I fear. But I do have some charms that might help with your epilepsy. They won't be free, and I might have to charge a bit extra, to make up for my . . . lost business." She fueled those final words with a slow smile and a glint in her eye.

"Not sure it's epilepsy." Hiram coughed and looked at the floor. What was going on with him? Was he sick?

Was he going to have a fainting spell right now, in front of the widow, just to prove that he could?

"How are you treating it now?" she asked.

"I . . . pray, mostly," Hiram said. "It's a charm I know." He then recited: "I conjure me by the sun and the moon, and by the gospel of this day delivered to Rupert, Giles, Cornelius, and John, that I rise and fall no more."

Michael found himself wincing in embarrassment. How could anyone take any of this seriously? Then again, who was he to cast stones? He sat in a fortune teller's little parlor, seeking information on a ghost.

Only he didn't really believe it.

Did he?

Diana's lips curled upward and she breathed out a little laugh. "It's a very sweet little spell, Mr. Woolley. Has it been helpful?"

"Some," he said. "I wouldn't call it a *spell*, exactly."

She stood. "Let me find something in the other room."

"Can I look at your books?" Michael asked. "I really like books."

"Help yourself." She limped out of the room.

Michael stood and perused the titles on the shelves. *The Elements of Astrology* by Luke Broughton was stuck in the middle of a dozen books with swooping characters that Michael guessed might be Sanskrit. Another book in English was called *Shatpanchashika*, and then he saw *Christian Astrology (Three Volumes Combined)*.

"Read out the titles," Hiram said. "Let's see if I

recognize any. Look for *The Picatrix,* or *The Discoverie of Witchcraft.* Or anything by Henry Cornelius Agrippa."

"Nothing like that," Michael said.

Hiram frowned.

Diana returned and took a seat. She held a cigar box, the word La-Zenda painted on the wood inside a red border. She opened up the box and retrieved a little silver cross. On it, etched in the metal, was a circle with a dot inside it and an arrow emerging from the circle, pointing upward. "Keep this with you, Mr. Woolley. Uranus is the planet that governs electricity, and this should stabilize your body. I see you have a Saturn ring. I would imagine your dreams are very vivid."

Michael reached for the cross and Diana pulled it away. "Sorry, my friend, but if you touch it, you might disrupt the energies. This is for your father. Foster father, I think."

"I guess technically he's my foster father, but I've been with him since I was a tot. He's the only dad I've ever known." Michael returned to the stool. "No points for guessing that one, though, since I have a pleasant nutmeg-like complexion, and my pap is the color of the sugar beets he grows and loves so much."

"I adopted him." Hiram stood, reached across the table for the cross, and sat back down, gripping the charm in his fist. "His father died in the Great War. He was my friend. Yas Yazzie."

"I recognize the name as Navajo." Diana smiled at Michael. "You have beautiful hair, and such nice brown eyes. So intelligent."

When had Michael's insides become oatmeal? He found he had no words. So this was what Pap felt... apparently, any time he saw a woman.

Michael remembered his manners. "Yes, thank you. Thank you, Mrs. Artemis."

"'Diana' is fine." She relaxed into her chair. "Can I get you something to drink? Tea, perhaps? I might have a beer."

"Pap's Mormon, and I'm . . . okay for now." Michael glanced at his father.

His pap had been staring at the woman, but now he dropped his eyes. "No, thank you. And thank you for the charm. If you have some . . . lore, maybe you know something about the ghost up on the Monument?"

"Lore?" Diana grinned. "Most people call it witch-craft."

"You're not a witch, I don't think," Pap said firmly. "I've dealt with witches. They're cruel. You don't seem like that kind of person." He cleared his throat, a bit too loudly.

"I can little afford to be cruel," Diana replied. "As a widow, a stranger in Moab, my standing is a bit precarious, and cruelty would only make my lot harder. As for witchcraft, well, there are some believers still, in the old ways, and I thank God there are. Does Mormonism have room for the old ways? We Catholics manage, but Catholics have always been keen on ritual and sacrifice."

Michael found himself intensely interested in the answer to that question.

His pap shrugged. "Some Mormons do. Fewer than once did, and fewer and fewer all the time. That's the way of the world; it changes. Do you know anything about the ghost?"

That answer was a disappointment. Leave it to Pap to stay on track.

The widow leaned forward. Her dress leaned with

her, showing a sudden fertile valley of cleavage. Michael knew better than to ogle. He stared at the spinning fan and wondered whether there was a setting to make it oscillate.

"The ghost in the new Arches Monument?" Diana asked. "My craft suggests...that is to say, I *believe*... it's poor Jimmy Udall. I have felt things, when I was up there...it's a spiritually powerful place. I find the Ute paintings especially fascinating. They're by the Turnbow Ranch, near the very fine arch up there. Have you been?"

Michael shifted his gaze from the fan, forcing himself to look at the widow's face. "We have. You're talking about..." He couldn't bring himself to say *Pants Crotch*. "The Bloomers. I guess the Turnbow Ranch was once the Wolfe Ranch?"

"It was," Diana affirmed. "The Turnbows moved in after Wolfe moved out. The stars suggest that it might have been a wolf that killed poor Jimmy. Have you heard of old Three Toe?"

Hiram looked over at Michael. "We have." Better Pap looked at him than keep on staring at the widow. Suddenly, her name seemed more than appropriate. She was a hunting goddess, all right. Times two.

Diana sighed. "Three Toe was a big wolf, pestering the ranchers, and taking more than his fair share of their livestock. Supposedly he was caught a dozen years ago, but who knows, really? He, or some other wolf, could have killed Jimmy, just like the stars told me. And without a proper burial, poor Jimmy could be strolling across the sandstone, alone and lost."

The widow had lost her smile. Tears shone in her eyes.

"I saw bite marks," Hiram said.

Diana Artemis nodded.

"Who is Jimmy Udall?" Michael asked. "Or, I guess, who is his family? Where can we find them to talk to them? Do they live somewhere in Moab?"

Diana nodded. "They're not well known in town, because his family squats on the Monument, so they only come in to shop. They live in a little dugout up there. I haven't seen it, but the stars tell me it's quite near the Bloomers."

"The stars sure tell you a lot," he blurted out.

Her laughter returned. "You're not wrong, Michael. May I call you Michael?"

"Michael is fine. Hiram for my pap." He wanted to ask if she really believed in all this mumbo jumbo, and in the things the stars told her, but he couldn't think of a polite way to put the question.

"You know," Diana said. "There are rumors of lost silver out in the desert. The bank was robbed in 1923, and supposedly, four bags of silver were taken, but only two returned. Jimmy might've stumbled on the treasure and gotten killed for it. Then his ghost would be restless, wanting his story to be known. Ghosts are like that."

"I thought the stars told you it was wolves," Michael said.

"I'm suggesting other possibilities." She smiled sweetly at him. "In case I am mistaken in my reading of the stars."

Hiram cleared his throat. "Did the Udalls ever come to see you?"

The widow nodded. "They were concerned about their missing son."

"And you told them wolves had killed him and left him a ghost in the desert?"

Diana Artemis shook her head slowly. "I lied to them. I said little Jimmy had died in a fall, and was in heaven. Tell me, Hiram, did I do wrong in giving them peace by telling a little lie?"

Hiram shook his head slowly. "I can't say you did wrong. It would have been better still if you could have given peace to the boy, too."

"Perhaps I don't have all your craft, Mr. Woolley. Anyway, I gave them more peace than they could get from that dugout church they attend."

"Dugout church?" Michael asked.

She nodded. "The Udalls have been spending Sundays with our local John the Baptist, Earl Bill Clay. He's an itinerant preacher, a wild-eyed zealot, you know the type." She grimaced. "Some call him Preacher Bill. I understand he calls himself the Reverend Majestic."

Michael thought for a moment. "But you don't think...the Udalls have found the missing silver?"

"That seems like...a really big stretch," Pap murmured.

And it didn't jibe with what the ghost had told them through the lantern.

"If the Udalls have become suddenly rich," Diana said, "they don't act like it." She turned and read the clock. "I do have an appointment. I apologize for cutting this conversation short. Hiram, if the charm doesn't help with your falling sickness, perhaps I can work your charts and see if I can find the cause of your malady, so we can attempt another approach. Maybe start by telling me your birthdate?"

"October 7, 1890," Hiram stared at his hat.

The woman nodded. "I can check if Saturn was in Libra at that time. It might be that, or it might be Mercury, which would explain everything."

Michael didn't know how a planet could be in a constellation. This whole astrology thing baffled him, and yet, ancient astronomers had an expertise he couldn't deny. Modern astronomy had come out of people's love of the heavens. Grandma Hettie had been a great one for reading the almanac, even if Hiram claimed he couldn't follow the charts.

Michael considered asking to borrow one of her books, to begin unraveling the mysteries of astrology, then thought against it. She wasn't running a lending library.

Diana gazed on Hiram, her face softening. "Saturn, the father, deliberate, but limited. Jupiter's energy is expansive, but not Saturn's. It confines, and yet, it's intensely practical. Saturn knows we are only limited creatures, bound by space and time."

Before Michael could give her his birthday, she rose. "The cross itself is five dollars. For my craft, I'll tack on a sawbuck. Is fifteen dollars acceptable to you, Hiram?"

Pap was up in his feet in seconds, reaching for his wallet in his back pocket. "Yes, Mrs. Artemis, that is fine. Just fine."

Fifteen dollars was steep, Michael knew it, but he also knew neither of them was going to dicker with the woman.

Pap paid her, and they left, hurrying back to the Double-A. Sitting in the truck, Michael leaned back and sighed. "She's too old for me, Pap, but she liked you."

"She's far too young for me." The wistful note in Hiram's voice suggested that he hoped it wasn't true.

Chapter Six

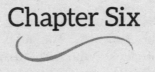

HIRAM LOOKED OUT THE WINDOW WHILE HIS SON drove silently through Moab. The effects of the economic downturn were visible, even in a place as small and innocent as this. Some of the houses had been abandoned, their windows boarded up; no wonder the bishop had been able to find a house for rent so quickly. Many of the business were closed. One rambling boarding house didn't have a single car in the parking lot.

The Udalls hadn't been home, assuming the dugout with the wax-paper window was theirs. Likely, their son Jimmy was the ghost. Was it possible that Jimmy had died in connection with ill-gotten silver, and that his family was somehow to blame? But that didn't explain the strange bite marks on the boy's body.

No, not on his body. In Hiram's dream. And what if Hiram's dream was mistaken? What if it was just a dream?

It could be the Udalls had left for work. Laundry

left on the line suggested that they hadn't packed up and left the Monument permanently. Unless they'd fled without any time to prepare. From what, though? The law? Something darker?

"Pap," Michael said. "Diana Artemis could be snowing us."

Hiram failed to understand his son completely. "What?"

"Bamboozling. Conning. Deceiving. Tricking."

"Yes, I follow you now," Hiram said.

"The Udalls came to the widow asking if she knew what happened to their son. Then she tells us oh, that ghost you're asking about, it's probably the Udall boy. Convenient. The stars told her? No, I bet she just knew about a missing kid, and guessed."

Hiram nodded. "But she knew it was a boy."

"Too bad we can't test this scientifically."

"Well," Hiram said slowly, "we can talk to the Udalls. And we can find out when their boy disappeared. Line that up with what we learned from the ghost."

"From the dancing kerosene lamp flame," Michael said tartly. Then he softened. "Which . . . might have been caused by a ghost."

It was a start.

Hiram held his hat in his hands, worrying the brim. He knew about the seven deadly sins, not because he was Catholic, but Grandma Hettie's knowledge had come from a wide variety of sources. Pride, envy, sloth, gluttony, greed, wrath, and lust.

Pride led the list because it could parade around as being a good thing, and Grandma Hettie had warned of it time and again. The Book of Mormon took a stern position against pride, too. If Hiram used his powers to force his own will onto the world, he might think he was the source of the greatness. A man always had to keep a tight hold on his humility, and a man who used charms...maybe more so. God had created him, the world, everything, and all good things came from God.

Hiram liked to think he had managed to avoid pride. And he'd worked through other sins, sidestepping them by keeping his mind on his service work. Envy gnawed at Hiram, though, when he saw a man with a simple life, a happy family, and the love of his community. Hiram wasn't a greedy man, nor prone to anger, and he liked to work. As for gluttony, Hiram kept that at bay by fasting.

So, he'd managed to do well with six out of the seven. He was left with lust. The lusts of the flesh, as Nephi called them in the Book of Mormon. He'd wanted Elmina with a fire that lit up his entire frame, but she was gone, and at his age, he'd thought those giddy, passion-fueled days were behind him.

But Diana Artemis had his heart thumping and his mind in a whirl. She had some kind of artificial leg, but it didn't bother him. She was beautiful, smart, and full of smiles. And she was a cunning woman, of sorts. She had mystery about her, she had secrets, like Hiram did. She'd understand him. She hadn't come out and said it, but she was an outcast like him, a widow who worked hexes in a sleepy little backwater Utah town. That couldn't be easy.

Hiram's best friend, Mahonri Young, was a librarian at Brigham Young High School. Mahonri insisted Hiram wasn't an outcast but a successful beet farmer in Lehi, a solid figure in the community, but was he respected? Not by his neighbors, and not by his church. People looked away from his Navajo son and were very careful not to say words like "witch" and "wizard" in Hiram's presence.

Hiram wasn't exactly an outcast. He didn't know a word to describe what he was...was there such a thing as an *incast*? A member of the group who was still not quite right? That was what Hiram Woolley was.

Bamboozled. Could the widow have bamboozled Hiram? He carried a bloodstone in his pocket, that prevented him from being deceived. But the stone could fail, if overcome by a more powerful charm.

Or if Hiram failed to keep a chaste and sober mind.

Hiram had stuck the silver cross in the bib pocket of his overalls. He liked that it was a cross, and though he didn't know much about Uranus—since it wasn't one of the planets you could see with your naked eye—a planet controlling electricity made sense to him. More than anything, he liked that Diana had touched it and given it directly to him. Her spirit would be in it, and he liked the idea, probably too much.

He sighed.

Michael frowned.

It was acceptable to like the widow Artemis. It would not even be wrong, Hiram thought, to fall in love with her, should that happen. What he couldn't do was dwell on her—

he forced his mind away from the track it had jumped to take on its own, filling with the image of her comely face, and the fair skin he had seen when she had leaned forward—

Hiram bit his own lip. A chaste and sober mind.

Chaste and sober.

Grandma Hettie had told Hiram stories about the saints, when he was young. Not Mormon "saints," which just meant church members, but Catholic saints. Bernard of Clairvaux had been one of her favorites; he was a man who had so valued his chastity that he had plunged himself into ice water on one occasion to defend it, and on another occasion had physically run away from a naked woman.

Hiram focused on the packed dirt street, imagining himself running away.

"Lunch," he said quietly. "We'll feel better with some lunch. Those biscuits were a long time ago."

"We have Bobette's sandwiches."

"Let's save those. It's good to have food on the road."

Michael turned onto Center Street and parked in front of a brick building, three stories high, with a wide porch out front. "Let's see if the hotel has some grub."

"But not too much." Hiram didn't want to run away from lust by indulging gluttony. Maybe Nephi would say that gluttony was a lust of the flesh, too.

"It's not a fast day for you," Michael protested. "Let's eat our fill. Or did you give all of our money to the widow Artemis?"

"Fifteen bucks." Hiram left the truck. "Thanks to Lloyd Preece, we can afford it."

Michael joined him. Together they loped into the lobby of the Maxwell House Hotel. Polished wood floors and ceiling fans reflected the low glow from brass lamps, making the whole place seem to shine, if only dimly. A few of the tables were crowded with men, chatting in loud voices. Across the far wall of the lobby ran the front desk; a staircase disappeared up to the right.

Hiram and Michael took an empty table by the window. The fans did a tolerable job keeping the place cool, though the full afternoon heat would laugh at the effort. He and his son would be out of there by then. Had something driven the Udalls from their home? And if so, did it have to do with the disappearance of their son? And was their son Jimmy, indeed, the ghost of the Schoolmarm's Bloomers?

Was their absence at all connected to the empty campsite lying on the same road?

A giant came over to their table, carrying two menus and holding a dog under one arm. No, not a dog—two dogs, because the sand-tinted head of a chihuahua protruded from the mouth of a border collie with a black back and a white chest. Stuffed, obviously. The man was at least seven feet tall and four hundred pounds if he was an ounce. Thinning blonde hair receded from a wide, grinning face, his nose a bit red, his eyes Scandinavian blue.

Hiram expected an accent, but the giant spoke American English perfectly. "Hello, gentlemen. No need to introduce yourselves. Hiram Woolley and his son Michael. I'm Leon Björnsson, and I run the Maxwell House. Me and my son, Arnie. He'll be cooking up whatever you want to eat. I'd recommend the chicken-fried steak, but order it quick, because we're about to turn off the fryer. In this heat, it might kill the cook!"

"Sir . . ." Michael furrowed his brow at the dogs. "I'll have the chicken-fried steak."

"Make that two." Hiram tried not to stare at the dogs. Some of the fur on the border collie's back had been worn down from petting, and the chihuahua only had one glass eye.

"Excellent choice! And I'll only charge for one."
The giant took both the menus.

"Oh? Is there a special?" Hiram asked.

"There is for you. You didn't charge Rex Whittle to
find the well." Björnsson headed back to the hotel desk.

"Hey," Michael said, "I'm beginning to see how the
cunning man thing can work out. We don't charge
people, but they know that, so they give us gifts.
Sandwiches and soda, and now steak? We don't have to
make a lot of money if room and board are provided."

Hiram grunted. At the words *room and board*, he
had to fight not to think of the widow's bungalow.

Several of the men at another table left their empty
plates and approached. At their head was a short man
in an old-fashioned black suit, including spats, and a
shoestring tie. Dandruff covered the shoulders of his
suit. He had iron-gray hair, a full head, but angry
red skin inched down from his hairline. Gray scabs
marked his scalp above his ears, caused by a bad
case of psoriasis.

"Hiram Woolley," the man with scalp condition said.
"I'm Erasmus Green, and I run the First National Bank
of Moab across the street. Welcome to our little town."
Green motioned to the two men behind him. Both were
older, with lined faces, one aged and the other marked
by the sun. Both wore nice suits, far newer than Green's.
"This is Banjo Johansson. He owns the mercantile just
around the corner on Main Street," Erasmus said.

The old man had a wrinkled ear, like a plum withered into a prune, but otherwise a pleasant face. Age
had given him a gut, a big bow of belly extended over
his belt, though his arms and legs were thin. He raised
a hand.

"And this is Howard Balsley. He's a prospector, but also helps out with the Monument and does a little bit of everything around these parts. Whatsit they call you, Howard?"

The sun-leathered man nodded. "A *park ranger*. It sounds fancier than it is. And it's not where I get my money from." His eyes were tiny compared to his face, as if his time outdoors had shriveled two grapes into raisins, giving him a permanent squint. He also raised a hand.

"It's nice to meet you all." Hiram recalled hearing Balsley's name. Something about mailing rocks to Europe. "Have a seat."

The three men pulled up chairs.

"How do you know who we are?" Michael asked.

Hiram could answer that. For one, it was a small town, and word got around fast—strangers in town was news in and of itself. For two, Hiram's bloodstone was beginning to bring him unwanted fame.

He managed not to sigh at the thought.

"Lloyd Preece." Green didn't bother to glance at Michael. None of the men did. It wasn't unexpected. Most people were enslaved by their prejudices. And if these men had been among the first settlers in the town, they might have fought Indians. There would be bad blood there. For his part, Hiram still couldn't hear the German language without getting a knot in his belly. He was just grateful that Lloyd Preece had taken a liking to Michael. It made things easier.

"Lloyd's a good man," Johansson said. "Me and him go way back. Why, I opened my store when he only had a dozen head of cattle. Me and Clem, we've been here a good long time."

"And yet you look so young and dashing," Michael said. Hiram had to admire his son's courage. How much should he try to curb the boy's tongue?

"Tell that to my wife!" Green said.

"Tell it to any goddamn woman who'll listen!" Johansson snapped.

The three men laughed. Green wiped at his eye. "Good thing we can dance. You've seen the two halls we have. We do have a good time there."

Michael settled into the conversation. He'd gotten them laughing, which was good. Michael did best when people were laughing with him. "I have to ask about Mr. Björnsson's . . . dogs."

"Petey," Green said. "Petey's the big one. Ask Björnsson himself. Leon is friendly enough, and he loved that dog. What's the name of the little one again, Howard?"

"I believe the little one was named Petey the Second," Balsley said. "Didn't last as long as the original Petey."

Michael blinked. "And he sewed them together . . . for convenient carrying?"

"Like he said. Ask Leon." Johansson sat with his arms clasped over his kettle of a belly. "You a farmer, Hiram?"

"Was it the overalls that gave me away?" Hiram asked. "Or the truck? I have a farm up in Lehi."

"How you getting along?" Balsley asked. "Depression and all, I mean. I heard it's been real bad on the farmers."

"It's been bad on a lot of people," Hiram said. "I still have my farm, so that's better than lots of folks."

"But you can find water," Johansson said. "You have that old timey magic going for you. Powerful, Lloyd

Preece said. They heard what you did up in Helper, and someone suggested we should have the widow Artemis find us a well with her stars and bangles, and he said no, get that cunning man down here. Good ol' Lloyd. He's keeping the Moab Co-Op afloat, giving them money, which is bad for my business, but I can't really fault him any. He has good Christian charity. Lost his wife a while back. Lloyd has a daughter. Her poor husband got kicked in the head by a horse and hasn't been right since. What's Lloyd's daughter's name? It escapes me." The old-timer knocked his head.

"Addy Preece Tunstall," Green offered. "Married to Guy Tunstall."

"Guy Tunstall." Hiram nodded. "I heard the name."

"Guy Tunstall is a hard-luck story," Balsley said. "Lucky enough to marry rich, and then he goes and gets his brains kicked out, so he can't even enjoy it."

"What kind of miner are you, Mr. Balsley?" Michael asked. "Coal, like they have up around Helper?"

"Uranium," Balsley answered, addressing Hiram. "And I wouldn't say 'miner' so much as 'prospector.' You wouldn't know it, but this region's rich with the stuff. Someday, we'll find better uses for it, but for now, it's mostly put in ceramics. You ever hear of Madame Curie?"

Michael laughed. "Of course. She's been researching the properties of radium, polonium, and other minerals for decades. She helped develop the x-ray machine."

Balsley had a laugh of his own, finally looking Michael squarely in the face. "Well, now, I didn't expect an Indian to know so much about science. She died last year, but there's still a market for uranium. I send some of it all the way to Paris."

Michael seemed not to take offense. "To Paris. She started a school there before she died. There and in Warsaw. Impressive. You must know the uranium miner with the camp up in the Monument, near the Udalls."

The question startled Hiram. How did Michael know it was a uranium prospector's camp they'd passed? He must be guessing, and trying to get confirmation of his guesses.

"Davison Rock?" Balsley said. "Sure I do. He's a man you should talk to. He knows as much as I do, if not more, and he's hungry for conversation. Nothing but him and the hoodoos out there in the desert, and if *they* start talking back to you, it's a bad sign. Davison Rock can be . . . difficult, though."

"All that time up in the hills has touched him," Johansson *tsk*ed and shook his head. "It's the goddamn heat."

"Difficult how?" Hiram asked.

Balsley made a face. "Oh, you get used to the heat. You live like a lizard, active in the mornings and the evenings, find a bit of shade and sleep the afternoon away."

Was that why the camp had been empty? If it belonged to Rock, the man might have been out working. "But a strange schedule doesn't make a man difficult. What did you really mean?" Hiram asked.

"I guess I mean that the line between lonely and nuts is sometimes hard to spot," Balsley said. "But Davison Rock isn't difficult at all compared to Earl Bill Clay. That man is a shyster, I tell you, a hobo who knows just enough Bible to get people to fill his collection plate. He acts crazy, but it's pure show business."

"I won't let him in my shop," Johansson decreed. "For one, I don't need anyone quoting the Bible at me."

Balsley looked at Johansson slyly. "You'd prefer it if he was quoting the Book of Mormon, Banjo."

Johansson shrugged. "Maybe if he knew a little Book of Mormon, I could find it tolerable. No. He's a menace all right. That crazy is no act, it's bone-deep and permanent."

Green frowned. "He's certainly a problem. Jack could get him on vagrancy laws if he was in town. As it is, he spends all his time out in the desert."

"Jack Del Rose is our sheriff," Johansson explained. "He's a good lawman."

"He's certainly kept my bank safe since he got the job," Green added. "Others failed. You know about the big robbery of 1923?"

"We heard about it," Hiram said.

"Well, the worst of the outlaws are gone, but we've had our fair share run through here." Green scratched at his head, then swept the dandruff off his shoulders. "Robber's Roost to the southwest is miles of badland that Butch Cassidy once used to keep hidden from the law."

"They talk about Butch Cassidy up at Helper, too," Michael said. "He robbed a big payroll up there and made all the mines switch to random paydays."

"We've had other bank robbers too, and a colorful history, but those are the old days." Green smiled. "The *bad* old days for us bankers. At least now, we all might not have much money, but we don't have many outlaws, either."

"You're lucky to be open," Michael said. "A lot of banks have failed."

Hiram didn't think these men were struggling. Their clothes were nice, they were clean, and they were all having a long, leisurely lunch on a Friday afternoon, before they went back to their work.

Hiram touched his bloodstone. It lay still in his pocket.

"Do you know anything about the ghost?" he asked.

Green slapped Balsley on the back. "That would be your area of expertise. You're the one up at the Monument the most, looking for your rocks, and taking food to the Turnbows."

"Wolfe Ranch," Michael murmured.

His son felt the coincidence. Wolfe Ranch seemed like an echo to the tales of Three Toe.

But was there such a thing as coincidence? Grandma Hattie had always been skeptical of the idea.

Leon appeared carrying a single plate and his dogs. He set the plate down in front of Hiram, and then went back for Michael's lunch.

"Show 'em Petey!" Johansson called to the big man.

"I will. Just sit tight." The giant ambled back into the kitchen.

"Ghosts?" Balsley grinned. "Do you mean like the election dreams of the Republican Party? Yeah, I hear weeping up there all the time. And it warms my heart."

"We are not talking politics," Green said. "And we aren't discussing religion. You're a religious man, aren't you, Hiram?"

Michael answered for him. "My father has a direct line to God. How do you think he found the well for Lloyd Preece?"

That made the men laugh more.

Leon returned with the other plate for Michael.

"There you go. You listening to these three old men gossip? Why, they're just hens. Hell, my dad used to have to sweep them out of the hotel with his broom to get them back to work."

"That's a load of cow biscuits," Johansson countered. "Bjorn would have joined us. He could talk longer than any of us and tell the bluest stories."

"Bjorn Björnsson? And we have Gudmund Gudmundson. Did you run out of names?" Michael asked.

More chuckles.

Leon fielded the question. "Icelandic names. Small country, short list of names, I always figured." Leon petted the dog-ensemble on his left arm. "As for Petey, he was the best dog I ever had. He was faithful, and I'll tell you what, a lot more faithful than my wife. She ran off. But Petey stayed with Arnie and me. Stayed and stayed. When he finally got sick, he crawled under the back porch and died. I figured, what the hell, you can't chase away loyalty like that, and now he's always with me. Ain't ya, Petey?" Leon wiggled the dog at Michael; the border collie's mouth stretched wide to permit the chihuahua head, which seemed to be on the end of an extending rod or something similar, to emerge. "Bark. Bark. Bark. Down, boy. Down." The giant guffawed, flinging spittle. "And Petey Two was a short-timer in this world, but there's no reason a short-timer has to be lonely."

Michael's eyes and mouth opened wide. Hiram wasn't sure whether to laugh or cry, the giant didn't seem to be making any kind of threat, so he stayed in his seat and watched.

Finally, Michael laughed. Then he relaxed, and reached up to pet the concentric dogs.

"Right," Leon said. "You thirsty?"

"These fellows aren't drinkers," Howard Balsley said. He raised a tumbler. "But I'll take a drink of Petey."

A drink of Petey? Hiram furrowed his brow.

Leon grabbed the chihuahua head in one enormous fist. Tilting the dogs back to face the ceiling, he tugged—and Petey Two's head came off, revealing the wide mouth of a bottle, taxidermied right into the body of original Petey.

"That's the stuff," Balsley said.

Leon grinned and poured half a glass of the contents of Petey into the tumbler. Hiram smelled the sharp tang of hard liquor and made himself smile, despite the oddity of watching alcohol pouring from the open mouth of a mangy stuffed dog.

Howard took a drink and grunted his appreciation.

The giant re-corked his dogs, swiveled left, and went back to the front desk.

The three old-timers rose.

Green spoke for them. "Well, we best let you to your lunch. If you need anything, Hiram, let us know. We hear you're going to stay on Lloyd's land and sight-see on the Monument. It's gorgeous country up there. Why, someday, I bet you Moab is going to be famous the world around for its great beauty."

"For the uranium," Balsley put in. "It's going to be as priceless as gold. We'll need something to power our spaceships."

Michael sat bolt-upright.

The three men left out through the door. The other men in the restaurant followed them.

"Spaceships?" Michael murmured.

"You handled that well," Hiram said.

Michael launched into his fried steak. The meat was drowned in gravy, lying next to a clump of mashed potatoes and a few spoonfuls of peas.

"Do you mean their casual bigotry?" Michael asked. "That's old news, bordering on the ancient. I think it's funny Howard Balsley is selling uranium to Marie Curie's school in Paris. And he didn't answer your question on the ghost."

"He didn't." Hiram touched his bloodstone.

"Or do you mean the fact that I just pretended that a stuffed dog was alive, so as not to offend its gigantic owner? Not just a stuffed dog, but a stuffed dog inside another stuffed dog. With a liquor bottle inside them both."

"That too," Hiram said.

Michael thoughtfully chewed a mouthful of steak. "I guess as a cunning man," he said slowly, "I'll have to do a fair amount of pretending. Not to mention evading the question, and . . . what was it you said? Keeping secret things secret."

"Yes," Hiram agreed. "That's what I said."

Chapter Seven

MICHAEL DROVE, HIS ARM OUT THE WINDOW, FEEL-
ing the wind. The road through the Monument wasn't
paved, but it was graded gravel and not well trafficked.
Michael found the absence of other travelers rather
surprising, given the scenic beauty around them.

To hit the road, they'd had to tack back north and
west toward Helper, turning east on a road that was
nearly invisible, and quickly climb up over a red rock
cliff onto rolling desert table land. This was the long
way, that was for sure.

Just in case, they'd picked up a full water can in
Moab before they'd headed out, along with a big bag
of flour to give to the Udalls.

The three old men back at the hotel were right.
Once people found the otherworldly geology of the
Monument, they'd come here in droves. As it was,
only the courageous made their way into the desert—
campers and scientists—or the more desperate, like
the Udalls and the people at the ranch. The Wolfes
or the Turnbows, apparently.

Michael stopped in front of a vast canyon of sandstone fins, red in the harsh sunlight. They gave the impression that a school of giant dolphins frolicked just beneath the sand.

"The wastes of Dudael," his pap murmured.

"Come again?" Michael asked.

"Something Gus Dollar said to me. Fallen angels in the wastes of Dudael."

Michael remembered the flies and fire at the bottom of the cavern, a lost place underneath the Kimball mine. "Gus Dollar tried to kill you, Pap."

Hiram nodded. "That doesn't make him a liar. But we don't need to talk about Dudael and fallen angels."

"Okay, we can talk about the ghost. You don't think he's a demon, do you? Or was Jimmy Udall killed by a fallen angel? Maybe that was what he meant by a wild animal. Maybe a possessed boar named Leon. Or was it Legion? We already have one Leon in Moab."

Hiram didn't say anything for a long time.

Michael had to prod him. "Why are we doing all this for the ghost? He's passed on, right?"

"He's dead," Hiram said. "But he isn't gone. He's lingering. The dead do that, waiting for the resurrection. The peaceful dead are here too, Grandma Hettie used to say. They're all around us, waiting for the last trump to sound so they can leap from their graves and meet the Lord Divine. But they're peaceful, so we don't hear from them. They're having a good time, experiencing what some call paradise."

"Jimmy Udall is the other kind."

Hiram nodded. "For him, the wait is a kind of prison. Not because he was a sinner, but because he was wronged. He's upset, I think about the way he died, so he's trying to let us know, so we can fix it for him."

"You want to help the dead, just like you want to help the living." Michael shook his head slowly. "Pap, you have a big heart."

"And the yet-to-be-born," his father said. "Everyone is co-eternal from the beginning, and everyone will continue forever. We are all one family." He consulted his map. "I think the turn off is just ahead. This map calls it Turnbow Road. At the very least, we can understand Jimmy's death. People want to be understood, alive or dead, and that might be enough to give him peace. And if it isn't . . . we'll see what else we can do."

Michael turned off the graded road at Hiram's indication. Turnbow Road was rutted, long tracks of dried mud in the soil, pitted and precarious. The Double-A had a high base, and so, while they went sideways a few times, it didn't rub its undercarriage on any of the exposed rock.

It was a bouncy, fun ride, and Michael loved negotiating his route through the desert. He'd drive off the road to avoid rocks or fallen logs, and when the road was entirely destroyed where it crossed a small gully—it looked as if a flash flood had wiped out the ramp entirely—he'd sidetracked half a mile to make his own crossing, always following his father's directions and trying to stick to the map.

It was problem-solving, and Michael liked solving problems.

When they reached the Udalls' dugout, there was a Plymouth Model 30U parked on the roadside. The car was brown, with chipped and flaking paint, and words painted on the side: DOCTOR STETSON'S ALL-GOOD SYRUP above, and below that, YOU'RE JUST 5¢ FROM A SMILE! A water barrel was strapped to the car's roof. Had the Udalls gone for water, was that why they hadn't been here, earlier? In any case, they were home now, and they didn't look as if they were flush with stolen silver.

The family was out in the shade behind a rise of red rock. Two dirty-faced toddlers in rough square dresses played in the sand with wooden cups. The younger seemed to be trying to build a castle; the older was trying to bury the younger in sand.

Michael and his father emerged from the truck. A big woman plucked her towels and washcloths off the line. She held the linen in front of her and stepped closer to her children. Her coveralls lay over a calico shirt, both bleached by washing and the sun. She had dark hair and dark eyes, and she squinted at Hiram and Michael.

"You the Stetsons?" Hiram asked.

She shook her head. "We just bought his truck off him, when he didn't know how to fix it anymore. Big city fool, more money than sense."

"So you're the Udalls?"

"Moses!" she snapped. Lowering her voice, she admitted, "Yes, we are, unless you got a writ."

From out of the dugout came her male twin. Same coveralls and the same calico. Michael noticed that the two little girls' dresses were made out of the same material, too. The man also had black hair, long and unkempt, and dark eyes.

Mr. Udall walked up to them in work boots. Same work boots on the woman as well. "Hey. What you two want?"

Hiram hefted the bag of flour down off the back of the truck. "Good day, Moses. I'm Hiram Woolley. This is my son Michael. Banjo Johansson had an extra bag of flour lying around, and if there aren't weevils in it, you might like it."

Moses frowned. "We ain't no hobos. We don't need no charity."

Michael considered pointing out that the double-negative was a positive vote in favor of charity, but he managed to hold back.

"It's old flour," Pap said. "If you don't want it, we'll take it with us. Like I said, it might be spoiled."

The woman set her laundry on a rock and came over to stand next to her husband. "We'll see if it is. And thank you."

"You're welcome." Pap set the flour sack down on a broad red rock.

"You some kind of errand boys for Banjo Johansson?" Mr. Udall asked. "Or just doing him a favor, seeing as you was passing through?" He twisted his waist to scan the desolate horizon with his eyes and barked out an unpleasant laugh.

"Coming to see *you*, in fact." Hiram smiled. "Banjo knew it, so he threw the flour on our truck."

"Us?" Mr. Udall's laughter and his smile collapsed. "What for? I don't owe nobody money."

"My son and I are interested in the ghost up around these parts. Folks think it might be your boy."

"Jimmy's dead," Mrs. Udall said. "He fell. He ain't the ghost. He's at home with Jesus."

"What you mean, *interested*?" Mr. Udall put in. "This some kind of game to you? You table-rappers or Quakers or something?"

"It's no game." Michael's mouth ran ahead of his thoughts, and he was surprised to hear how earnest he sounded. "Do you mind talking about him with us? We'd like to help."

"Help us?" Moses Udall squinted.

Hiram nodded. "And your boy."

The woman crossed her arms. "Who are you?"

"Just people," Hiram said. "But people who have experience with things like ghosts. I came to town to help Lloyd Preece find a well for Rex Whittle. Dowsed for it."

"Sometimes people call us cunning men," Michael said. Oddly enough, it felt good to say it.

"Better than that goddamn sheriff." The woman spat into the dirt. "He called it a wolf attack. Three Toe, he said. I don't believe it. Jimmy had a rifle. We didn't hear a gun. We didn't hear nothin' that night."

"Dammit, Priscilla!" Moses Udall thundered. "You can't be blaspheming. The Reverend Majestic says we have to keep our speech perfect as God is perfect, or we'll end up worse than Roosevelt."

Roosevelt? Michael resolved that, if he ever entered the ministry, he'd call himself the Reverend Majestic.

"He's damned by God, Moses, that Jack Del Rose is. Damned to hell." She spat again. "It's no blasphemy to say it. You take on the job of sheriff, you take on the responsibility, and he ain't done his job, not by half!"

Moses spat also, as if prompted by his wife.

"The Reverend Majestic?" Pap asked. "Is that Earl Bill Clay? Preacher Bill? Is he around?"

"Preacher Bill shares the word of God for today," Mr. Udall answered. "God's ways are not our ways, and not the ways of the Roosevelt Administration.

Preacher Bill says to have faith and keep our heads down, and we do, mostly. Only we don't trust the sheriff. He's worthless. Not a bad man. He just ain't a good lawman."

And yet Erasmus Green, the banker, thought highly of him. Wasn't it just like the law, to be on the side of the wealthy?

"He didn't look for the body," Priscilla said. "He didn't do no lawmanning. He called it wild animals and that was that. Or he said Jimmy left us 'cause of how hard the times are. He said maybe Jimmy might have found work in Grand Junction, over in Colorado, or rode the rails. Jimmy was a good boy. He wouldn't leave us."

Moses' next words came out hard. "October last, Jimmy took the rifle out to hunt. Maybe catch an antelope. He never came back. I found the rifle up near the arch. No blood. No sign of Jimmy. Saw deer tracks in the sand, big ones. I'd a swore it was elk, maybe, but no elk would be out here in the desert. Not much to eat."

"Have you seen many wolves out here?" Hiram asked.

"Coyotes are out here," Moses grunted. "Not many wolves, since wolves like elk. Lot of meat there. I took down some elk in the La Sals last December, after Jimmy left us for his great reward in heaven above. Wolves in the La Sals are more likely than out here."

"Though you did see big deer tracks," Michael pointed out. "Maybe a herd of big deer is on the Monument, and wolves are hunting them."

Moses nodded slowly.

Priscilla's frown had turned darker. "Thanks for the flour. But you should leave and not bring up bad memories."

"We're sorry for your loss," Pap said. "We'll be on our way. But if you remember anything, we're camped down near the river near Lloyd Preece's homestead."

"Lloyd's a Christian," Moses said. "He doesn't trouble us if we're on his land, and we've even done chores for him a time or two. Ain't hardly another Christian body, though, and it's only a matter of time before we're sent on out from here. Howard Balsley says the government is going to take all this land. For tourists. I guess I can see that. It sure is pretty out here." He paused. "Pretty, but in a sad way. Dust and death, and shapes God Almighty Himself can barely imagine."

"You could say the same about life, I guess." Pap tipped his hat. "Good day to you folks. We're sorry for your loss."

Moses nodded at them. "You have a good day."

Priscilla curtsied.

Back in the Double-A, Michael went to turn around, but Pap pointed onward. "Let's go see about the uranium prospector. He might have seen something."

Michael cranked the wheel and sent the truck over a big shelf of rock, keeping his speed down and his tires off the sandy road so he wouldn't wash the Udalls in dust.

"Glad they took the flour," Pap murmured.

"Why do they stay out here?" Michael asked. "Is there no better place for them?"

His father left the question unanswered.

Where the road passed a long stretch of slickrock, they found the campsite again. This time it wasn't empty; beside the tent stood a Ford Tudor, which was an awfully nice car to be out in the middle of the desert. A man hurried from the tent to his cooking stove, balanced on a low table assembled from pieces of long sandstone, kicking up dust as he went. Beside the stove lay cylinders and boxes without any immediately obvious uses—prospecting equipment? Then he grabbed a pack, turned it upside, and shook out the contents.

Michael drove up next to him.

The man wore work pants and a nice shirt that would've looked better under a suit jacket. His suspenders were black silk. His shirtsleeves were rolled up, showing sunburned arms, as burned as his face and neck. The man had a pronounced Adam's apple and a shock of dark hair, white with dust.

He ran up to the truck, kicking up more dust from his brown shoes. Not boots, those were shoes. The prospector pushed his face in through the window on Michael's side. His eyes crowded close together on either side of a nose like a beak. The stench of him, sweat and stink and liquor, washed into the cab. "Have you seen it?"

Michael considered driving on. This guy wasn't right.

"Maybe," Pap said. "What are you looking for?"

The man stepped back, laughing. "The secrets of the universe. The rocks, the answer is in the rocks. History. All the history of the world. Power in the stone. Stones. The universe is in the stones. You haven't seen it, have you?"

Michael felt the prickle of fear. Stones. As in a seer stone? Or a bloodstone? He leaned back. "I believe this falls into your area of expertise, Pap."

His father got out of the truck and stepped slowly around the front.

The prospector faded slightly back.

Pap held up both his hands. "I'm Hiram Woolley. That's Michael in the truck. We can help you, if you let us."

"Davison Rock." The man looked as if he were about to say more, but then he slammed his mouth shut and swallowed hard. His next words were a bit more coherent. "I'm Davison Rock. I'm fine. I'm all right. As right as rain, as they say, but there isn't rain in the wilderness. It's the Great Basin. The Sierra Nevadas take the rain. The Rockies over there, they take the rain. History is under my feet, history all the way back to the first day of creation, do you hear me? Moment zero!" The man laughed, but then tears fell from his eyes.

He staggered back, retreating.

Pap drifted to Michael, still in the truck, the engine idling. Pap leaned against the truck, his arms crossed. "He's drunk. Maybe we'll come back when he's sober."

"You don't want to wait around for him to sober up?" Michael suggested.

Hiram shook his head. "If we'd come in on foot, I'd wait, but it'll be hours and maybe not until the morning. That's a long time to wait when we're not sure he knows anything useful at all. We'll come back tomorrow."

Michael felt his brow furrow. "Maybe you Mormons aren't wrong about staying away from alcohol."

Hiram grunted.

"Coffee, though," Michael said. "That seems all right."

Hiram squinted at the sky. He walked around the back and got in the passenger seat.

Michael turned the truck around, driving across sand and slickrock, until they were headed back north.

"You know, he wasn't wrong," Michael said. "The Great Basin is in a rain shadow. As for the universe being in the rocks, that's correct as well. The elements are all there, the building blocks of life along with inanimate things. He might be an interesting person to talk to once he dries up. I mean, he's saying it in a crazy way, but what he's saying isn't wrong."

Pap took off his hat and wiped the sweat from his brow, smoothing down the little hair left on his scalp. "That's kind of you, son. Always look for the good in people. Nine times out of ten, you'll find it."

On the drive back, they stopped to look at a grand valley. Its cyclopean walls leaned in until they almost touched, an impossible geometry that only seemed possible if some gods had laid hand to hammer and chisel to lay the cliffs out that way.

Only there were no gods. No, erosion made the landscapes, time, water, and long eons, as powerful as any deity.

Michael thought of what Davison Rock had said about stones. "Only . . . you don't think the prospector was talking about a seer stone, do you? All that talk about secrets of the universe, and seeing things in stones?"

"I don't."

Michael thought of the widow Artemis and her collection of books. He was curious about the astrology, the stars, the planets, but he also was interested in the geology of the area. Stars and stones, the desert definitely had its secrets. He found that so much more interesting than the heaven that Jimmy Udall had failed to find.

Chapter Eight

MICHAEL TURNED OFF THE ROAD, CUTTING THROUGH the junipers toward their camp. In the darkness, the trees loomed up like wild beasts, sudden and startled and aggressive. Hiram resisted the urge to tell Michael to slow down.

Instead, he looked at the cliffs to the south-east and saw a light that must come from Preece's house; he'd promised to update the rancher on information he collected about the ghost, and it was early enough yet that he wouldn't feel uncomfortable knocking.

The Udalls had known Preece and had described him in friendly terms. Did Preece know, or suspect, that the ghost was Jimmy Udall's? He hadn't offered that information, which suggested that, if he knew it, it was information he wanted to keep hidden.

With the sun gone and the warm summer air melting into a cooling breeze across his face, Hiram closed his eyes. Why was he always so tired? He found himself thinking of the widow Artemis...the curve of her lip... the curves of...

The truck cracked to a halt, bouncing all thoughts of the widow from Hiram's head.

The truck ticked but all else was silent. Even the river's gurgle was lost in oppressive quiet. The air felt heavy, like the world was preparing to grieve. Hiram tried to trust his instincts. Grandma Hettie said a person's intuition was God talking so quietly, only the heart could hear it.

Something was off, and while he didn't much like violence, sometimes a weapon was necessary. He thought about warning Michael that things weren't right, but then thought against it. If his son wasn't feeling anything, Hiram might be mistaken.

While his son got out of the truck, Hiram reached into the glove compartment. He took out the Model M1917 revolver marked with the initials *Y.Y.* and *H.W.* and pocketed it. Then he was out of the Double-A with Michael following him through the junipers.

"You'll go talk to Mr. Preece now, right?" Michael said. "He's the one who wanted to know about the ghost."

Hiram briefly considered taking an icy bath in the Colorado River. He feared it wouldn't work, his mental images of Diana Artemis seemed so warm and real. "We're staying on his land, so it seems only fair, doesn't it?"

Michael nodded. "Also, you're thinking he's rich and maybe he's in a position to help the Udalls, whether or not the ghost is their son Jimmy. And, no offense, Pap, but your sense of duty is going to drive you to go report to him before we eat. Right?"

"I feel so predictable." Hiram laughed. "If you want to get a fire started and some food going while I talk with Preece, I think that would be a fine idea."

Michael sighed. "I think if I'm learning this cunning man craft, I'd better learn all of it. It's like how doctors have to practice bedside manner, and lawyers have to practice rubbing their hands together while laughing in a sinister fashion. Let's go tell Lloyd Preece we think the Udall kid is dead, but we have no idea why."

Hiram felt slightly uncomfortable with the words *the Udall kid*. He would have preferred *Jimmy Udall*; using the dead child's name seemed more respectful. "It should be a short conversation."

"That'll leave us lots of time to ask him for money."

"Not for ourselves."

"Never. *But* ... if he offers a meal, or gas money, or a gift..."

"We'll try to refuse," Hiram said.

"Right," Michael agreed. "We'll *try.*"

Their Redwings crunched on the dry soil across the valley. Hiram smelled wood smoke and meat as he stepped onto the plank porch. Up close, he could see that the cabin was nice, but not new—its most recent coat of paint was flaking off, but in the yellow light coming through the curtains and the windows, he noticed spots of a different paint color underneath. The building had a distinctly masculine feel from the outside—a stuffed elk head was nailed to the wall on the porch, above two wooden chairs whose Spartan simplicity was relieved by a pair of mismatched, worn cushions. The junipers grew right up to the walls of the cabin, huddling around its windows and crowding the edge of the porch.

He pulled open a screen door; standing inside, he knocked on the solid wood behind. "Mr. Preece!"

"I'm not saying that the smell of that stew is making me hungrier, Pap, but..."

"Okay." Hiram grinned. "If he invites us in for *dinner*, I won't say no. I won't even try."

The light inside went dark.

"Mr. Preece?" Hiram called. He put his hand near his overalls pocket and the revolver, just in case. "Lloyd? Everything all right?"

"I'll get my flashlight." Michael swung his knapsack around in front of him and dug inside.

The cabin door swung open. In the dark interior, Hiram could see nothing, and before he could open his mouth to call again or step aside, something slammed into his face. He collapsed, lights flashing in his vision.

"Pap!"

Hiram grabbed at his attacker and managed to wrap his arms around the other man's legs. The assailant fell, tumbling forward over the edge of the porch and dragging Hiram with him. They rolled in the dust.

A light snapped on, and it blinded Hiram.

Knuckles struck Hiram in the cheek and in the jaw. Hiram punched back and connected with bone. The other man lurched away, groaning and cursing.

Hiram smelled alcohol and urine and the stink of a body that hadn't been washed in a long time. And something else—rot? He climbed to his feet, reaching inside his shirt to touch the comforting iron disk of his chi-rho medallion. "Shine the light on him!" Hiram's own vision was an explosion of colored blotches.

He reached for the revolver in his pocket and found it gone. Had he dropped it, falling from the porch? Did his attacker have it?

Fear gripped Hiram's spine.

"I'm trying—ooph!"

Hiram heard thumping sounds on the porch and

Michael's light disappeared in a sudden crash of glass. He turned and leaped back onto the porch—

in time to take another haymaker to the jaw.

Hiram sailed backward, crashing to earth on his back, full length in the dust. He pawed at the amulet and couldn't find it. Had he lost his protection? Was it failing him?

Improbably, he found himself remembering the widow's cleavage.

"Hey!" Michael yelled. "Get the hell off me!"

Hiram stood up and saw a big shadow racing toward him. Lowering his head, he threw a shoulder into the place where he guessed a stomach should be. Somehow, he missed, and hurled himself onto the ground. Then a boot kicked him in the chest, and then another in the gut, and then the gut again.

Bang!

Bang! Bang!

Hiram saw the flashes of gunfire, and the kicking stopped. His head spun too much to see, but even over the ringing of his ears, he heard footsteps running away into the night.

"Pap!" Michael called.

Hiram groaned.

"My flashlight's busted, Pap. Where are you?"

"Here." Hiram groaned as he rolled over and tried to stand. "Please tell me that you're the one shooting."

In the darkness, Michael found him and stepped under his shoulder to support him. "Sorry I swore, Pap."

Hiram coughed, his ribs hurting. "I don't know, it seemed appropriate to *me*. I don't think you hit that fellow, though. Or if you did, you only grazed him, because he got away clean."

"Yeah, what happened? You're a great fighter, but that guy cleaned your clock like Jack Dempsey giving Jess Willard dancing lessons. Lucky I found the gun where you dropped it."

Hiram coughed. "Caught me by surprise, I guess." He reached into his shirt and found his chi-rho medallion. He hadn't lost it, after all. Had it not helped him, then? Or would his beating have been even worse without it?

Or had the amulet helped Michael find the gun?

Suddenly, he remembered the smell of Diana Artemis, and his blood ran cold. A chaste and sober mind.

He'd be powerless without a chaste and sober mind.

He needed to concentrate and keep his thoughts pure.

"I wasn't aiming to hit that guy," Michael said. "I wasn't sure I could tell you apart in the darkness anyway, so I shot at the sky."

"Good work."

"I don't think it was Lloyd Preece," Michael said. "Preece smells better."

"Maybe we accidentally interrupted a burglary. Preece must not be home." Hiram straightened; his back felt as if it might snap in two. "Let's get back to the camp and see how much damage Mr. Dempsey did to my beautiful face."

"Are you nuts, Pap? We're going to go in the cabin, and you're going to sit down and let me look at your face. And if Mr. Preece has any scotch, we'll—"

"I don't need a drink." Hiram's jaw felt numb.

"We'll *clean your wounds*, Pap," Michael said. "You're bleeding. I don't know if you noticed, but you took several shots in the kisser as well as a couple of kicks to the breadbasket."

"I noticed."

"So we're going in and taking care of you where we can get some decent light." As he spoke, Michael pushed Hiram toward the front door.

"Right. Okay, you're right, of course. But let me go first, just in case."

Michael laughed out loud but let Hiram go first. Hiram took the pistol back. He'd counted three shots, which meant that he had two left, since he habitually left the hammer over an empty chamber, for safety.

"We're armed," Hiram said in as commanding a tone as he could muster. Then he stepped inside.

Nothing attacked him. Now that he was past the door, Hiram could see the tiny blue dot in the far corner of a kerosene lamp turned low. Red and purple spots still impaired his vision. Stepping carefully, he crossed the room to the light, Michael at his side.

"I smell . . . something," Michael said. "Something I don't like."

Hiram turned up the light.

Lloyd Preece lay on his back in the center of the room, still and covered in blood.

Beside him stood a sofa and a table. In the corner was a cast-iron stove. Beside the door was a pegboard with hats hanging from it. Above a cold fireplace hung a bolt-action rifle, and beside the same fireplace leaned a double-barreled shotgun. Other hunting paraphernalia and trophies decorated all the walls. Dark doorways suggested other rooms.

Hiram handed Michael his pistol. Michael raised the revolver and shouted. "Is anyone else here?"

Hiram knelt beside Preece to check his pulse and breathing. Nothing. The man's throat was slashed wide

open and his shirt was soaked in gore. It wasn't blood
that Michael smelled—in death, the man's bowels
had released.

"He's dead," Hiram said, as if announcing the fact
to himself. Michael left him to search the rest of the
house. Hiram wanted to help, but his head was still
whirling, his vision was uncertain, and he felt nause-
ated. He had to sit down.

"There's a study over here!" Michael called. "Books
and ledgers! And...uh...a queer little statue thing."

Hiram stared down at the body. If the man who
had killed Lloyd Preece had then knocked Hiram
down, then perhaps Hiram had narrowly avoided being
murdered himself. He smelled garlic and mustard,
faintly, and he murmured his charm against the falling
sickness. "I conjure me by the sun and the moon, and
by the gospel of this day delivered to Rupert, Giles,
Cornelius, and John, that I rise and fall no more."

But shouldn't Diana Artemis's cross ward off the
fainting spell without Hiram's charm?

The thought of the widow Artemis came wrapped
in flesh and sweet scents, though; would her amulet,
too, fail, when Hiram's mind was wracked with lustful
thoughts as it was?

Hiram pinched his own earlobe, fiercely, to bring
his mind into focus. He took deep breaths, and the
garlic and mustard smell retreated, to be replaced
again by the smell of feces—that, and not blood at
all, was the real smell of human death.

Should they chase the killer? But he already had
a head start, and in the darkness Hiram and Michael
couldn't move fast enough to catch up.

"This one's a bedroom!" Michael yelled. "And a

little washroom." He returned to the parlor, revolver down at his side. "No one here but us."

Hiram dragged himself up onto the sofa, feeling a seizure tease at the edges of his mind but then recede. "We need to tell the sheriff. He'll be in Moab."

"You sure, Pap?"

Hiram frowned. "Of course. Why?"

"Because last time you and I were near a murder scene, we became suspects. Right now, there's no reason for anyone to think we were involved. Maybe we should just go down to the river and camp and let someone else find Preece in the morning."

Hiram's eyes had trouble focusing. He looked at the hat rack. "You make good points, son. But even if there was a reason for us to become suspects, I'd still want to report it." It would be the right thing to do, and right now Hiram wanted to be very careful to do the right thing, to restore his chaste and sober mind. "But in this case, there's simply no reason anyone would blame us. Even if we are the ones who report the crime."

Michael nodded slowly. "I guess we know what the murder weapon was."

"Well, that's really the sheriff's business, but ... what weapon do you think killed Preece?"

"That fancy silver knife he was flashing yesterday." Michael stooped to the floor, and when he stood he was holding the knife's sheath. The weapon wasn't in it.

"I guess I'm lucky I didn't get stabbed," Hiram said. "Unless the knife is still in here somewhere." Hiram tried to get up to look, but nearly fainted with the effort.

"Sit, Pap. I'll do the searching."

Michael set the sheath down again and looked for the knife. Hiram gazed at the hats on the pegboard, trying to figure out why he felt that something looked wrong. Then he realized what it was.

"It's not here, Pap," Michael announced. "I think you're lucky you didn't get stabbed."

Hiram nodded, then pointed. "Is one of those hats a lady's hat?"

Michael plodded over to the row of headwear. "Oh yes," he said, plucking a round blue cap from a peg. "Very fashionable in about 1929, and therefore worn by all the girls in Provo this spring."

"Why does that feel wrong?" Hiram asked.

"Because the whole point of fashion is to wear things when they are fashionable, and not six years later."

"No, I mean—"

"I know what you mean, Pap." Michael cracked a grin. "Preece is a widower. *Was* a widower. So whose hat is this?"

Hiram considered it. "Probably his daughter's. Addy Tunstall."

"Or a lady friend," Michael added. "Nothing wrong with a widower having a lady friend, is there, Pap?"

Hiram flinched.

"That guy who beat us up," Michael said. "You think maybe he's that prospector? Davison Rock?"

"I smelled booze," Hiram said. "A lot of it."

"So did I. And stinky man-beast."

"But he would have had to come running down here, hell-bent for leather, to beat us by the footpath. I've never known a drunk to have that much ambition, or that much staying power."

Michael shrugged. "Maybe he drove. People drive

drunk all the time. Maybe he took some faster road that we don't know."

Hiram nodded. "And I thought I smelled something else, too. I thought it smelled like rot, or decay. Maybe I was smelling Preece's body?"

Michael looked down at the body and shuddered. "No, he smells a little like blood, and mostly like, uh, other stuff. He isn't rotting yet." Michael waved his hand to shoo away flies, which were beginning to crawl over Preece's corpse.

"Let's get that covered." Hiram stood and hobbled, over Michael's protest, into the bedroom. A spare sheet folded and sitting on a set of shelves would do fine; he brought it back, chased away the flies, and covered the body. "Any idea what uranium smells like?"

Michael's eyes widened. "The stone? Uh, I don't know, stones don't usually smell like anything."

"Sure they do," Hiram said. "You know what sulfur smells like. You're just not used to sniffing rocks. But I thought . . . look, you're the *Popular Science* reader here . . . doesn't uranium have something to do with decay?"

Michael laughed. "Yeah, but not like that, Pap. It's the decay of isotopes. Look, it's like electrons and stuff."

Hiram chuckled, feeling foolish. "One of us needs to get the sheriff, and I think it should be you."

Michael hung the woman's hat back on its peg. "You feeling a spell coming on?"

Hiram shook his head. "Take the revolver, in case the killer is still out there. When you get to the truck, take a moment and reload. Keep the gun next to you. Drive into town and tell the sheriff what we saw. Tell him I'll be here watching the body to make sure nothing is disturbed."

"And if he asks me questions about, for instance, the knife?"

"Answer them. We're not guilty."

"And if he asks me questions about, for instance, the *ghost*?"

Hiram smiled ruefully. "Tell him the truth. Tell him some people think your pap has a special talent with ghosts, and apparently Mr. Preece was one of them. I expect if the sheriff has his eyes open, he'll already know we came into town to do a bit of dowsing."

"It's not illegal."

"It's not. Just... not as common as it used to be. But mostly, let the sheriff know that Mr. Preece has been killed, and then come back here and get me."

Michael nodded. "But I'm not leaving until you pick up that shotgun and check to make sure it's loaded. That crazy bastard might try to jump me in the darkness, but he might come back here and attack you, too."

Hiram didn't admonish his son for cursing. The man who'd beat him did indeed seem like a crazy bastard.

Chapter Nine

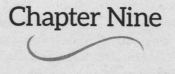

HIRAM HELD THE SHOTGUN AND STOOD IN THE
dark study, watching out the window toward his campsite. He felt on edge and fearful, chanting Psalms and
praying for Michael's safety, until he saw the headlights
of the Double-A snap on. When the truck rolled onto
the road that led back into Moab, he took a deep
breath and wiped sweat from his brow.

The cabin had two external doors, and they were
both locked. Lloyd Preece's corpse was covered, though
no doubt there were flies creeping under the sheet
on the ground. Corruption was born into the human
species, and the sheet was really just a way of whiting
the sepulcher, or being polite to the dead. And also, it
was less unsettling to sit in the same room as a corpse
with its throat slashed when the corpse was covered.

The murder, Hiram reminded himself, was not his
business. Grand County had a sheriff. Lloyd Preece
had kin, and this was their affair. Michael would
bring the sheriff, Hiram and Michael would give their

statements as witnesses, and then they would be done. They could leave.

But no. He had yet to give Jimmy Udall peace.

But Hiram didn't want the attention that being close to a murder investigation would bring. He preferred to be completely invisible to the public and to the authorities. Invisibility was freedom. Invisibility was peace.

If he had known a hex or a prayer that would reveal the killer, Hiram would have used it anyway, alone in the cabin, and nudged the sheriff in the right direction. Hiram knew charms for investigating crimes—Grandma Hettie had taught him that that was one of the traditional tasks of the cunning man or woman, going back to medieval England, when the king's officers might not always be accessible, or might not be friendly—but those charms required labor. Divination by clay balls or sieve and shears, for instance, could identify the guilty among a set of suspects, but the cunning man first had to find the suspects, and the divination would only work if the guilty party was included.

The Eye of Abraham was another charm used to solve crimes. It caused a guilty person to weep, but you had to lead the criminal into the presence of the written Eye, which meant that you had to figure out who the criminal was on your own, and then the Eye confirmed your conclusion. And the corpse of a murder victim, Grandma Hettie had sworn, would start to bleed again in the presence of its killer, but did that still hold true with a body that had been emptied of blood and stuffed, as human bodies were treated these days? And if it did, what mortician in

Grand County would let Hiram Woolley lead a procession of murder suspects through the funeral home to test it? A frog's tongue on a person's breastbone would compel him to tell the truth, but you had to find the criminal and put the tongue on his chest to get a confession.

And, again, the murder was not Hiram's business. Was the ghost of Jimmy Udall even his business? Hiram quickly decided that it was. Jimmy himself was suffering, had been killed in some strange and unresolved way, and needed Hiram's help. Jimmy's parents, too, were people who were in no position to get help from any other sources. Widows and orphans and the poor, this was Hiram's mission, and he didn't need to get back to the farm with any urgency.

He felt a little uneasy to be investigating a ghost with Michael. A few months earlier, Michael had been ignorant of the fact that Hiram was a cunning man at all, and now he was taking turns with the Mosaical Rod. Was the transition too fast?

Michael was becoming a kind of apprentice to his father. All things considered, though, Hiram would rather that Michael's first hexes involved healing chapped udders on cattle or helping a goat that had eaten barbed wire and ulcerated its stomach than dealing with the unquiet dead.

Or a murder.

Were the ghost and the murder connected? Hiram stretched out in a leather chair behind a desk in the darkened study, able to see the corpse in the other room and the front door from where he sat, and laid the shotgun down. He saw no obvious connections, other than geographical proximity. Lloyd Preece had expressed interest in the ghost—but it had been seen near his land, and Hiram had personally observed that Preece was a generous man who liked to help the poor.

A bit like Hiram himself, though with much more money.

Hiram remembered Preece's joke about wanting to be seen to be rich. There was probably truth to that, but a man could take the sting out of his own pride by acknowledging it and laughing at it. The two best targets for laughter in this world were a man's own self and the Devil—mocking one's own vanity was a jab at both of them.

A mirror hung on the wall of the study. It was large, maybe five feet tall and three wide, its frame was heavy, and it hung from two thick iron nails. Hiram stood and examined himself in the mirror—he looked gaunt, unshaven, and tired. The mirror's glass was cracked right across Hiram's face, thrusting the image of his head, from the eyes up, a couple of inches to one side.

Hiram chuckled at his own vanity.

And the human-looking bitemarks on Jimmy Udall's ghostly form?

Turning, he saw Lloyd Preece's corpse, stretched out full-length beneath his improvised shroud. And who would have wanted to kill Preece? He was a good man, generous, and unlikely to inspire the rage or jealousy or hatred that would drive someone to murder him.

Envy, perhaps. Preece was wealthy. Only a wealthy man could fork over forty dollars without batting an eye, for the sake of a neighbor. Or a hundred dollars, to jobless men on the road. Wealth could inspire envy.

Or perhaps, the way Preece had acquired his wealth

had led him to make enemies. Preece was a rancher. Had he stolen land, or water rights? Had he rustled another man's cattle? The wall behind Preece's desk was entirely covered by a built-in bookcase, with swinging glass doors, which kept dust off the books. Hiram opened the doors one at a time to see what information Preece cherished: scriptures, and a few commentaries on them; land surveys; genealogies; ledgers full of ranching data that Hiram had a hard time deciphering when he flipped through the pages; the eleventh edition of the *Encyclopedia Britannica*, published just a few years before the war; a thorough collection of almanacs. Hiram thumbed through several of the almanacs. He understood the weather predictions well enough, and appreciated the agricultural tips, and didn't mind the advertisements. The star data was mostly over his head—it was a part of Grandma Hettie's lore he'd never mastered. Preece had a shelf full of diaries, the kind with the dates pre-printed in them, that you bought at a drugstore. Hiram felt embarrassed and guilty, but he looked through a couple of the volumes and saw nothing obvious; Preece's entries were lists of things done, either on the ranch or in his calling in the bishopric. Many dates were simply blank; a few were circled.

On one of the shelves, he found the statue Michael had referred to. It was indeed queer: a single head, with three faces, looking away from the sculpture's center. Hiram picked up the sculpture; it was of heavy stone, and the carving was crisp and beautiful. This was a work of art, something Lloyd would have paid good money for. The faces represented no one Hiram could identify, but seemed to be a child, a youth, and a man. Probably the same person, in three stages of life.

It wasn't a likeness of Lloyd Preece, though, and it looked so fantastic, it probably wasn't an image of any of Lloyd's kin. Just art, then.

Hiram set the statue down and left the study. In the cabin's main room, he was struck by a sudden observation and stopped. The walls were covered with the signs of hunting: a deer's head, an elk's, several long guns, maps, hunting jackets. But the room didn't contain a single picture of Lloyd Preece with a trophy, or in hunting gear, or holding a fish.

Odd, for a man who participated in the hunt, and who was aware enough of himself to joke about his own vanity. But maybe choosing not to put *himself* in the images of the hunt was a way to keep that vanity in check?

Hiram wandered into the man's bedroom; even in the weak light coming from the main room, he could see that the bedroom was tidy and cheerful. A dresser stood in the corner, and on top of it rested a vase containing flowers that were just beginning to wilt—a sign of a woman's presence? Had his loneliness led Lloyd Preece to trespass across some woman's marriage vows, inciting an angry husband? But Hiram was a widower, and that fact hadn't led him to—

an image of Diana Artemis's hips as she turned and limped away from him flashed into Hiram's mind. He blinked hard and cleared his throat, trying to force his unruly thoughts back into their ordained track.

A man could put flowers in his bedroom without doing it for the sake of a woman.

And what about the man who had burst from the door and attacked Hiram? He was a likely candidate to have committed the murder. He might be Davison

Rock, who seemed to be unbalanced, by drink if not by derangement of the mind or soul. Had he and Preece quarreled over mineral rights? Perhaps Rock wished to collect uranium on the rancher's land, and Preece had said no—was there enough wealth in uranium to lead a man to kill?

It seemed unlikely, though Howard Balsley had said his wealth hadn't come from his park ranger job. Where did it come from then? And if Rock were sufficiently deranged, perhaps the financial aspect of it wouldn't matter. Perhaps being denied was cause enough. He had seemed pretty worked up about the secret history of the world that was printed in the rocks.

There was another insane man living in the wilderness. The preacher. Hiram closed his eyes, trying to remember exactly what he'd heard, but all that came into mind were images of the widow's curves, so he opened them again.

Something about the end of the world. And preaching in a dugout up in the canyons. Hiram hadn't seen any church marked on his map, but the map wasn't especially detailed, and the kind of church that was located in a cave—if that was literally true—probably wouldn't be on anyone's map.

Well, the sheriff would know about both these men, no doubt. And it was the sheriff's business, after all, not Hiram's.

What about the fact that the murder weapon seemed to be Preece's strange dagger? And that Bishop Gudmundson had a similar knife? What was the meaning of that weapon, and did it connect the two men in some way that would lead one to kill the other?

The dagger looked vaguely Masonic. Hiram was not

a Freemason; like his lack of grimoires and arcane languages, his unfamiliarity with Freemasonry sometimes bothered him. Perhaps a network of brothers would be an aid to him, especially if those brothers included men who had lore like his own. Perhaps membership in a lodge would give Hiram access to the kind of books he didn't own, but wanted. Perhaps in his current situation, it would shed light on this untimely death.

In any case, no one had ever put Hiram's name forward for enrollment in a lodge, and it didn't seem likely that it was about to happen now.

Also, Preece and Gudmundson had been very much at ease with each other the day before. And they were in the same bishopric, which could only mean that when Gudmundson had been called to be bishop, he had asked Preece to be his counselor. Those were callings that were yoked together, involving long hours of intimate cooperation in serving the congregation—such as moving Ernie and Bobette Smothers, for instance. You didn't invite a man you hated to be your counselor, you invited a man you trusted, a man you thought to be competent.

Hiram shook his head. None of this was his concern.

Nor was it Michael's problem. He and Michael would lay the ghost of Jimmy Udall to rest and go home.

Was Michael right to worry? Would he and Hiram end up being accused of this murder? Or of the murder of Jimmy Udall?

It wouldn't happen, Hiram decided. They'd stick around town and try to help the Udalls, but once he told the sheriff what he knew, Lloyd Preece's death was out of his hands.

❖   ❖   ❖

Michael made sure the revolver was set to an empty chamber before he started driving; he didn't want it to go off when the truck bounced over one of the potholes pitting the road, or when Michael reached down to check that the weapon was still beside him on the seat. Michael felt pride in the fact that his pap hadn't reminded him to do that, and more pride in the fact that he had remembered to do it himself. He should probably get a gun, too.

Pap would hem and haw and drag his feet, and Michael ultimately wouldn't do anything that his pap was really opposed to, but in the end, Hiram wouldn't stop him. In part because they were often in the wilderness, and a gun was a useful tool. Usually to warn off bears or to hunt, but once in a while, because some maniac out there lay in the darkness, looking to commit murder.

This was not Michael's first experience with a night-time killer. Frankly, his misadventure in February had been much more frightening, since it had involved some kind of pit demon or fallen angel, or both—Michael had never quite understood the boundaries separating those categories, and Hiram was either unable or unwilling to explain. The demon had killed multiple people, several right in front of Michael's eyes.

Michael had had bad dreams for a few weeks after that, and he had been surly with his father. Fortunately, Hiram Woolley was a patient man, able to take his son's sharp tongue and reply, in due time, with love.

Michael loved his pap. So he was proud that he was practicing good firearm safety as he pushed the Model AA Ford down the canyon toward Moab as fast as it would go.

The drive into town took maybe half an hour,

though Michael's racing thoughts made it seem longer. The first sign of town was the faint glow of lights as Michael turned left between two high walls enclosing a narrow canyon, and into a broader valley. Then Michael was soon passing the first streetlights and buildings.

Lights were still on in the houses, but most of the businesses were dark. As he entered Moab itself, it occurred to Michael that he wasn't really sure where to go. The sheriff would have an office, but it might not even be in Moab, since the sheriff was the chief law enforcement officer for the county. Maybe the sheriff's office would be in Green River, or Floy.

The businesses still open were dance halls, saloons, and hotels. A hotel seemed like the place where he'd excite the least resistance and attention, so Michael pulled over at the Maxwell House Hotel, parking the Double-A on a dirt side street. As he stepped from the car, Michael smelled the Colorado River.

Men in suits and cowboy hats stood in the hotel's lobby, drinking liquor from shot glasses and congratulating each other on the success of their businesses. As Michael opened the door, several turned to look at him, as if they were expecting someone. When they saw who he was, their expressions fell.

Michael ignored them and pushed forward to the hotel front desk. A young man with a caramel complexion and one front tooth missing from a polite and charming smile wishing Michael good evening and asked whether he had a reservation.

"More of a camper, myself." Michael knew he shouldn't be joking, not with a dead man only recently murdered. However, he couldn't help himself. He felt strangely calm. Or was that shock? "That's Pap's preference, you understand. As soon as my ship comes in, I plan to live in nice hotels exclusively."

The clerk continued to smile. "Are you the new telegraph boy, then?"

Michael laughed and jerked a thumb over his shoulder. "With an urgent message about stock prices for the Rotary Club here? Buy railroad shares! Sell beef! No, I need to talk to the sheriff."

The clerk's smile collapsed into a neutral expression. "He's not here. These are ranchers, mostly."

"Oh, yeah." Michael turned and looked at the men. He spotted Erasmus Green and Banjo Johansson, drinking with men he didn't recognize. No sign of Howard Balsley. Lloyd Preece had said something about being about to find him at the hotel. Too bad he hadn't left just a few minutes earlier; he might be here enjoying a little liquor right now, and hearing from Hiram and Michael about the dead kid.

No, he had to think of him as *Jimmy Udall.*

Michael was slowly coming around to accepting the possibility of ghosts. The idea he was communicating with someone's spirit would be exciting, if true. Yet, he wasn't entirely convinced that only a ghost could be responsible for the behavior of the lantern flame he'd seen the night before, but he was totally certain that his pap wasn't trying to trick him. Hiram Woolley believed in the ghost, so Michael thought he could, too. After all, he'd seen a demon before, so what was so challenging about thinking there might be ghosts in the world, too?

Though *had* he seen a demon, really?

Maybe he had been confused. Maybe he and his pap had *both* been confused.

"Look," the clerk said, "you want me to give you

directions to the Grand County Courthouse? That's where he has his office. If he isn't there, there will at least be a deputy on duty."

Michael took the directions and drove the few blocks to the courthouse. The lights here were electric and on, throwing bright yellow sheets of light out into the street in two directions from the corner where the courthouse stood, bulky and shadowed in the darkness. Michael left the truck out front, with the revolver out of sight in the glove compartment, and entered.

Two men in khaki shirtsleeves and slacks sat at a desk in the reception room. One was bone-thin and beet-red, studiously working at a crossword puzzle on the desk. The second man was older, bald and whiskered, with big sideburns that sprouted from his wrinkled face. He squinted at Michael, his right eye completely closed. A big gold cross lay on his uniformed chest, hanging on a thick gold chain.

"You're not one of my deputies," the man with the bad eye said. "Usually, that means you're a concerned citizen here to report a crime, or you're a member of the American Automobile Association who's lost his map. Fifty-fifty. You did pull up in a truck, that leans me toward the AAA. On the other hand, you look more like an Injun down from the Uintah and Ouray than a tourist. Maybe a farmer. Do I know you?"

"I'm looking for the sheriff," Michael said. "I have to report a murder."

"So much for the Triple-A." The man sighed and leaned forward, taking the newspaper and pen from the other man at the desk.

"Jack," the second guy protested, "I just figured out that nine across is Cincinnatus."

"Hold that thought," Jack said. "I have to take notes, and I left my notepad in my other pants. Now then, boy, you said murder."

Was this guy kidding him? "Can I see the sheriff?" Michael asked.

"You're looking at him. Jack Del Rose, Grand County Sheriff. Did you want to report a murder or not?"

Michael nodded. "Lloyd Preece. He's a rancher—"

"I know Lloyd." The sheriff jotted down a note. "Where's the body?"

Michael found that his hands were shaking. "He's been killed at his cabin up the canyon. My father and I stumbled across his body because we're camping on his land. And there was a guy who came rushing out of the cabin. We didn't see him, but he smelled like alcohol. And...like maybe he hadn't bathed in a while. Maybe years."

The sheriff jotted down another note. "Okay, we're on it." Then he handed the pen and newspaper back to the other man.

"Do you...do you want to follow me up the canyon?"

"I know where Lloyd lives," Del Rose said. "I can find my own way there."

Michael found himself furrowing his brow. "Are you going to come up *soon*?"

"Sure," Jack Del Rose said. "Just as soon as Russ here writes down Cincinnati."

"Cincinnatus," Russ said.

Michael hesitated. On the one hand, the sheriff didn't seem anxious to rush to do his duty. On the other hand, was that Michael's problem? And maybe if he pushed, he'd only draw attention to himself.

"Seven letters," Russ said, "drilled the Continental Army at Valley Forge."

"Craftsman," the sheriff suggested. "I use a Craftsman drill myself."

Michael forced himself not to shake his head as he left.

Michael was still feeling shaky when he pulled off at Preece's cabin. When he told his pap the cavalry was coming, but was going to take its own time, Hiram only ran his fingers through his hair.

"You get some sleep, son," he said. "I'll watch the house, make sure nothing comes in to trouble the body."

"You're tired, too."

Hiram nodded. "But you have to drive, so I need you alert."

Michael was too tired to argue. He left the crime scene, which was a strange way of thinking about the house, and drove back to their camp. His father had enough guns for a second Great War, and so Michael had taken the revolver. He did like the feel of it under his pillow.

Despite the evening's excitement, or possibly because of it, Michael fell instantly asleep.

Chapter Ten

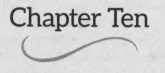

ON SATURDAY MORNING, MOAB LOOKED DESERTED. Hiram and Michael filled the Double-A's tank at a gas station. While Michael talked with the gas station attendant, Hiram drifted out into the main street to stretch the sleep from his eyes, ponder, and watch.

The events of the previous night had left him stretched thin. Fighting always took it out of him, chi-rho medallion or no. And then, after the hours Hiram had spent mulling over the puzzle of Preece's murder, the sheriff's deputy who had finally arrived had been virtually indifferent. He hadn't even taken a statement from Hiram, just shooed him away and told him to come down to the courthouse in the morning.

Should that indifference tell Hiram something?

The attendant finished, and Hiram joined his son in the Double-A. "It's odd that the sheriff himself didn't come out to talk to us."

Michael chuckled. "Well, he did such a bang-up job with the Jimmy Udall case. Maybe he has this newest murder firmly under control by some means we can't see."

"Is this some kind of Buck Rogers thing? Mind rays or something?"

"I was thinking magic," Michael said. "Maybe he'd do that thing you told me about, with scissors."

"Sieve and shears." Hiram chuckled uneasily.

"Do you think they're connected?" Michael asked. "The two murders?"

"I don't see how."

"I bet they are," Michael said. "Preece showed a lot of interest in the ghost. Except the thing is, Jimmy's body wasn't found. The murderer left Preece's body where he killed him."

"Or maybe I surprised him so he couldn't move it," Hiram noted. "But the deaths were eight months and maybe twelve miles apart. That doesn't exactly suggest a link."

"To the sheriff's, then?" Michael asked.

"Yep. You mind staying in the car?"

Michael had a way of saying the wrong thing at the wrong time, and Hiram didn't want to get sideways with the sheriff. He didn't want the trouble, he didn't want the fame. He especially didn't want word of his connection with this murder to get back to Bishop Smith. John Wells had enough headaches already.

"Trying to keep me out of that exciting crossword puzzle action, eh?"

Hiram chuckled.

"I can stay outside, Pap. But I think you need me in on this. I'm a keen observer. Don't worry, I'll keep my mouth shut. We're partners, right?"

Hiram surrendered.

The Grand County Courthouse was a blocky red and white sandstone structure off Main Street. Michael pulled up on the street; there was plenty of parking.

The court parts of the building seemed to be closed, but the front doors were open to give access to the sheriff's office. Inside, the ceilings were high, and they followed signs to the door marked GRAND COUNTY SHERIFF. Men's voices in low tones came from the room.

Hiram knocked on the doorjamb. Michael stood behind him.

Sheriff Jack Del Rose was older than Hiram expected, bearded and bald. He wore his uniform well, his black shoes shined to a gleam. He squinted at Hiram and gripped the gold cross that hung around his neck.

Hiram struggled not to touch the cross in the bib pocket of his overalls, his new charm against the falling sickness. The charm had worked, so far, hadn't it?

Gudmund Gudmundson stood with the sheriff in the office, beside a large desk. Gudmund's arms were crossed on his chest, the corners of his mouth turned down. "Hiram," the bishop said, "I can't thank you enough for coming to the sheriff so quickly last night. I feel awful about Lloyd. I can't...can't believe anyone would want to kill him."

Del Rose nodded. "Yes. Mr. Woolley, isn't it? You're a good citizen. I appreciate you waiting for my deputy last night. We had a bit of a busy evening, and I know that left you sitting around awhile."

A busy evening? Michael had described crossword puzzles. Hiram smiled. "Didn't want coyotes to get at the body."

Gudmundson shuddered. "I visited Lloyd myself

yesterday. To think, if I'd been a little later, maybe the evening would have turned out differently."

Hiram nodded. "Or if we had returned a little earlier." Perhaps even just *minutes* earlier. Perhaps if Michael had simply driven straight to Preece's cabin rather than to their own campsite, Preece would be alive. "I guess you must have been there in the afternoon?"

"Late afternoon. You and your son were out on the Monument?"

"Pretty country." Hiram stepped farther into the office. The window was open. Cool air leaked in, smelling of the sage in the sunshine.

Michael shuffled in as well.

The sheriff stuck out a hand. "I met your son last night, Mr. Woolley. I'm Sheriff Jack Del Rose, and unless you're a suspect, you can call me Jack."

Hiram shook the hand. "You can call me Hiram. Even if I *am* a suspect." He nearly kicked himself for the dumb joke.

The sheriff turned to Michael. "You know, I didn't think of it last night, Williams Drugstore has a fine display of Indian carpets and jewelry. You might be interested."

"I've never been to the Uintah and Ouray Reservation." Michael's smile was tight and forced. "I was born *Navajo*. And thanks, we've been meaning to get to the drug store. My pap is a big fan of ice cream."

The sheriff chuckled and chewed a lip. "Best ice cream around, and don't tell Banjo I said that."

Gudmundson didn't laugh. He looked stricken.

Del Rose cleared his throat. "Deputy Pickens collected the body last night. It's a shame. His throat was cut ear to ear, lying on his own living room floor, though of course you two both know that. Helluva thing. No question of accidental death or natural causes."

Hiram's eyes went to the knife at Gudmundson's side. Preece had had his throat slit, and his knife was missing. Why did the rancher and the handyman have such strange, and similar, blades?

Gudmundson noticed the stare. The handyman unsheathed the blade. "I was just in to talk to the sheriff about the knife."

"Deputy Pickens noticed that Lloyd's knife was missing," Jack Del Rose said. "When I called Bishop Gudmundson here this morning to let him know his counselor wasn't going to make it to church tomorrow, I mentioned the knife, and he came right over."

"In case the sheriff needed to know what the missing knife looks like," Gudmundson said.

Michael brightened. "That's a fine piece. Can I see it?"

Gudmundson handed it over and then sucked in a breath. "Lloyd and I picked up a pair in Salt Lake. We were up there for some reason, found them in a curio shop, and the dates were just too perfect, so we had to get them." A shadow passed over his face. "I don't know what I'll do with him gone."

Hiram saw the markings on the knife; characters across the hilt looked Hebrew to his eye, and there were two different abstract geometric designs etched into the blade, one on each side. Were they the same as the markings on Lloyd's knife? "What do you mean, the dates were perfect?"

Gudmundson nodded. "I'm no astrologer, you understand, but those signs on the blade ... one of them is the sign of the planet Jupiter. And the other is Aquarius."

Hiram struggled not to feel self-conscious of his limited knowledge in this sphere. "So your star-sign is Aquarius? Was Jupiter in Aquarius when you were born? Or are the signs perfect for some other reason?"

"That's not my birth-sign." Gudmundson cracked a grin. "I'm not sure what my birth-sign is, frankly. The curio-shop owner told us that these knives were Jupiter knives, that they would channel the energy of Jupiter into a man. And on the day I was born, Jupiter was in the constellation Aquarius, so this knife fits me."

Hiram grunted. "And was Lloyd Preece also born when . . . Jupiter was in Aquarius?"

"No, his knife had a different sign. One that matched his birth. Taurus, I think."

All the talk of stars had Hiram thinking of the widow Artemis and her alluring walk. The more he tried to shut out the images, the harder they pushed to get back in.

"And the Hebrew?" Hiram wished he could read languages, too. Especially Hebrew.

"*Adonay* on one side, that means Lord. And *Elohim* on the other. According to the shopkeeper."

Michael peered closely at the signs and characters. Knowing Hiram's son, he'd memorize every marking.

"You two wear these daggers to church?"

Gudmundson laughed. "We used to. Used to joke we needed to go back up to the curio shop and get one for the second counselor, too, that's Jeff Webb, until he asked us to stop teasing him about astrology. It made him uncomfortable. So for church, I leave the knife home."

The sheriff sighed. "So, Preece's knife is missing,

and it might be the murder weapon. And it looks just like this one, only one of the signs will apparently be different."

The sheriff was talking an awful lot about his investigation. But it suggested that he didn't think Hiram was the culprit, and Hiram found he was curious.

"Any idea who would want to kill him?" Hiram asked. "And why the killer would use his own knife?"

The sheriff backed up and stood against his desk, which was sparse. He crossed his arms. "That's just it. Lloyd was well liked. He was one of the most important people in this town, everybody's extra grandpa, people loved him. He helped with money, with property, hell, the Udalls have been squatting on his land for years now, and they aren't alone. I can't imagine who would want to hurt him."

Michael gave the knife back to Gudmund. "I'm no expert, but whoever took Mr. Preece's knife is probably the one who killed him."

"Feels like an intimate crime," Hiram said. "Killing a man like that with his own favorite knife."

"Or a crime of opportunity," Jack Del Rose suggested. "If someone got mad at him, mad enough to kill, maybe that was just the weapon to hand."

"He had it when I saw him yesterday," Gudmund sheathed the dagger. "Clem and I left his place, just fine in the afternoon, and then we headed on over to the dance at the Woodmen's last night."

The sheriff exhaled. "I think it was a stranger. Someone passing through, or anyway, someone who isn't really part of the community."

Hiram feared where this was headed. He kept quiet.

Michael didn't. "Sheriff, me and Pap found the body.

I hope we aren't suspects, but you're sure welcome to search our campsite for that knife."

"You're not," the sheriff agreed. "No, son, I was thinking of some other folks. Like those men in their truck you helped, Bishop."

Gudmund shook his head. "Maybe ... but I wouldn't think so. Don Pout is keeping them busy."

Del Rose didn't pause. "Well, there's two other outsiders out in that desert. For one, we have that preacher hobo, Earl Bill Clay, who's off his rocker."

"Preacher Bill knew Lloyd, all right," Gudmundson said thickly. "Lloyd gave him money and food, and I warned him not to. You encourage someone like that, he'll keep coming back, and the day you tell him no, he might hit you on the head and take what he wants. Much safer to let the church feed him. But Lloyd was also generous, generous to a fault."

"Or maybe Lloyd didn't tell the preacher no," the sheriff suggested. "Maybe the Reverend Majestic is simply insane. Too much sun, too much Jesus, maybe he saw one of the demons of the W.P.A. in Lloyd, or thought he did." Del Rose grinned.

Gudmundson grunted. "If I had to choose someone, a stranger, it would be that uranium fellow. I know Howard Balsley says he's the genuine article, but the prospector isn't right in the head, either."

"Too much sun and science?" Michael asked.

Del Rose laughed so hard both eyes shut. "That's a bright boy you have, Hiram. The truth about the prospector might be a bit simpler than all that. He drinks. He's spent a night or two in my jail because when he hits the sauce, he's not himself. He might have gone up to Lloyd, wanting the mineral rights on a stretch of desert, and when Lloyd refused, the prospector killed him. Took off with the murder weapon."

"What about the missing silver from the 1923 robbery?" Michael asked. "Could Mr. Preece have found it? Or maybe the prospector found it, Davison Rock, that's his name. They might have fought over it. My dad and I met him yesterday, drunk as a skunk."

Del Rose chuckled, and Gudmundson harrumphed.

Del Rose hitched up his belt. "Lloyd wouldn't pick a fight over money. He was one of the richest men around these parts. Now if the prospector got tired of the uranium game, and he thought Lloyd was rich, he might have gone to Lloyd to get the silver. Or maybe Preacher Bill gave in to his own greed. Now, that might be a motive. You talk to anyone for five minutes, and they'll say Lloyd Preece is rich because he found that missing silver."

"But we know that's not true," Gudmundson said quickly.

Hiram stuck his hand in his pocket, feeling the bloodstone. It lay inert and calm.

Del Rose nodded. "No, it isn't true. For all sorts of reasons."

"It's not Three Toe," Michael said. "We know that for sure."

Del Rose tittered. "So you've heard of our Three Toe? Why, that wolf was caught a long time ago. Measured eight feet long. I saw the pelt myself and checked out the paws as well."

"New movie at the Ides," Gudmund said. "*Werewolf of London.* I ain't seen it myself. Maybe it's the ghost of Three Toe come back as a man?"

"I saw it in Lehi," Michael said. "There weren't any

ghosts. Just a strange herb in Tibet. It's a metaphor for our need to fight our baser instincts. It was pretty good."

Hiram fought off feelings of disappointment. "What? When . . . I thought you went to a dance."

"Sorry, Pap, I kind of lied." Michael grinned at Hiram. "Anyway, my risk of accidentally necking with some girl was much lower at the movie. I went alone. And as for the murder, I'm pretty sure we have a new moon going on, and don't werewolves come out when the moon is full?"

"If only lying were the worst of our misdeeds around here," Del Rose took in a breath and blew it out. "Well, Mr. Woolley, thanks again for your help, both with the well, and with poor Lloyd. If you give me your address, I'll keep you posted on the investigation." He took a pad in a leather notebook and a pencil and went to hand them to Hiram. "Send you a newspaper clipping when we catch the guy."

Michael intercepted the writing implements. "My penmanship is better. You'll thank me. Reading my pap's pigeon scratch is a brutal experience."

"That would be fine." Hiram said. "Michael and I will probably head back to Lehi soon. It is beautiful country, though."

"How did your ghost hunt turn out?" Gudmundson asked.

"We're pretty sure the ghost is Jimmy Udall's," Michael said.

"Oh?" the bishop asked. "So now what?"

"I feel for the Udalls." Hiram shook his head. Then he asked, "So, sheriff, are you going to go out and bring in Davison and Preacher Bill?"

"I sure will," Del Rose said. "The prospector is easy

to find, at his camp by the Udalls'. As for Preacher Bill, I can't very well comb every canyon for him. There's hundreds of miles of slickrock mazes out there, and half of it is too rough even for a mule. But I don't have to search for him because I know where he'll be. Later this afternoon, at four o'clock, he holds services out in Frenchie's Canyon south of the river, near Castle Valley. Some kind of crackpot, holding Sunday services on Saturday."

"Seventh Day Adventist?" Hiram asked. "Or a Jew?"

Del Rose said nothing. The silence turned awkward.

"I came in this morning to give my statement," Hiram said. "If you want it."

Del Rose nodded. "You found the body. You leave the crime scene as it was?"

"We put a sheet over him," Hiram said.

"Anything else to add?"

Hiram tried to remember clearly. "When we approached the cabin, the light was on. I knocked, the light turned off, and then a man opened the door and attacked me. He knocked me down, and then ran off into the woods when Michael fired into the air."

"You get a look at his face," the sheriff asked, "or anything else that would identify him?"

"He smelled like liquor," Michael said.

"You mentioned that." Jack Del Rose grinned. "That's not what we'd call a distinguishing feature in the policing business."

"And decay," Hiram said. "Like he was carrying around rotten meat in his pocket."

Del Rose jotted down some notes on a little pad of paper on the desk. "Anything else?"

Hiram shook his head.

"I guess that's it, then," the sheriff said.

Gudmundson cleared this throat. "I'll escort you out, Hiram. I was just leaving. Jack, you let me know how I can help."

"I will. And thank you both for coming in."

Hiram walked down the wide corridor with Bishop Gudmundson, Michael trailing.

The bishop kept his voice down. "I appreciate you coming in, Hiram. Jack Del Rose is a decent fellow, though he's not the Federal B.I., but he's also not the only authority around here. Don't worry. I'll do some asking around."

Hiram stopped and gripped Gudmundson's arm. It was muscled and hard, a working man's limb. "Revenge won't do anything for Lloyd, Bishop. He was a man of peace, and it served him well."

Gudmundson lowered his head, gulping in air. "Maybe Lloyd was killed because he was a man of peace. But you're right, Hiram. This isn't the Old West."

"And you don't want to get mixed up in this, especially you. You're the bishop, so be the bishop. Go comfort your flock, get ready for the funeral, finish moving in the Smothers family, feed the poor. See how those migrant fellows are doing, the ones whose truck you fixed. Let other people find the criminal."

Gudmundson nodded. "You're right." He raised his head. "But if you have any magic that can help, Hiram, I'd beg you to use it."

Hiram's shoulders suddenly felt very heavy. "I plan to." He let his hand drop.

Gudmundson grinned, his lips pulling back to show even yellow teeth. "Well, now, that's the best news

I've heard all day. We have a cunning man helping us. Lloyd will have justice."

"We'll try," Hiram said.

Gudmundson slapped Hiram on the back. "There are grand forces at work here in Moab. Look out at the Monument, and tell me there's no God."

Hiram liked Gudmundson. He liked the feeling of camaraderie he had with the man, too; they were both people of faith, people who served, men who worked with their hands.

Out in the sunlight, Michael watched Bishop Gudmundson walk away. Then he turned to Hiram. "Pap, that knife looked pretty sophisticated, and it was made of silver. I'm not buying the story that Mr. Gudmundson is selling, getting those knives with Mr. Preece in Salt Lake. If I was a betting man..."

"Boy."

"A betting young man," Michael finished, "I'd put my money on the widow Artemis. If she etched the Uranus symbol into that cross, maybe she made knives for those men. Maybe, I don't know, they never paid her, so she killed Lloyd with the knife she made. Or at least she might tell us where they *really* got the knives."

Hiram didn't respond. He felt his heart thud in his chest, and a knot of lust settled into his belly. Seeing Diana did make sense, though he was afraid he had another motive, one that had nothing to do with daggers.

Chapter Eleven

HIRAM DAWDLED BY THE TRUCK, TO THE VISIBLE annoyance of his son. It was still relatively early Saturday morning. They stood beside the Double-A, parked on the street in front of Diana Artemis's house.

"We could try to find her phone number," Michael suggested. "Assuming she has a telephone."

"I'm being silly, aren't I?" Hiram felt embarrassed and nervous. He wanted to see the widow again, and desperately. What might this be doing to his charms?

Hiram stuck his hand in his pocket and gripped his heliotropius. "Michael, tell me a lie."

Michael looked at him skeptically. "I love Moab with all my heart and soul."

The bloodstone remained cool, unmoved. "Another one."

"I'm certain that Jimmy Udall is in Greece, on the island of Mykonos, enjoying the sun."

Again, his bloodstone did nothing. Hiram removed it from his pocket. He handed the heliotropius to

Michael. "Son, I'm not concerned about you lying to me about seeing that movie in Lehi."

Michael waited and squinted. "What am I supposed to feel?"

"It's like a pinch." Hiram frowned. "It's not working."

"Right." Michael shook his head. "Your magic rock isn't pinching me." His son caught himself. "Okay, that came out a little sharper than I intended. So, what's the problem?"

"I had that big meal yesterday, that steak, which was a luxury I didn't need. It could be that." Hiram waited for his son to react to the lie. "Feel anything?"

Michael wrinkled his nose. "Not a thing. Sorry, Pap. Am I letting you down?"

"It's probably fine." Hiram could hardly admit to himself what he was feeling, and he certainly didn't want to discuss it. "Let's go talk to the widow. If it was Sunday, she might be out. She said she was Catholic, right? And I think maybe she has a slight French accent."

"I thought I heard one." Michael passed the heliotropius back to Hiram, who stuck it in his pocket. This time, his son went first, down the path beside the house.

Hiram knew a French accent when he heard one. He and Yas Yazzie had avoided the red lights and ladies of the evening during their time overseas. Other doughboys had fallen into infidelity, but not them.

But there had been a woman, a French woman, and like Diana, she had been a young widow. The Kaiser's war machine made widows and orphans; it created despair and fear. For that matter, the English and the French and the Americans had created widows and orphans right back.

Hiram stopped walking. He smelled perfume,

Monique's perfume, and her shy smiles. Such pretty dark hair, like Diana's, it had fallen in ringlets down her pale face, smudged with dirt. Wars were dusty, muddy, bloody things, and they darkened faces as well as souls.

Monique had been with them, those last mad days, when they'd raced through the trenches, untangled themselves from the barbed wire, and smelled the gas and the corpses. Through that hellscape, she'd been with them, until the very end. She'd wept over Yas's body, in the burned-out church, ancient enough itself, though the chambers below the basement were far older, pre-dating Rome.

Hiram hadn't cried. It was unmanly to cry, especially in front of a woman. He had done so later, when he was alone. Monique had looked at him with tears tracking down the dirt on her face.

He hadn't lost himself completely to her beauty, but he had certainly noticed it.

"Pap?" His son's voice came from a great distance.

Hiram smelled the spicy smell, garlic or mustard, fried in sugar. Maybe, he was remembering Monique cooking for them, a small piece of beef, going bad, in onions and butter.

Michael caught him before he fell, and Hiram didn't—quite—lose consciousness.

He leaned back against the fence.

A big woman in a house coat and big slippers—*Hausschuhe*, that was the German word—appeared, coming around the front of the house. She had her hair in curls, covered, like Elmina had worn hers.

Hiram found a verse of Matthew running through his head. *And if thy right eye offend thee, pluck it*

*out, and cast it from thee: for it is profitable for thee
that one of thy members should perish, and not that
thy whole body should be cast into hell.*

"You, sir, are you okay?" the woman in the *Hauss-chuhe* asked.

Another voice answered. "Yes, Edna, this is Hiram
Woolley and his son. They've come to see me."

"Easy, Pap," Michael said.

Hiram sank until he sat on the gravel, feeling the
rough rock under his palms. He clung to his consciousness. He couldn't pass out in front of Diana.

"What is the trouble with him?" Edna asked from
her back steps.

"Just a little faint," Diana answered. "He fasts too
much."

Edna laughed. "A man should respect his own
appetite. Especially if he's a working man."

Hiram opened his eyes. Diana crouched in front
of him, and her beauty hurt. Why had she never
re-married? Why hadn't *Hiram*? Why hadn't he found
a nice Lehi woman to take care of him? No, he'd
have taken care of *her*, and done a better job of it
than his father ever had.

Hiram would keep her safe from sickness and disease. He'd failed with his mother, he'd failed with
his wife, but he wouldn't fail Diana.

"Sorry." He blinked. "I'm a little light-headed."

"I should have told you to wear this against your
skin." Diana drew near, and he felt the heat from her
body, a soft hand on his head, and then she pushed
the silver cross from his breast pocket into his hand.
He hadn't felt her grab it. "Say your charm, Hiram.
You know, your prayer. Your faith is strong."

Embarrassment caught Hiram for a moment, but then he remembered she was a cunning woman. He slurred his charm. "I conjure me by the sun and the moon, and by the gospel of this day delivered to Rupert, Giles, Cornelius, and John, that I rise and fall no more."

He felt better. He couldn't smell the spice and the sweetness, only the soft fragrance of the woman in front of him. Michael fanned him with his own hat.

Out of habit, and not a little vanity, Hiram smoothed what was left of his hair.

Edna had come down as well and she stood over them. "Well, his color is coming back."

"In the summertime, red is better than white," Michael said. "In the winter, white is his natural shade. How are you feeling, Pap?"

He looked into Diana's pretty green eyes. "We apologize if you don't see clients on Saturday. We should have called."

"And look, she's fixed you up, just like that," the woman said. "Diana is a godsend. She cleared up my arthritis, so I can quilt again. 'God moves in a mysterious way His wonders to perform; He plants His footsteps in the sea and rides upon the storm.'"

Hiram climbed to his feet. "Well, Mrs. Artemis, it seems the powers of Uranus were not quite enough for me. Though I didn't pass out."

"I do have something else that might help," Diana said.

Edna reached out a hand, perhaps to touch him, and then withdrew it. "I'll put some tea on. Tea will fix anything. Or would you prefer coffee?"

"I'd like some water," Hiram took his hat from

Michael and held it. "I'm sorry I caused you any concern, Mrs. Artemis."

"Let's get you into my house," she said. "It's the best time of day, cool, but not too cold. This desert does like to change its temperatures."

Michael found a joke. "The weather in Utah changes more often than some of my friends change their underwear."

Edna wailed laughter. Diana smirked.

Hiram shook his head. "Michael."

"We know about underwear and boys," Edna said. "I raised three sons and a husband." She walked back up her steps and into her house.

Hiram kept a grip on his son as they walked down the path and into Diana's cottage at the back of the yard. Once in the parlor, he took his place on the couch. His pride was hurt, and he had to let that go.

Or his craft might not work again.

Though his charm against falling sickness had worked. Or had that, after all, been the Uranus cross?

"I won't apologize again," Hiram said, "though I want to."

"We have greater concerns than that." Diana sat in a chair, while Michael took up his stool. "I heard about Lloyd Preece."

"Already?" Shock was evident in Michael's voice.

"Small town," Hiram murmured.

"And when a pillar in a small town is removed, everything tilts immediately." Diana sighed.

"Mrs. Artemis..." Michael started.

She held up a hand. "Diana. Please. And if you refer to me as the widow Artemis, you'll break my heart, young man."

Michael colored. "Never that."

Hiram's eyes went to Diana's legs. She wasn't wearing stockings, and he saw one shapely leg, and one made of wood, falling to a simple black shoe. The craftsmanship was excellent, smooth as a natural limb, and an excellent match to her flesh leg. He wondered how far that wood went up to meet flesh.

He tried to swallow, but his mouth had become a desert. Her dress was blue, this one with flowers that appeared to be lilacs.

He shifted his gaze to her face with some effort. This dress plunged in an uncomfortable way. "We have questions about Lloyd's knife."

"Can I get a piece of paper?" Michael asked. "I can sketch what I saw."

Diana provided him with a notebook. Michael had to pass over many pages to get to a blank sheet. He drew a rough picture of the weapon. "This isn't Lloyd's knife, though. It's Gudmund Gudmundson's. We ran into him at the sheriff's office."

"I'm familiar with Gudmund's knife," Diana said. "It was created to harness the powers of Jupiter."

"Did you make the knife for him?" Michael asked. "Or inscribe the signs?"

"No." She pointed at one of the signs, a circle quartered by a cross, with smaller circles at the tip of each arm of the cross. "This means Jupiter."

"I don't remember that one from reading my horoscope in the newspaper." Michael grinned, maybe to show he didn't really read his horoscope in the newspaper, or maybe to show there was a limit to how seriously he was taking this whole conversation.

"First of all," Diana said, "Jupiter isn't one of the

twelve houses of the Zodiac, so you wouldn't see it in the newspaper, in any case. But secondly, this is not the sort of symbol you see in the newspaper. This is called the 'Seal' or 'Character' of Jupiter, and it's only used in serious magic."

"Not for reading the future?" Michael's grin didn't falter.

"Not for trying to decipher in which way the stars and planets will influence the future," Diana said slowly. "Instead, a knife such as this is used to draw the power of the stars and planets to the wielder's aid."

"To what end?" Hiram asked.

"To the ends of Jupiter," she said. "Power and prosperity."

"It hasn't worked that well for Gudmundson, then," Michael said. "He's a handyman, while his buddy Lloyd Preece got rich. Maybe the bishop's dagger is broken."

"Maybe," Hiram demurred. "What's the other sign?"

"This one, you might see in a newspaper." The image was of two parallel, jagged lines. "This is the symbol of the sign Aquarius. This knife was crafted to channel the power of Jupiter to the benefit of its wielder, a person born when Jupiter was in the constellation Aquarius."

"When would that have been?" Michael asked.

Diana leaned back. Hiram had a hard time listening to her words, her face was so interesting. "Jupiter travels around the ecliptic at the rate of approximately one sign per year, not counting periods when it is retrograde. Without consulting an ephemeris ... I think in about 1914, and before that, 1902."

"Gudmundson could be thirty-three," Michael said. "That all seems to fit. He says he got it in Salt Lake, along with another one, that Lloyd carried. They were up there together. Found them in a curio shop."

"It could be," Diana said. "I could consult with the spirits."

A knock, and Edna came in, carrying a tray, with a tall glass of water and a complete tea service, including a little kettle. She set it on the table. "Here you go, my friends. I'll be in the house if you need me."

"Thank you, Edna."

The woman retreated.

Diana stood and closed the drapes. Only a dim light was left, until she took three candles, marked with more astrological symbols. "Michael, could you move the tray? There's a table near the door. We'll get to the refreshments in a minute."

Michael took care of the water and the tea.

Diana left and returned with a glass orb and a sterling silver stand, with more signs carved into the metal. She placed the crystal ball on the table and adjusted the candles.

Hiram tried to ignore the bad feeling in his belly.

Michael's eyes were bright, expectant.

Hiram prayed silently for protection, touching his chi-rho medallion. But would the Lord Divine provide him shelter in his current state?

Diana closed her eyes and put her hands over the clear crystal of the ball. The candles were still for a moment, and then they flickered. "Spirits. From the east, from the west, from the north, to the south. Show me the truth of Lloyd Preece's murder."

The drapes, covering the window, stirred. Was that wind? Or had souls come to them in the room?

Hiram closed his eyes. He didn't want to see

anything in that crystal ball, and he didn't want any spirit to fix its unseen gaze on him or his son.

"I see something," Michael whispered. "In the orb. The candle flames, maybe, or a face. I can't... I can't tell."

Diana let out a breath. "Two knives, two men, two good men, in a barren land. Lloyd, is that you?"

Hiram prayed Lloyd wasn't there, that he'd found peace in the arms of God. But little Jimmy Udall hadn't found peace. Would Lloyd?

"Treasures," Diana murmured. "Treasures and greed, evil in the hearts of men."

Hiram couldn't help it; he opened his eyes. Two candles had gone out and their wicks smoked, perfuming the room with a sweet, waxy smell. He'd rather just smell Diana.

A fly buzzed through the room. The name of the demon he'd trapped in the caverns of the Kimball Mine came to his mind unbidden. He didn't let it form in his head; names were powerful things.

The last candle went out. Diana sat back in her chair. "Well, my friends, the spirits didn't tell me anything, unfortunately. There is greed involved, but that doesn't require much imagination. It wasn't a crime of passion that took Lloyd from us."

"Money is a better motivation, I guess," Michael said. "Though you said something, Mrs. Artemis. Sorry, but Diana isn't coming out of my mouth too easily. You said Jupiter was in Aquarius. I don't get how a planet can go through a constellation, when the constellations are much, much farther away. And... it spends a year in a constellation? And what's the ecliptic?"

Diana laughed, stood, and opened the drapes. She

swept her crystal ball up, took it back to her bedroom, came back, and retrieved the candles. The beaded curtains clicked each time she passed. Once her things were put away, she set the tea service back on the round table. "I do have a book you could borrow, Michael. You have to promise to give it back. Losing even one volume from my little library would be a sorrow I couldn't bear. And remember, I've buried a husband."

"Thank you," Michael said.

Diana snapped her fingers. "I almost forgot. Do wear the cross against your skin, Hiram, but I have something else for your falling sickness. I know you eschew tea, but I have a special blend of herbs— chamomile, passionflower, and valerian root—which should help you. I will give them to you gratis, since the Uranus cross wasn't as effective as we hoped."

She rummaged around in her room and gave him a small, fragrant mesh bag. "Steep this three times in hot water. Adding your falling sickness prayer wouldn't be a bad idea. Drink it in the morning. I'll continue to seek guidance from the spirit world."

They chatted more, drank water and tea, and then said their goodbyes.

Hiram and Michael walked back to the truck, both quiet. They stood under the big cottonwood in Edna's front lawn while Hiram took a length of twine from his toolbox and threaded it through the Uranus cross, knotting the string and then putting the cross over his head, under his shirt, against his skin. The shade was welcome protection against the sun already heating up the air.

"I really did see something in the crystal ball."

Michael held the borrowed book against his side. "And I have to admit, when you told me you were a cunning man, I figured you'd do stuff like what we just did."

Hiram thought for a long time. "That felt like a parlor trick, Michael. I don't think Diana is a witch, but she might be a bit too modern for me." But was the widow looking into a crystal ball really any different from Hiram looking into a peepstone?

"She did seem to understand the whole Jupiter knife thing."

Hiram nodded. "But I don't see any reason why the knives matter. I think someone just killed Lloyd for some perfectly ordinary reason, and used his own knife to do it, because that was the weapon at hand."

Michael laughed. "Well, if you married her, I'm not sure I could call her Mother. If Freud is right, I'd have quite an issue there."

"I've heard strange things about Freud." Hiram decided not to ask for more details. "Let's get something to eat. And some hot water. I'd like to try the tea."

Chapter Twelve

"HMM," MICHAEL SAID, RUNNING OVER THE DINER'S menu. "I really expected something more exotic from the best diner in Moab."

"Your appetite for caviar is going to leave you disappointed, son." Hiram cracked a grin.

"In a town named *Moab*, shouldn't there be, I don't know, gefilte fish, or matzo soup, or at least *something* Jewish?"

Hiram chuckled. "I see we're going to have to work on your Bible knowledge. Moab was one of the *enemies* of Israel, not a Jewish land. Most famous for human sacrifice, if I recall correctly."

"In that case," Michael said to the waitress, who tried to smile blandly, but whose tapping of her pen on her order notebook noticeably picked up speed at the words *human sacrifice*, "I'll have two fried eggs and toast."

"Give him a side of bacon, too," Hiram said. "And orange juice. Growing boy. Just eggs and toast for me."

He'd already gotten the hot water, and the little bag from Diana lay on a saucer. He hoped it would work.

He wanted something to work. He felt unsettled.

The waitress stepped away, her shoes clacking.

"Human sacrifice, eh?" Michael asked.

"The king sacrificed his own son to save the city," Hiram said. "He was sacrificing to his gods, I guess, but the Israelites besieging him were so horrified, they just pulled up stakes and left."

"Speaking of the king's own gods, what did you make of that odd little statue on Lloyd Preece's shelf?"

Hiram had forgotten the statue entirely. "I hadn't made anything of it. I took it for art. Maybe something Lloyd himself did as a young man. Or, generous like he was, maybe he bought it from some local artist to encourage him. Why, did you make something of it?" He stretched his memory. "Isn't there an old Greek story about man being three different creatures, morning, noon, and night? A riddle of some kind?"

"The riddle of the sphinx." Michael squinted for a moment, then changed the subject. "Dad, we can't leave Lloyd Preece's murder investigation in the hands of Sheriff Del Rose." Michael's voice was urgent, and his facial expression somewhere between indignant and horrified.

"You're worried he's not competent." Hiram sighed.

"No," Michael said. "Clearly, *you're* worried he's not competent. I'm worried that he's an *idiot*!"

Hiram lowered his voice. "Maybe say that in softer tones. This is a small town."

"The whole world's a small town. That doesn't mean it's wrong to seek justice."

"I'm in favor of justice." Hiram nodded. "Almost as much as I'm in favor of mercy."

"Pap," Michael said, "I told him there was a dead man. A rich, important dead man, a nice guy, bled out in his own home. And the sheriff practically yawned in front of me. And then *hours* later he sent his deputy around. And he could barely be bothered to hear your account of what happened, he was more interested in telling me where I could buy rugs and jewelry! Mercy just doesn't figure into this—there's a killer on the loose, and no one to stop him."

"Mercy always figures into everything." Hiram sipped the tea. It tasted weak and flowery. "The sheriff is investigating *now*."

"Don't you think Lloyd Preece deserves better than whatever investigation that jackass comes up with?" Michael asked. "Preece was generous with us and with everyone. He was the best kind of rich man, as far as *I* can tell. And he was *slaughtered*."

Michael was right. Hiram took a deep breath and sighed. "Okay. But officially, if anyone asks, we came here to dowse a well and we're sticking around because there's a ghost out on the Monument."

"Both of which are true." Michael nodded, a satisfied expression on his face.

A woman sat down at their table. She wore a violet-colored blouse, and a black skirt that fell below her knee. In her hands she clutched a small purse. She had a soft, rounded face and short dark hair, and she struck Hiram as vaguely familiar.

"You must be Lloyd Preece's daughter," Michael said immediately. "He called you *Addy*. Our condolences."

Michael was a full minute ahead of Hiram mentally, but of course he was right. The woman, in her thirties, perhaps, was the spitting image of her father, and the only conceivable reason she could have sat down at the table with them was that she knew her father was dead, and she had heard something about Hiram and Michael in connection with his death.

Hiram dreaded the idea that he might be becoming famous.

"Condolences," he mumbled.

"I prefer *Adelaide*." She nodded at Michael and then at Hiram. "You're Hiram Woolley? The dowser, up from Lehi?"

Hiram nodded. He meant to say "yes" verbally, too, but before he could, Adelaide was talking again.

"I need your help," she said. "I think my life is in danger."

Michael's posture snapped to attention, and Hiram's thoughts came into focus.

"Who do you think wants to hurt you?" Hiram asked. She'd spoken with her voice lowered, though she sat up and smiled as if everything were normal; he tried to do the same.

Did she think someone might be watching them?

"Whoever killed my father," she said.

"So you don't know who that is," Michael concluded. "Any guesses? You must think it's someone who might be here in town."

Again, Michael was quick as lightning. That mind would make him a formidable cunning man—or a scientist.

Or both? Maybe Michael could teach geology at a university and also be master of the craft of stones— there were more stones with special properties than just bloodstones in the world. For that matter, he could prospect for uranium on the side, too.

"I have no idea," she said. "But I know why he was killed."

From her handbag she drew a folded sheet of paper. She unfolded it carefully and set it on the table where Hiram and Michael could see. The sheet looked something like a dollar bill, but half again as large, and on thicker paper, with a blue watermark. It bore the name and address of a bank in Denver, but its largest lettering said: *Pay to the bearer $500 upon demand.*

"Is that real?" Hiram struggled with what he was seeing. He'd heard of bearer bonds but had never touched one with his own hands. If genuine, the sheet of paper basically amounted to a five-hundred-dollar bill. "Was this your father's, Mrs. Preece?"

"Mrs. Tunstall, as it happens. Married name. It's real as far as I know. My father gave it to me yesterday and told me to be ready to get out of town. He said there was lots more where this came from, and then, there's a fortune to be had in a man's good opinion of himself. He said we'd all go together, even my husband Guy, and start a new life."

"You father didn't like Guy?" Michael asked.

Adelaide Tunstall shook her head. "No, it wasn't like that. My father was a very successful man, because he worked hard and took risks. Being successful meant my father could provide for many people, including us. My husband..."

"Is not a very successful man," Michael concluded.

"No," she said. "Not in that way."

"But you don't think he and Guy might have, for instance... fought about money?" Michael was asking a very hard question, but his voice was mild, as if he were inquiring about the weather. That was a subtlety he might not need as a geologist, but that would serve him well in the cunning man's craft, or in the practice of law.

"No. No!" Adelaide's eyes grew big, and then she laughed. "Look, you'll understand when you meet my husband. Guy just wouldn't have it in him. Some women marry their fathers, but other women marry to get away from their fathers. I . . ." She shrugged. "After growing up with a man who worked hard and was ambitious, I married a man of a different type. I don't think Guy's hit anyone in his life. I don't think he had the will, even before he got kicked in the head by that horse."

Hiram sat back and tried not to look stunned while Michael talked. Lloyd Preece gave every indication of being a pillar of his community, a deeply rooted and settled man. What would make him want to flee? And was it a sudden flight, or had he been preparing, saving up money for the purpose?

Was it to save his good opinion of himself? Did that mean someone had involved him in an enterprise that was shameful or criminal?

"Your father gave the impression of being wealthy, Mrs. Tunstall," Hiram said. "Do you know where the money came from?"

"He was a rancher, Mr. Woolley. He ranched for forty years and he was good at it. And he was quick to spend money to help other people, but he didn't spend very much on himself. When I was a young woman, I asked him if I could get a tattoo—it was a strange whim I likely picked up from reading too many magazines. He told me I could, so long as the tattoo was the phrase, 'a penny saved is a penny earned.' That new truck is the only thing I can recall him buying for himself in years. He still lived in the cabin where I grew up when he could have built a mansion in town."

The new truck, Hiram thought, and the Masonic silver dagger.

"So you're saying," Michael asked slowly, "that you have a tattoo with a Benjamin Franklin quote in it?"

Adelaide laughed. "I'm saying my father got rich by being careful with his money."

"You don't know anything about buried silver?" Hiram asked. "Money from a bank robbery?"

"I've heard the rumors." Adelaide seemed to consider. "It's possible Dad had money I didn't know about. Frankly, if you were going to have bank robbery loot fall into the hands of any man in Grand County, Lloyd Preece would be a good one to choose. Wherever it came from, a lot of cash flowed from him into local charities—firemen's pensions, poor relief, public parks, as well as churches. That's right, churches plural, not just *his* church. And I've seen him hand a twenty-dollar bill to more people down on their luck than I can remember."

Hiram nodded. "I saw that myself."

"Might he have taken money for the mineral rights on his land?" Michael asked.

"Or is it possible that he made any enemies in developing his land over time?" Hiram suggested.

"You mean, someone who would want to kill him?" Adelaide shrugged. "It's possible, but if any of those things are true, I don't know about them. What I know is that my father wanted to leave the state, and he apparently had been setting aside cash to be able to do that. Then someone killed him. I need help."

"I'm not much of a fighter," Hiram said.

"That's not true," Michael protested. "I've seen you go up against four men and come out on top."

Hiram frowned. "I don't like to fight." He turned his eyes to Adelaide. "But I have a truck, if what you need is a ride out of town."

"What made you turn to us?" Michael asked.

"My husband's cousin Dick is a coal miner in one of the camps outside Helper," Adelaide said. "He told us about what you did at the Kimball mine, earlier this year."

That would be the bloodstone, spreading Hiram's fame. Hiram sucked at his teeth, wishing he could ask Adelaide exactly what she had heard. He wished he could be anonymous, an unknown, a man on the street. Good works seemed more noble when they were anonymous, but also, he'd rather that anyone who was opposed to him not see him coming.

On the other hand, Adelaide Tunstall had come to him because of his reputation, and that gave him an opportunity to help her.

"You need a ride out of town," he said. "And your husband, of course. Do you have children?"

She nodded. "Three."

"I guess we could fit everyone in the truck." Michael looked skeptical.

"I'll strap myself to the back," Hiram said. "And Mr. Tunstall with me. We'll all fit. But where do you want to go, Mrs. Tunstall?" He held up the bond. "Denver?"

"You don't have to drive us that far," she said. "Get us

to Provo and we'll catch a train to . . . somewhere else."
Abruptly, her eyes took on a guarded, shy look. "Maybe
it's best if you don't know where we end up, exactly."

"I agree." Hiram nodded.

"We can go right now," Michael said.

"We can't," she shot back.

"You need to pack?" Hiram asked. He was offering
her a graceful way out, in case she was having sudden second thoughts. The narrow eyes Michael shot
his way indicated that Michael knew it. If Adelaide
Tunstall feared for her life, why wouldn't she want
to flee immediately? It was Saturday, so the children
shouldn't be in school, and any job she'd walk away
from was a job she would be abandoning in any case.

If she wanted more time, maybe she thought she
knew where her father's money was, and she wanted
to go collect it.

Fair enough. That was none of Hiram's business,
though it did make him feel as if perhaps he was
helping someone who was about to become rich, rather
than helping someone who was on the way to poverty.

But she feared for her life, and her fear seemed
reasonable, and Hiram could help.

Besides, he wanted to go see the Reverend Majestic
Earl Bill Clay preaching.

She nodded. "I do need to pack. And I need my
privacy. Believe me, I feel better just knowing you'll
escort me out of town."

"I don't want you to be alone, though," Hiram said.
"Would it be okay if Diana Artemis came with you
while you packed? With the two of you, I think it's
much less likely that anyone will attack you."

Adelaide hesitated. Was that reluctance on her face?

"Or we could come, Mrs. Tunstall. Couldn't we, Pap?" Hiram nodded.

"Help from Mrs. Artemis would fine," Adelaide said. "She could keep an eye on the children while I gather my things and Guy's." No one seemed to think that Guy Tunstall was competent. Not even his wife, who didn't mention him as a source of safety for her, or even suggest that he would help her pack.

"We'll accompany you to her house," Michael suggested.

"That leaves us little time to get to the other places we wanted to get to this afternoon." Hiram thought of the uranium prospector and the wilderness preacher. The waitress approached the table with two plates in hand, and Hiram smiled apologetically at her. "I'm sorry, but could we get those eggs packaged to go?"

Encouraged by a fifty-cent tip, the waitress quickly wrapped the eggs and bacon both inside the toast, to convert the meal into a pair of sandwiches, with orange juice in a paper cup.

"You eat," Hiram told Michael. "I'll drive to the widow's." He tried to sound noncommittal about it. However, he found that he liked the idea of driving to Diana Artemis's house very much.

"And if you have a fainting spell?" his son asked. "Magical tea notwithstanding?"

"Drop the sandwich and grab the wheel."

Hiram drove, and Adelaide Tunstall followed in a newish red Ford Cabriolet.

"Do you think they know each other already?" Michael asked around bites into his egg sandwich that caused yolk to well up and flow around the thick sourdough toast, sinking into the bread's grainy pores.

"Or do you think Mrs. Tunstall's hesitation is only because she wants some time to look for the money?"

"We don't know that she wants to find the money," Hiram said.

"No, but you were thinking it, too. And it is rather odd she asked for privacy. And then agreed to let Diana help her."

Hiram nodded. "It is odd. And you're right, it might be about the money. We are strangers to her, and men besides. If the money was rightfully Mr. Preece's, then now it does belong to his daughter. But I hadn't considered the possibility that Mrs. Tunstall might already know Mrs. Artemis."

"So formal, Pap. I know you think of Mrs. Artemis as Diana. You can probably think of Mrs. Tunstall as Adelaide."

"Adelaide, then." Hiram chuckled. "Diana's reputation is none too good. That might just be the ordinary talk one hears about an adult woman with no fixed man in her life."

"You say that like it's fair, when you know it isn't."

"It isn't fair. But it's ordinary."

"Well, if the two women start punching each other, which one should we help?"

"If they fall to blows, we pull them apart until they cool down."

Hiram parked the car in front of Edna's bungalow, careful to leave the shadiest spot for Adelaide Tunstall. She parked behind them and stepped out of her car as if hesitation was the furthest thing from her mind.

They passed into the back yard and had only reached the front step when the door opened. Diana Artemis smiled.

And Hiram forgot what he was doing there.

"Ahem," Michael said.

Hiram tried not to look at her legs, or the curve of her shoulder, or to think about the fact that she was a cunning woman—if not exactly like Hiram, then sort of like Hiram—and a widow.

"Ahem," Michael said.

Hiram looked down at his feet.

"So we're here," Michael said to Diana, "because Mrs. Tunstall needs someone to be with her this afternoon while she packs."

"For a trip," Adelaide said. "Hello, Di."

"Hello, Addy. A trip sounds lovely. I'd love to help. I have some appointments, but I can reschedule them."

Appointments.

Diana would be giving up work to do this, and it was essentially a favor for Hiram. He was a little surprised they'd greeted each other by their first names, and that they had a certain familiarity with each other.

Hiram fumbled in his pocket and found the remaining twenty-dollar bill Lloyd Preece had given him. He handed it to Diana. "This is paid work," he said. The words sounded blunt and awkward when they came out. Diana smiled and raised her eyebrows.

"That's a lot of money to help a girl pack," she said.

"It might be dangerous," Hiram said.

"Should I take a gun?" she asked.

Michael tilted his head at Hiram and raised his eyebrows.

Hiram cleared his throat. "I don't think you need to worry that much. But, just in case—wear this." He removed his chi-rho amulet and handed it to her.

His own heart was troubled by her presence. He

desired her and he knew it, and his desire was clouding his ability to perform even simple charms. But that didn't mean the medallion wouldn't work for her.

She accepted the gift and settled it down on her lovely throat.

Hiram was struck by the thought that he had exchanged amulets with Diana Artemis; he wore her cross, and she wore *his* cross, in the form of the chi-rho medallion. He wanted to make clear that even though it was a bit like exchanging rings, Hiram had no such intention, but he couldn't bring out the words.

"Why don't we meet back here," Michael suggested. "Say, sundown?"

"Eleven p.m.," the widow Artemis countered. "And turn your lights off before you get to this block. At sundown, there will still be traffic on the street, but by eleven, you'll know that anyone on the road with you is following you."

Michael and Hiram got back into the truck, Michael taking the wheel.

"Well," Michael said, "they didn't punch each other."

"They didn't." Hiram's appreciation for the widow had grown. She'd dropped her entire day to help Adelaide. She risked losing clients, which meant losing money. He was glad he'd given her the chi-rho amulet, though he was worried for the women. If the murderer thought the Preece fortune lay in the hands of the daughter, they might be in trouble. However, it was unlikely they'd get into trouble in town, in broad daylight, the two of them—three, including the husband.

"The Saturday wilderness services don't start until four o'clock." Michael drove them down onto Main

Street. "We can run up to the prospector and see how soused he is. Then we can motor on down to Frenchie's Canyon. Pretty sure we can make it. Sound like a plan?"

Hiram nodded. Then he sighed.

Chapter Thirteen

MICHAEL DROVE PAST THE UDALLS' PLACE TO GET to Davison Rock's campsite. The Udall family was gone, perhaps on their way to Preacher Bill's Saturday services. Or was he the Reverend Majestic?

"So, when you become a traveling preacher, how do you pick your name?" Michael asked.

Pap said nothing.

Michael pondered more. "I guess if I were preaching the Bible, I'd have to go by Michael Yazzie. Woolley is a terrible last name. It sounds so... animal. But extinct animal, like a woolly mammoth. Or do I go all in with Michael Yazzie Woolley? Like Williams Jennings Bryant?"

"I have no idea," Hiram said.

They bounced over a rock, and the entire Double-A shuddered. Heat shimmered in waves off the dirt track winding like a rattler's path over the rocks and across the sand.

"People would want me to have a more native name. Like Michael Yazzie Deerhoof or something.

Michael Nightwolf. No, that would be my detective name. Preach the Bible by day. Solve crimes by night."

"I think science by day will get you a more stable life," Hiram suggested.

"Tent preaching by night? But when will I solve crimes?"

"On the weekends. Is it fun for you to taunt me like this?"

"Well, it's more fun than talking about murder, ghosts, and what-not. I can't believe Lloyd Preece is dead. It feels surreal." Michael frowned, slowed, and had to adjust his wheels so they rode over another outcropping of rock. They went up a ridge, piled with stones, to get them onto a shelf of slickrock, which they traversed before bouncing down the other side, springs creaking. "You don't think Lloyd was there, in Diana's room, with us, do you? I swear, something moved in the crystal ball."

"I'm not so sure," Hiram said. "Loaning you the book was generous. And the silver cross might have helped me. I didn't pass out. Now I've got the cross against my skin, and we'll see about the tea."

Michael winced at the heat and the sunshine blazing through their windshield. "If we were to use science, heaven forbid, to test the efficacy of the cross, you would track how you felt for a month without wearing it, and then wear it for a month, keeping a journal. Then we would know. We could do something similar for the séance. Have a séance, every day for a month, and then write down what we see, in a clinical environment."

"I don't think it works that way," Hiram said. "Some-times, when you try to measure a thing, you lose its essence. Its power. And you must treat these things seriously, or they won't work at all."

"And this is the problem, Pap, with the whole system. If sometimes your spells work, and if sometimes they don't, you can't prove anything." Michael didn't want to attack his father's beliefs, but he himself felt baffled. He'd seen the fly demon in the Kimball Mine. He'd felt the dowsing rod plunge in his hands. The magic wasn't complete horse crap, and yet, it seemed to him that it must be. Why hadn't his pap been protected against the murderer the night before? Why wasn't the bloodstone telling him when people were lying? Those questions couldn't be answered because magic was magic and not science.

"I don't like the word 'spells.'" His pap sighed. "If I were constant, my charms would work, powered by the Lord Divine, to help this troubled world." He turned away. "God is constant. I am weak. My faith is weak. I'm sorry, Michael. Grandma Hettie would have been a better teacher. She was the most constant person I ever knew."

Michael pulled up on the stretch of slickrock that descended to the prospector's camp. "Pap, you're not weak. I've seen you fight. And you made it through the Great War. Maybe God asks too much of you. Maybe He's the problem."

Hiram grinned. "He did a pretty good job with the world. And He did a fine job with you. That strengthens my faith more than anything."

"Me?" Michael felt astounded. "I'm your loudmouth atheist son."

"Agnostic," his father said.

Michael didn't argue. He pulled up alongside the prospector's camp.

They parked beside the Ford Tudor and piled out of the truck. The camp had been cleaned and straightened.

The large-nosed prospector himself stood under a tarpaulin, creating his own shade with collapsible metal poles. He'd set up a folding table—not wood, but metal, and it was covered with mineral specimens, a scale, and a complicated looking machine: a box, a long wand, a cloth cable. He held a magnifying glass up to his eye and examined a rock.

. He set the glass down and surveyed Michael and his father. "Hello. Have we met? That truck looks familiar." His accent sounded slightly English, but not quite.

Michael answered for them both. "We drove by here yesterday, but you seemed distracted. I think you were looking for something. I'm Michael and this is my father, Hiram."

"Hello, Michael, Hiram. The name is Davison Rock." The man paused and hooked his thumbs in his suspenders. He was in the same shirt that he'd worn the day before, the underarms stained, the sleeves rolled up. "I was looking for a hunk of pitchblende yesterday. I found it." Davison winced and folded his lips together. "But how can I help you today?"

Michael saw he was ashamed. He'd known he'd been rip-roaring drunk, and yet, he wasn't about to apologize or talk about it. Michael didn't blame him.

Pap took over. "Lloyd Preece was murdered last night in his cabin down by the Colorado River."

Davison furrowed his brow and shook his head. "Why, that's a damn shame. Lloyd was a good man, and we were near a deal for the mineral rights to his land."

"Near a deal?" Pap asked.

Davison saw where that line of thinking was leading. "Why, I didn't kill him. I was asleep by sundown yesterday."

Michael tried to soothe things over. "We don't think you did, Mr. Rock. We're just trying to help."

"Because the sheriff is incompetent." Davison nodded. "I knew that after I was in town ten minutes. But I won't be grilled by you, or by anyone."

"Actually, we came to talk to you about a ghost yesterday." Michael made sure the prospector saw he was smiling. "See? We're not police. And we're harmless."

"A ghost?" Davison shook his head, laughing a bit. "I've heard stories, but I've not seen a thing. I had a crazy night a few months ago, back in February, when I nearly got run over by a herd of deer one night. And I heard howling—might have been wolves." Davison's eyes went from Hiram to Michael. "Last night, in order to get to Lloyd's cabin, I would have had to drive, or take the cable car, or swim. I was in no condition to do any of those things."

February... might that have happened to Rock at the same time that Hiram and Michael were helping the miners of the Kimball Mine? Probably not. Probably it was just coincidence.

Michael felt bad for the guy. He wasn't wrong. He'd barely been on his feet the day before. "Mr. Rock, I couldn't help but notice the irony in your being named Rock. Which came first, your interest in geology or the name?"

Davison tilted his head. "I've loved rocks since I was a boy, but my interest couldn't predate my birth."

"I thought it might be a made-up name," Michael said. "Like Harry Houdini."

"The secrets of the universe are in the stones," Hiram murmured.

"That's right," Davison smiled. "We're standing in

the middle of a million years of history, my friends. Do you realize human civilization is less than ten thousand years old? We've been here a miniscule amount of time. And yet, the rocks upon which we stand were once an ocean bed, three hundred million years ago. We would have been underwater here. Think of it, a world without people, populated by all manner of life, now extinct. The forces of pressure and time are staggering. Millions of years of history."

Michael felt a thrill go through him. "Yes, this stone was once sand, but underneath the water, it was pressed into rock. That and time, buried deep below the crust of the earth."

Davison took his right hand and put it on top of his left. He tilted his right upward. "And then, the land was lifted up by volcanic activity, where the wind and rain eroded the softer detritus away and eventually ate through the stone itself."

Pap kept quiet. Of course, Pap thought it was all created by God in seven days, or some other old-timey notion.

Michael couldn't help but think of the majesty of the land being carved by the eons and the weather. The geology around them had been crafted by a higher power, certainly, and it had nothing to do with the world of the spirit.

"So tell me about uranium," Michael said. "I don't know much. I know the mineral releases particles, alpha, or beta, I can't remember, and that the rock itself degrades. You can detect that with the Geiger counter, can't you?"

Davison again, smiled, showing fine white teeth. "Hans Geiger, German physicist, came up with the idea to detect radiation from unstable minerals in 1908. It wasn't until 1928 that it was perfected by his student, Walther Müller, so men like me could buy it." He patted the box with the long wand. "Do you know how the Geiger-Müller tube works?"

Michael couldn't stop grinning. "You bet I do. Basically, the particles move through the tube, which contains an inert gas. Those particles conduct electricity, enough to make the speakers on the main unit crackle. We're actually hearing the electrons." Michael liked the way Davison was looking at him. "I read a lot of *Popular Science,* and basically any book I can get my hands on." He thought of the astrological tome from Diana and felt a little silly. What would Davison think of him reading about how stellar activity ruled human lives, and how a person could summon down the power of the planet Jupiter through the constellation Aquarius?

Was this how Pap felt when Michael teased him about his charms?

"That's right," Davison said. "You have it exactly. To think, the stones themselves are a whirl of activity... as if they were alive. What we think is solid is actually atoms spinning around each other. It makes one question the solidity and the veracity of the seen world."

Pap was listening closely. "So there is an unseen world?"

"Indeed." Davison lifted a mottled stone of black, gray, blue, and copper colors. "You think this is solid, and so it would seem. But it is mostly space. In each atom there is a nucleus at the center, protons and electrons are spinning around the nucleus, and yet, the space between the particles is vast. This stone is mostly empty space."

The grin Pap brought to his face was priceless. "And maybe God fills those cracks. Could there be room in your science for a bit of divinity?"

"It would be hubris to presume that we understand the mysteries of the universe." Davison nodded. "I have no issue with religion until men use it to control and cheat other men. In fact, out here, on the stones of this long-dead ocean, I can't argue there is a presence here, a force, that I cannot see or weight or taste. Perhaps one day we shall develop the technology to study it. For now, we may call it God."

The uranium prospector flicked a switch on the box on his table. That box was mostly the power source and the speaker unit which powered the rod in the tube; the rod would be surrounded by an inert gas, neon, or helium, or argon. Davison swept the Geiger-Müller tube over mottled rock. The speakers on the box clicked away. "For all we know, God is a particle of energy filling the world."

"And evil?" Pap asked.

Michael felt a bit embarrassed by the question.

Davison took it in stride. "Evil is far simpler. Men kill for love, for money, or out of drunken rage. Most of the time what we call evil is human stupidity, a willful ignorance, or desperation caused by circumstances. I do not understand God, Hiram. But I have at least *seen* evil."

Michael clapped his hands. "Mr. Rock, I do believe that was one of the best speeches I've heard in a long, long time. And to see an actual Geiger-Müller tube working? This is amazing. And see, Pap, if his instrument is working correctly, he'll get the same results, time and again."

Pap nodded. "The problem isn't God, Michael. It's His instruments."

That made Michael clap again. "A very fine argument, Pap. I applaud you."

Hiram looked away.

Davison set the wand back on the table and turned off the unit.

"What do you do with the uranium?" Michael asked.

"Sell it," Davison said. "Or try to. Marie Curie and her husband, Pierre, needed several tons of uranium ore to create even a few grams of radium, which has been shown to help cure some cancers. That ruled the market, for a time, but now the prices are dropping precipitously. Uranium can be used in some ceramics, and in other textiles, but that isn't where the future lies. Physicists in Europe: Enrico Fermi, Otto Hahn, and others, are unlocking new secrets every day, using unstable elements like uranium. My plan is to find a large deposit of either pitchblende . . ." He raised the mottled rock. "Or carnotite." He motioned to a powdery yellow stone. "And wait until the prices increase. Then, I can help provide the scientists with the fuel to power the future."

"Or destroy it," Michael said. "Isn't there talk of using the particles as a weapon? And yes, I do read Flash Gordon and Buck Rogers."

"If we could unlock the power in the atoms," Davison said, "that could be used to do any number of interesting things. But you're right, such energy could be used to kill. And hence, we return to our discussion on human evil, which seems to be on the rise. If anything, European fascism and its attendant hatred and intolerance is truly of man, and nothing divine resides in it. And communism, for all its fair words of international brotherhood, peace, and sharing, seems to be little better with respect to practical outcomes."

Michael thought any talk of human government should include some talk of the diabolical.

Pap didn't take the political bait. "Mr. Rock, so if you did find a deposit, you wouldn't sell it right away? Don't you need the money?"

"I don't," Davison said. "Look, I know I must look odd out here, but I assure you, I have all the financing I need. I can prove it. Erasmus Green should be at the hotel later this evening. He runs the First National Bank of Moab. He can vouch for me, as can Howard Balsley, who knows as much as I do about geology, if not more."

Pap nodded his head, his eyes downcast. "Mr. Rock, we're not police. You're not a suspect as far as I'm concerned."

"But I know the sheriff doesn't see me with such forgiving eyes," Davison said. "I've had dealings with him."

Michael remembered Sheriff Del Rose saying Davison had been locked up for public drunkenness. It was hard to believe that this scientist, this intelligent man, would ever spend a single night in jail. Michael thought of Pap's comment on faulty instruments.

"Let's do this," Davison said. "I'll meet you at the hotel at seven. I've had about all I can stand of my cooking out here. I'll eat a meal, we'll talk to Mr. Green and Mr. Balsley, and I can assure you, I had no dispute with Lloyd Preece, over money, or mineral rights, or anything else. Lloyd was a very wealthy man. And I . . . let's just say I'm comfortable."

Michael was thrilled to spend more time with Davison Rock. They had a literal world of things to talk about.

"We'll meet you at the Maxwell at seven then," Hiram said quietly.

On their way back to the truck, Michael went over the timeline of their evening: see the Reverend Majestic at four, meet with the scientist at seven, and then escort Adelaide to Provo at eleven. Quite the evening. He was glad that Diana had the chi-rho amulet—if it worked at all, that is, it was good that she would be the one carrying it. What other craft did she have to protect her and Adelaide's family? He hoped it was enough. He found himself surprised by the idea, and oddly comforted. Having a cunning man, or a cunning woman in this case, seemed like a handy thing.

Michael drove them up and back around to the highway. From there, they continued on toward Frenchie's Canyon on the south side of the Colorado. They'd show up a little late for the Reverend Majestic's Saturday afternoon theatrics. Michael didn't feel too bad. He didn't expect to miss any important doctrine.

Pap touched his shoulder. "You liked the prospector, didn't you?"

Michael rolled his eyes. "Of course, I did. He's a scientist. I want to be a scientist. I don't mind Lehi, most of the time, but Pap, it's not exactly a hotbed of intellectualism. You're right, I don't want to fight crime. I'll need to get to college before too long."

"You do." Pap sighed. "I'm curious to see what Earl Bill Clay can tell us. I smelled Davison Rock, and while he was a working man out in the sun, he wore a cologne. The man I fought last night stank and not just of booze. He smelled like carrion."

"And no seer stones were involved." Michael had wondered about that the day before. After talking with the prospector—geologist was probably a more accurate description—Davison wouldn't go around looking for angels in hats.

"No, no seer stones," Hiram said. "I think Mr. Rock is an innocent man."

"Maybe a man didn't kill Mr. Preece." Michael's mind had been opened by his time with the uranium prospector. If God filled the void in atoms, what else might they find there?

Chapter Fourteen

"MANY ARE CALLED," THE REVEREND MAJESTIC Earl Bill Clay howled from the top of his pulpit, which was an upended wooden crate with *Sears, Roebuck* stamped on the side in black letters. "But few are chosen. And why are the many not chosen?"

Hiram and Michael had parked down by the Colorado River, about five miles up the canyon from the Preece cabin. Cars were everywhere, some parked dangerously close in the weeds next to the green waters.

Hiram and his son had then marched up a short trail into Frenchie's Canyon.

There, the Reverend stood in front of a wall built up of slabs and chunks of red rock, filling in the underbelly of an overhang on the top of a long sandbank. Water might flow down this canyon, which was narrow enough to become really dangerous in a flood, but there was no water in sight now.

The canyon was mostly in summer afternoon shadow, but the spot where the Reverend stood was bathed in pink and orange light. This made the Reverend himself—a bear of a man, unshaven, with bright red hair and beard, who was dressed in mismatched parts of several tuxedos of differing sizes and who hopped up and down from the crate to emphasize key points, always jumping with both feet at the same time and landing on both feet—look like a purple bear.

Dotted along the sandbank, the Reverend's parishioners were seated on the front rows on chunks of red stone, with the back rows standing. Hiram immediately recognized the Udalls: same calico shirts, same overalls, same boots. They looked more like brother and sister than man and wife. Well, the Bible did say that Moab had other issues besides just human sacrifice.

To one side, despite his assurances to the contrary, sat Rex Whittle. Not far from him, Hiram recognized Don Pout, the man with the tiny nose and long eyelashes who had been at the dowsing. He saw one of the migrant workers, too, the short man who smelled of tobacco. Hiram and Michael stood in the back, near the top of a stone-choked path that led up this narrow canyon from the river below.

"Why are the many not chosen?" the Reverend Majestic hollered again.

"Why?" Rex Whittle called out.

"Tell us!" bellowed an old woman Hiram didn't recognize.

"Because of the dragon!" The Reverend leaped up into the air, pulling his knees up into his chest and then coming down on both feet simultaneously. Gravel in the sand crunched. Plumes of dust rose to cover the Reverend's legs.

Hiram winced, thinking how much such a jump

would hurt him. He had to admit, though, that it made the sermon lively.

"So, Pap," Michael whispered. "Is that the guy who attacked you?"

"In the darkness, I didn't see much," Hiram murmured. "And once that fellow hit me, my vision became entirely unreliable. Funny as this sounds, I'd like to get closer and try to *smell* him."

"That doesn't sound funny at all," Michael said. "That sounds disgusting."

The Reverend paced back and forth. For all his energy in leaping, he walked with a severe limp. Something was wrong with his right foot; he stepped on it as if only the heel had feeling, or as if his toes were broken and he was afraid to flex them. His mismatched tuxedo imitation was equaled by his wearing two mismatched boots—the right boot looked as if it might have been Army-issue in the war, and the left was an oversize cowboy boot that swiveled around his calf like a rolling bucket at every step.

"The dragon has us all in its grip, and do you know how you can recognize it?"

"How?" This from Don Pout, whose voice trembled at the weight of his own question.

"Telegraph!" the Reverend bellowed. "Telegraph! Telegraph! Telegraph! Not to mention the gold standard, and the Works Progress Administration, and the Panama Canal—Satanic all!" He leaped up again and this time landed on top of the crate, arms windmilling briefly to catch him from falling.

"See, Pap?" Michael said. "That's religion for you. Maybe you Mormons can add a little of his circus to your act, fill those pews."

"Where is the room for the little man in all this, eh, Mr. Roosevelt?" The Reverend stabbed an accusing finger at the sky. "You speak with a honeyed tongue, but I see the Rolls Royce you drive! I know the wolves you send out among the human flock, to eat our flesh and to make you and your kind fat!"

"Earl Bill Clay!" a voice bellowed to Hiram's left.

Hiram turned to see Sheriff Jack Del Rose and a couple of deputies in khaki pants and dark olive jackets. The deputies held nightsticks.

"Everybody except Preacher Bill needs to clear out," Del Rose bellowed.

A few of the parishioners at the fringes of the crowd crept out past the law enforcement men.

"Now!" the sheriff roared.

The crowd ran. They streamed past Hiram to rush down to where their cars and even in some cases their mules waited; in a minute of busy motion, the desert amphitheater emptied out.

Hiram and Michael stood still.

The Reverend Majestic leaped into the air one more time, now landing in front of the only opening in the rough stone wall, an irregular door beneath an irregular sandstone lintel. He wheeled to face the lawmen, nearly falling over as he pivoted awkwardly on his bad right foot. When he finished his pivot, though, he held a silver knife in his hand.

"Can you smell *that*, Pap?"

"That's Preece's knife!" One of the deputies started forward, brandishing his nightstick. "I'm going to kill you, you vermin!"

Hiram sucker-punched the deputy, landing a solid right fist on the man's temple. The deputy tumbled to the sand and lay still—should Hiram grab the night-stick? But he wanted to defuse tension, not raise it.

He stepped into the path of the lawmen, deliberately dropping his hands to his sides, his fingers not curled up into fists.

"Pap," Michael said. "The guy with the knife is *behind* you."

"Tell me if he makes a move." Hiram nodded, feeling sweat slicken his back and palms. "Sheriff, you can't kill this man."

"Don't get all excited, Hiram," the sheriff drawled. "Russ Pickens didn't really mean he was going to kill anyone. He just meant that suspects sometimes come out of the arrest process a little bit worse for wear."

"You don't know that this man killed Preece," Hiram said. Even as he said that, he smelled the Reverend Majestic, and the combined reek of alcohol, stale sweat, and corruption was unmistakable—this was definitely the man who had knocked Hiram down, charging out of Preece's cabin. "He might have a perfectly reasonable explanation as to why he has Preece's knife."

"Yes, I do!" Clay howled. "The knife is Satanic!"

"You heard him." Jack Del Rose chuckled. "That sound reasonable to you?"

"It's not the craziest thing I've heard." Hiram's mouth was dry. He swallowed, and that didn't help.

"And then I thought maybe I could sell it for money!" Preacher Bill yelled.

"*That* sounds downright *sane*," Michael quipped.

"Once I exorcised all the evil spirits of the Franklin Delano Roosevelt Administration out of it!"

"This is nuts." Sheriff Del Rose sighed. "You came

by my office this morning to make your statement, and that was helpful, Woolley, but now I've got my man and you're getting in my way. And you're doing it on purpose. Stand aside, or I'll arrest you for obstruction of justice. And I will remind you that arrested suspects sometimes come out slightly worse for wear—which is *none of your business.*"

"He might be guilty," Hiram admitted. In fact, Hiram thought he most likely *was* guilty, and he envisioned himself testifying at Clay's trial about the night of the murder, and his blind fistfight with the hobo preacher. "But he gets arrested like any other suspect, and no one roughs him up, and then he gets a trial."

"Guilty of what?" Clay asked.

"Why do you care, Woolley? Why do you care if Pickens saves the taxpayer some money by doling out the punishment this guy is going to get, anyway?"

"Look at him," Hiram said. "He's a madman. Jesus had mercy on madmen. If I want Jesus to have mercy on me—"

"Spare me the Jesus talk!" Del Rose barked. "I had enough of that to last me a lifetime before I was ten years old."

"Guilty of what?" Clay screamed. "Guilty of the taint of the dragon? Guilty of being a man-eating wolf, like all the other man-eating wolves in this valley? Guilty of the Fall of Adam?"

The downed deputy, Pickens, was stirring, and the other deputy started to help him to his feet.

"Earl Clay," the sheriff called. "You're under arrest for the murder of Lloyd Preece!"

"Lloyd Preece? Lloyd Preece?" All the menace and imbalanced madness fell instantly out of Clay's voice. "Why would I murder Lloyd? He fed me. He gave me money."

The bloodstone in Hiram's pocket lay inert. Did that mean that Clay was telling the truth? Or was it one more instance of Hiram's craft failing him, because of his erotic obsession with the widow Artemis?

But in any case, he believed Clay. There was madness in the man, but innocence as well.

Hiram backed toward Clay, raising his hands slightly from his side, but still not balling them into fists. "Why do you have Preece's knife, Reverend? You took it from his house, didn't you?"

"He was already dead when I got there! I took it from his body!" the Reverend howled. "I told you the knife was Satanic! The knife killed my friend, the dragon killed him, the world killed him! And I took the knife to destroy it, because maybe if I destroyed the knife, he would come back!"

"Yeah," the sheriff said slowly. "Or maybe you could sell the knife for money like you just confessed. That would be after Lloyd Preece refused to give you a dime and you killed him."

"Maybe," Clay said.

"I'd keep quiet," Michael muttered. "You're not helping your case."

"Just promise you won't beat him up," Hiram said to the sheriff.

"I'm not promising shit," the sheriff said. "Get out of the way now or you get to see the inside of my jail. Hell, I'll throw you and your new best pal in together."

Hiram heard the thud of running feet.

"Pap!" Michael yelled.

Hiram dropped forward, curling himself into a ball to avoid a knife-blow from behind that he felt certain was imminent—

and threw himself under the sheriff's legs.

The two men collapsed to the ground in a tangle. Past the sheriff's khaki-colored knees and olive-green midriff, Hiram saw Earl Bill Clay duck into his stone dugout. "You can't see me!" he yelled. "I can hide in here!"

The two deputies were having none of it. They charged the door, nightsticks up—

and the first one went reeling away as a red rock the size of a man's head struck him in the face. Blood spattered on the sand, and Hiram saw a flash of silver.

"That's it!" yelled the standing deputy, Pickens, as he pulled his gun. "Come out, you!"

No answer.

"Now, or I shoot!" Pickens yelled.

"No!" Hiram called.

Bang! Bang! Bang!

The deputy fired into the dugout as he ran into it. Sheriff Del Rose stood and dragged Hiram to his feet, glaring through his one half-open eye. "To hell with arresting you. I should just shoot you, and say it was an unfortunate mistake after you wouldn't get out of our way. Might have to shoot your boy, too, and that would break my heart, but I tell you what . . . I know how to get over hurt feelings."

The sheriff smelled of sweat and too much coffee. Over the sheriff's shoulder, Hiram saw Michael stoop and pick up something from the red sand near the dugout doorway, pocketing it quietly.

"I only wanted to prevent violence," Hiram said softly.

"Lying bastard," Pickens said, emerging from the dugout. "You punched me right in the noggin and I wasn't even looking at you."

Hiram shrugged, but kept an even gaze on the deputy.

The sheriff shoved Hiram aside. He managed to keep his feet.

"Pickens, what the hell?" the sheriff growled. "You kill the guy?"

Pickens shook his head.

Michael stepped quietly away from the lawmen.

"Then what? You go in there, made friends, and you decided to leave him alone, after all?" Del Rose's brow furrowed, perplexed. "Maybe you wanted to leave him for me, like a present?"

Pickens looked embarrassed. "He disappeared."

The sheriff drew his gun and a flashlight and stationed himself beside the doorway.

"It's broad daylight," Michael said. "Why the flashlight?"

"Shut up, kid," Del Rose spat.

"Better than 'Injun,'" Michael murmured. Then, "Oh, it's going to be dark in that cave. Right."

The sheriff screamed, "I'm coming in, and I'm more than ready to shoot you."

Then he slipped into the dugout.

Hiram followed.

The space inside was small and dark. Hiram tried to follow the beam of the sheriff's flashlight with his eyes, and he saw a wedge-shaped corner that angled down and back, until the sand underfoot finally met the overhanging rock wall. On two sides, the sandstone rocks had been stacked into such a tight wall that almost no light shone through the chinks between them.

"I'll be damned," Del Rose said. He turned slowly, staring at the walls and shining his light up at the rock face, as if he might find a hidden staircase.

Hiram's own flashlight was in the Double-A. "Sheriff, would you mind shining your light over here? In the corner."

"Go home, Woolley."

"Don't you want to find your suspect?"

"You mean the one that you let go?"

"Just . . . humor me, would you?"

Del Rose shone his light into the corner Hiram indicated. "What do you think you're seeing?"

"Do those furrows look like a body might have crawled into that corner?" Hiram asked. "And look at the sand at the base of that rock in the corner. It's heaped up, like someone pushed the rock into place from the other side."

"You're thinking that was an exit, and after the crazy guy crawled out, he pushed in a rock behind himself."

"I think he had enough time," Hiram said.

"Fine." The sheriff pointed his gun at Hiram. "You go take a look. I'll cover you."

That had not quite been Hiram's plan. He reached to touch his chi-rho medallion and was reminded that he had given it to Diana Artemis.

"Okay," he said. Then he lowered himself to his hands and knees, crawling back into the corner. "Reverend Clay, I'm coming your direction," he called out. "I'm not going to hurt you. I believe you were Lloyd Preece's friend."

The sheriff snorted.

Hiram lowered himself onto his belly. "The way I see it, you went to ask him for money. Preece was a generous man, he gave to people all the time. He'd given to you before. But you found him dead, and that made you upset. Maybe you were distracted or maybe you thought you could really help him, but you grabbed the knife, and that's when you heard me knocking on the door."

"What are you doing, helping plan his defense?" the sheriff asked.

Hiram had reached the rock in the back corner. He pushed at it experimentally, and it moved—no weight rested on it, and a breeze blew through the cracks around it. "Maybe you were afraid that I was the killer, come back to kill you too, or to take the knife. So you turned down the light, and when I knocked again, you attacked me."

"Jesus, Woolley." The sheriff sounded disgusted.

Hiram pushed the rock all the way through. The space beyond was not totally dark—so, not a cave? "There's definitely an opening here."

"So the preacher had an escape route planned, did he?" Del Rose chortled. "That strike you as innocent?"

"It strikes me as paranoid," Hiram said. "Or maybe just well prepared." He dragged himself through the opening, and found himself in a vertical shaft, which appeared to have been formed as a wrinkle of open space where two masses of sandstone met. The floor of the shaft was sand, and pale light shone from above. Hiram looked up and saw, for just a moment, a pair of dangling legs silhouetted against the last light of the evening sky.

"Woolley?" the sheriff called.

"Preacher Bill!" Hiram yelled. "Reverend Clay!"

The legs pulled themselves up over the lip of the sandstone and disappeared.

Sheriff Del Rose crawled into the shaft. He stood, and the two men nearly filled the space. The sheriff looked up. "He climbed out the shaft."

Hiram nodded. "Surprisingly agile for a man with a limp."

"I should arrest you. I really should."

Hiram sighed. "You'd have a case."

"Yeah." Del Rose squinted at him. "Get out of my sight, farmer."

"You're not going to climb up the chimney?"

"So that maniac can drop rocks on my head? No, thank you. My men and I will have to figure out how to get up onto the top of the cliff and keep searching. Maybe get some dogs or something."

"I think he's innocent."

"Shut up."

Hiram dropped to all fours and crawled out of the chimney, and then stood to exit the dugout. He walked into the barrel of Pickens's revolver, and the deputy's sour stare. Michael stood off to the side, sweat on his face.

"I should shoot you," the deputy said.

Hiram nodded, tired. "The sheriff said a similar thing. He decided against it and let me go."

Pickens seemed to consider the possibilities.

"Come on, Pap," Michael said. "Let's get out of here."

Pickens settled for snarling, and Hiram and Michael walked down the canyon toward their truck.

"Doggone, Pap," Michael said, "you really think the crazy guy is innocent."

Hiram didn't have the heart to talk about the bloodstone and his doubts. Instead, he just said, "I think he was in the wrong place at the wrong time."

They climbed down the boulder-strewn slope. They reached the Double-A, parked in a clump of junipers. All the other vehicles were gone.

They got into the truck.

Michael didn't start it. "Pap, I have a question about obstructing justice."

"I wasn't obstructing justice," Hiram said. "I was trying to . . . prevent another murder."

"Right. The crossword deputy wasn't about to stop at a beating." Michael was quiet for a moment. "So you're saying, you wouldn't want to actually obstruct justice. For instance, by holding on to evidence."

Hiram was still full of adrenaline and couldn't think straight. "Probably not a great idea, no. You can go to jail for it, even if Sheriff Del Rose's deputies didn't beat you to death."

"That's what I thought," Michael said. "So, I make it about 5:15. It's about forty-five minutes into town. That gives us an hour to kill."

Hiram opened the door, closed it, and leaned in the window. "I need a walk and time so I can think and pray. I would suggest you do the same."

Chapter Fifteen

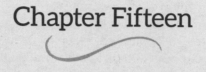

MICHAEL SAT ON A FALLEN COTTONWOOD TRUNK, open book across his lap. He'd finished his perusal, for now, and watched the shadows growing longer as the sun headed toward the western horizon. He liked sitting next to the river, reading, and smelling the rich stew of the water. But after his studying, he found himself in a baffling state: exhausted, interested, incredulous, and excited, all at the same time. He'd spent the hour reading about the minute mechanics of astrology, and he was looking forward to moving his body again, and resting his mind a little.

First, dinner with Davison Rock, then they'd have to rendezvous with Diana and Adelaide Tunstall. Michael liked the way the uranium man thought and talked, he liked his slightly funny accent, and he liked the idea of a person of science with secret reserves of money. He looked forward to dinner.

Michael had to wonder what Guy Tunstall might be like after getting kicked in the head by a horse. Severe brain injury might do all sorts of terrible things to a person. The brain was the seat of consciousness, after all, though Grandma Hettie used to claim that the ancient Hebrews and Egyptians believed a person thought in his heart. And the soul? Where might that lie?

Pap returned, as silent as ever, and they drove into town. Moab seemed its usual quiet, tiny red self. That boded well for Diana and Adelaide. If there had been trouble, such a small burg would've been in an uproar, especially after the murder the day before.

Michael parked outside the Maxwell House Hotel. He and his pap went through the doors into a room full of smoke, chatter, and the fog of liquor. The place was full of men. The dance halls and saloons in town must be going begging for business; all the town's men seemed to be at the Maxwell House Hotel.

"A toast!" a man Michael didn't recognize shouted, raising a shot glass. "To Lloyd Preece and his never-ending river of twenty-dollar bills!"

"To Lloyd Preece!" the crowd shouted.

Hiram murmured along with them, nodding agreement. "To Lloyd Preece."

"This is a wake," Michael said to his father in low tones. "We don't do wakes, do we?"

"We Mormons? It's not a particular part of our culture, but we don't especially object, either."

"Oh, good."

Gudmund Gudmundson stood beside Clem, both in neat, dark suits. On Clem in particular, this clothing looked shockingly wrong; on Gudmundson, the suit just suggested to Michael how, in the right circumstances, people might call the man "Bishop." Gudmundson looked respectable, like someone whose word you would accept. Both Gudmundson and Clem were next to the sheriff at the bar with other men from town, some dusty cowboys off the range, and still further men in shoestring ties, bow ties, or the thick-bottomed ties, like Oliver Hardy wore. Michael had seen *Sons of the Desert* a couple of years earlier.

Gudmundson, Jack Del Rose, and Clem stood with a few other men Michael didn't recognize, and all were drinking soda pop from bottles: grape and orange Nehi, Hires Root Beer, and Coca-Cola. So that was the Mormon crowd. They seemed to be having as much fun as the others, at least.

Near the back, in the far corner, Erasmus Green sat at a table with his pals, Banjo Johansson and Howard Balsley. The hotelier, Leon Björnsson, sat with them, petting his stuffed double-dog Petey.

Green and his friends sat in the same place Michael had seen them the day before. Davison Rock was at the same table with Green, and he had a cup of coffee in front of him. Michael was glad. He never wanted to see the geologist drunk again.

Michael and his pap headed over to the seated crowd.

The men rose. They wore the best suits in the room, by far, and Erasmus Green even had a top hat on, though the shoulders of his coat were spotted with dandruff. "Hiram! Michael! Sit with us! We were just talking about Lloyd. Heck, everyone in here is talking about Lloyd." The banker's cheeks were flushed and the whiskey bottle in front of him was nearly empty. So this was the non-Mormon crowd. Half the men had smoldering cigars clutched between their fingers.

Michael shook hands with Davison Rock. No one

else offered. That was fine. Let Pap deal with the rest of them. Michael really only wanted to talk with Davison, anyway.

Lloyd Preece's knife was heavy in his pocket. Michael didn't like the idea of going to jail for obstruction of justice, but when Preacher Bill had dropped the knife, he'd grabbed it. He *had* to—he wanted to see what was on it and how it differed from the bishop's knife and how both compared to what he was reading in the widow's book. He didn't really have a plan for what to do with it; vaguely, he thought he might put it back in the Reverend Majestic's dugout, and then maybe leave the sheriff an anonymous tip. In the meantime, he'd confirmed that this knife—Lloyd's Preece's knife, supposedly, and the weapon that had killed him—had the Seal of Jupiter on one side and the symbol of the constellation Taurus on the other.

Again, this matched with what the bishop had said. Apparently, that meant that Lloyd Preece had discovered the knife in a curio shop, realized it was for Tauruses and that he was a Taurus, and had bought it.

No, that wasn't quite right. The knife was made to channel the power of Jupiter for a wielder who was born in a year when Jupiter was passing through Taurus. Which, apparently, Lloyd Preece had been. That was not the same thing has having Taurus as your birth-sign.

Michael wondered what Davison would make of the dagger, the signs on it, and the supposed power it drew from Jupiter. Davison might accept that the forces of the stellar bodies at work could indeed affect humans in some yet unknown way. Heck, *gravity* was a mysterious force that stars exerted on each other from a distance, even though no one quite knew how. He was far more open-minded than some of the books Michael had read. Maybe Davison Rock could thread his way through the maze of science and religion so as to be able to have them both.

Could science and religion mix peaceably? Michael had read about the Scopes Monkey Trial in 1925, and what he knew of the proceedings made such a proposition seem unlikely. The minute you gave creation over to evolution, God seemed like a kid without a penny in his pocket, whistling his way home. If men evolved out of monkeys, without a guiding hand, just because of how they reproduced, what was left for God to do?

Give power to charms, Pap might say. Answer prayers. Help the poor.

But clearly not all the poor, or there wouldn't be poor people anymore.

Michael sat next to Davison. Pap sat in the middle of the group.

Green said in a loud voice, "Let me go on record as saying that Davison Rock is a fine man, a committed entrepreneur, who just might transform Moab from a hot, dry cow town to an internationally famous mining destination, the uranium capital of the world!"

"Hear, hear!" Howard Balsley lifted his frothy mug of beer. "Davison Rock, it's a pleasure to know you."

Davison lifted his cup of coffee. "Thank you, my friends." By contrast with the other men of Moab, Rock's accent made him sound like a duke.

They nodded agreeably to him, maybe to acknowledge his thanks, maybe to affirm that it was a good thing Davison Rock wasn't drinking with them. His coffee didn't seem to bother them.

Pap said something to Leon, and the giant thundered, "You'll want the fried chicken tonight, Mr. Woolley. And it's on us. Let me go get Arnie on it." He rose, shoved the Peteys into Pap's face, and did his barking routine.

The men laughed, and the giant pushed his way through the throng.

"We need it, now that Lloyd and his robbery silver are gone!" someone barked. Michael couldn't tell who.

Erasmus Green touched his top hat. "No, no, no. I was there on the day of the robbery. Do you want to hear the story?"

"Tell us again," Banjo said, his face bright red. "You love to tell the story."

Davison smiled at Michael. "This is what you call local color. And you'll like the fried chicken. I had it myself right before you got here. My apologies, but I was too hungry to wait."

Green stood. "April 27, 1923, I'll never forget. I saw the door to the bank open. I go inside, and then?" He struck his head. "Out I went. I was bound, gagged, and I had to watch as three men wearing bandanas blew open my vault with dynamite. And then the safe inside. And the idiots with their explosives, they destroyed all the paper money, and it went sprinkling down like so much confetti!"

"That would've killed me dead!" Banjo guffawed.

"The three men left with how many bags of silver?" Green asked. "How many have you heard, Mr. Woolley?"

Pap blushed as all the attention fell on him. "I heard four bags."

"No!" the men around them roared.

"There were two bags of silver!" Green held up two fingers. "Just two. Not four. And our esteemed sheriff, Mr. Jack Del Rose, slept through the whole thing!"

"Not this damn story again!" That was from the sheriff, at the bar, where Gudmund and Clem patted him on the back.

Davison raised his eyebrows at Michael. "See? Good thing Sheriff Del Rose is popular, because he's not exactly a crackerjack lawman."

Michael didn't respond. He wanted to hear the rest of the story.

"To be fair," Green said, "Jack was only a deputy back then. Joseph Tyler wore the big badge, God rest his soul."

Leon Björnsson returned and sat in his chair, petting his stuffed dogs bald. He flicked loose hairs onto the floor. "What did I miss?"

"Bound and gagged," Banjo said.

"Two bags of silver." Leon knew the story.

Green continued, holding the attention of the men. He could have been on a stage. "Sheriff Tyler, with young Jack spitting fire at his side, found the robbers, all three of them, out in the desert, and yes, on Lloyd Preece's land, and yes, on what is now a monument of nature consecrated to the commonweal of these forty-eight United States of America. The robbers weren't exactly geniuses. They didn't have many supplies, and I think they were rather surprised that they'd gotten as far as they did."

"They never made it to the Robber's Roost," Del Rose shouted. "We got 'em."

"I know what you are thinking, and yes, it's sad," Green said. "A lot of my money was lost in the explosion.

But there are two happy endings to this story." Again, Green emphasized his point by waving two fingers around.

"The first? I had insurance on the deposits," Green said. "So in any case, the good depositors of Moab were always going to be covered."

"Tell 'em about the second," Gudmund hollered.

Green grinned. "So Sheriff Tyler and the trustworthy Jack Del Rose retrieved the two bags of silver, but they might have gotten a bit overzealous in their dealings with the robbers. Because when I counted out the silver that the lawmen returned to me, I'd made a thirty-dollar profit. Along with the money from the insurance, and a certain tithe, I was actually paid for the little bump I received on the head."

Michael had to laugh. It was a funny story, almost a bit hard to believe, and then the men rumbled into another yarn about outlaws.

What did *a certain tithe* mean? Wasn't tithe money you paid your church?

Davison knocked Michael on his arm. "Here's your dinner."

Another giant, this one only a little older than Michael, brought over plates of fried chicken, fried greens, and big slabs of corn on the cob, slathered in butter. Michael's hunger hit him, and he dove in. Arnie Björnsson slid a Hires Root Beer bottle in front of Michael, and then wove his way back to the kitchen.

"You know," Green said as the second outlaw tale ended in the bandits running away from an abandoned house, convinced that the migrant child living inside was a ghost, "all signs point to that hobo preacher, Earl Bill Clay. As Lloyd's killer, I mean."

The men muttered.

Banjo frowned. "We have other strangers in town. Take Diana Artemis, for instance."

Leon lifted the Peteys. "Bark, bark, bark, Banjo. Petey loves the widow Artemis. Both the Peteys do. She's a woman down on her luck. I, for one, like that she found a home here."

"Since we're telling stories," Banjo said, "you've heard about Louisa Parker, have you?"

Leon waved a hand. Green frowned. "Louisa Parker likes to drink." He shot a look at Davison. "She's not the best witness."

Banjo shrugged. "Yeah, but it's a bit strange. She goes to the widow Artemis to get her stars done, and when she leaves, she's missing her mother's emerald ring."

"Or Louisa pawned it for more money to buy booze." Leon gripped his dead dog tight. "She wouldn't be the first. She's Catholic, and Catholics drink."

"As do uranium prospectors," Davison threw in.

That brought out a fresh round of laughter.

Howard Balsley leaned in to speak in a low voice to Hiram; Michael was close enough to hear. "Other folks say that the widow Artemis gets by selling more than fortunes or reading tea leaves. If you know what I mean."

Michael was surprised at how angry he felt at Balsley's words. The fun had turned into gossip, and not very nice gossip at that.

Pap didn't respond, but he clenched one fist until his knuckles were white.

Green scowled at Balsley. "Come on, Howard, let's not get mean. Those are just rumors."

"They most certainly are," Leon agreed. "Don't piss

off the Peteys. They'll both bite your damn face off!"
More barks from the dead dogs.

Balsley colored. "I'm sorry, fellas. I've had a bit
much. Actually, I had my stars done by the widow,
and she said I should lay off the sauce. Too bad the
water wagon left town today."

That brought new chuckles.

Michael chewed on a chicken leg, the grease heavy
on his tongue, the skin flavored and delicious. He set
the bone down on his plate. He was glad the other
men had put Balsley in his place about Diana. This
talk about getting one's stars done did open the way
for his question for Davison. "What do *you* think of
astrology, Mr. Rock?"

Davison sipped his coffee, grimacing at the bite.
"It's ancient, and antiquity tends to throw white robes
and an aura of respect around any institution. But
honestly? Anything that tells me what my destiny is
surely must be suspect."

"So you're skeptical." Michael wasn't about to admit
that he was . . . not quite convinced.

"I try to be skeptical about everything," Davison
said. "That includes religions and anything resembling
religions, such as spiritualism or tarot cards or this
new interest in the occult. I have to admire the widow
Artemis making her living talking to ghosts and telling
people that July is going to be lucky for them. Do
you know where the term con artist comes from?"

"A confidence artist," Michael said. He lifted corn
to his lips, greasy from the chicken.

From Davison, "Exactly. A con artist gets you to
have confidence in him, and then he can say whatever
he wants as long as you pay him. Or her."

"I've seen some strange things," Michael said. "I can't explain them."

"You're young yet. Wait, and you may find explanations." Davison made a face. "Sight is only one of our senses, and not a very reliable one. If you see a stick in the water, you might think it's bent, but pull it out, and you see it's straight. The light hits the water in such a way to trick the eyes. I'll need proof of anything, confirmed proof."

"The scientific method." Michael chewed down corn.

"Precisely." Davison paused. "Belief is a powerful thing, a very powerful thing, and you can't quantify it, and it can do some good. I believe in the future of uranium in Moab, for example. However, I'm not looking for investors for my operation, not yet, anyway, because the minute I try to inflict my beliefs on another person, I've crossed a line."

That was the thing. Michael had proof. Rain fell on the Woolley farm when other homesteads went dry. His pap had found the well using a dowsing rod, and Michael had felt the hazel wood jump in his own hand. Did it work every time? No. And yet, maybe his pap was right. Humans were iffy instruments, even at the best of times.

"Always keep an open mind," Davison said. "But the minute the evidence contradicts your findings, adjust your hypothesis, and keep experimenting."

"I couldn't have said it better myself." Michael set the denuded cob on his plate.

More stories were told, more whiskey drunk, and Michael downed three bottles of root beer, a fine lingering dessert for a large meal. The hours peeled away in all the talk.

As eleven o'clock approached, Banjo stood. "Well, my friends, I have a wife who likes me home when she goes to sleep. I must be off."

"No!" came the raucous reply.

Both Michael and his pap had finished their dinner. They had an appointment to keep. Michael bid good night to Davison, his pap shook more hands, and they left the smoke for the clear air of the Utah sky, cool with the night. Few lights twinkled in the buildings of downtown Moab.

His pap was scowling.

"You okay?" Michael asked.

Pap shrugged. "I will be, once Adelaide and her family are safe."

Michael still felt the sting of Balsley's low-voiced accusation against Diana. "What did you think of what they said about the widow Artemis?"

Pap sighed long and hard. "She's pretty. She's single. Men will talk. It's none of our business, but it's a damn shame."

For his father to curse like that meant he had strong emotions on the subject.

Michael was taken aback.

Pap continued. "Many women have been brought low by idle talk. Women have been accused of witchcraft simply because they didn't fit in, whether they had any craft or not. And you can bet those people in Salem didn't hang any witches or cunning women who were friends of theirs."

Michael had never thought about that possibility, but he'd met one witch before, Gus Dollar, and the shopkeeper had used every trick in the book on them.

"Evidence," Michael said. "Look for evidence to

prove any theories. Pap, she did have the names and addresses of men in her notebook. Remember when I had to draw the symbols I saw on Bishop Gudmundson's knife? I saw them when I was paging through. Some were starred."

"Did you see birthdays?" Pap asked.

"I saw dates, at least." Michael put the pieces together. "So she was collecting information for their star-charts. I guess that's right. I hate that I have these doubts about her now. Satan doesn't need to do much. People are trouble enough in the end."

"They are," Pap replied. "Let's hurry. We'll pray for Diana. In the meantime, you remember how this gossip made you feel . . . and don't you ever pass on similar talk about anyone."

Michael nodded. For the first time in a long time, he felt he could get on board with prayer.

Chapter Sixteen

WHEN MICHAEL PARKED THE DOUBLE-A IN FRONT of Edna's bungalow, Diana was standing out in front, her shadow swallowed in the dark skirts around the cottonwood tree. In the night, she appeared ghostly as she stepped to Hiram's window.

There was something about her that tugged at Hiram's mind, but it was drowned out by the things about her that tugged at Hiram's other parts. The sight of her left him breathless.

There was no sign of Addy Tunstall's red Ford Cabriolet.

"Is everything okay?" Hiram asked.

Diana nodded. "The Tunstalls are inside. I just wanted to get a look at you, all to myself."

"Hey, I'm here," Michael said.

She winked at him. "I meant the plural you."

"We'd better get going." Hiram cleared his throat.

"Addy is lucky to have men like you two to protect her. Men with strong muscles, from working the farm."

"For your information," Michael said, "what you mostly get from working a farm is dirt under your nails and a callus in the palm of your hand from the gear-shift of the John Deere. Also, lots of splinters and a strange tan."

"I just didn't see her car," Hiram said.

"She parked it a few blocks away," Diana explained. "We thought it might draw attention, parked here."

Hiram nodded.

Diana patted the door of the Double-A as if she were stroking a beloved horse. "She's packed. The kids and Guy are here, too."

"No one gave you any trouble?" Hiram asked.

"Not a lick." Diana smiled. "Your jewelry worked perfectly, so I figure you're going to want it back, now." She leaned forward, pushing a cloud of sweet scent in through the window, and filling Hiram's eyes with a very distracting view. She pulled the chi-rho medallion off and handed it to Hiram, who put it on.

He found that he had mixed feeling about getting his medallion back. He'd be grateful for the additional protection, but she was no longer wearing something of Hiram's—

her hat. She was wearing a hat, he realized, and it looked just like the hat from the cabin. The one Michael had said was six years out of fashion. Or maybe it *was* the hat from Lloyd Preece's cabin.

A cold icicle of fear and doubt stabbed into the warm, confused droning of Hiram's heart. Of course, there would be two such hats. Or of course, if needing to pack had required Adelaide Tunstall to go to her father's cabin, perhaps Adelaide had *given* the hat to Diana Artemis.

But why would the Tunstalls go to Lloyd Preece's house to pack, if they hadn't been there for years?

He realized he was sitting silently. "Well, ma'am, maybe tell them to come out now, then."

Diana went inside, and Hiram and Michael exited the truck. Hiram began anchoring rope to the truck's bed, so that he could strap the family's belongings down tight, and also to create a safety harness for himself and Mr. Tunstall. He thought Adelaide and the children would fit into the truck's cab with Michael, but that would just about fill the Double-A to capacity.

"Did you notice the hat?" Michael whispered.

Hiram nodded.

"You realize," Michael said in a low voice as he looped the rope through an anchor ring, "that this means Mrs. Tunstall went back to the cabin looking for her dad's money."

"Seems like a reasonable bet," Hiram agreed.

"So what you have to ask yourself," Michael said, "is what Mrs. Artemis was thinking. She and Adelaide obviously knew each other. They called each other pet names. Di and Addy, but when you suggested Diana stay with her for protection, Mrs. Tunstall was reluctant."

"Small town," Hiram said.

"Maybe Adelaide was less than enthusiastic about spending time with Diana because she knew Diana and her father were . . . ooh la la. Which would also explain why Diana might have left a hat at Lloyd Preece's cabin."

The idea hurt Hiram. "Maybe. Or maybe she'd just heard the rumors about Diana and didn't want those rumors to rub off on her."

"And if Diana and Lloyd Preece were indeed...
ooh la la...then maybe she knew he had a stack
of bearer bonds. And maybe she was happy to go
watch Adelaide's kids because it meant she might get
a chance to look for the bonds. Or maybe Adelaide
would lead her to them."

"These are guesses."

Michael frowned. "Of course, they're guesses. And
if Diana Artemis is willing to rob a family trying to
leave town for fear of their lives—might she have
been willing to murder Lloyd Preece?"

"Hold on, now."

"Pap, what about the hat?"

Hiram sighed. "What about the hat." It wasn't a
question.

"Sorry to infringe on your romantic inclinations,
Pap." Michael blew out a breath.

"I don't...there's no..."

"Or look," Michael continued, "maybe there were
other extenuating circumstances. Maybe Lloyd tried to
force himself on her, or he owed her money, or she
was trying to break it off and he attacked her. But we
ought to go take a look inside Preece's cabin, and if
the hat is no longer hanging on its peg, then it's the
one perched on Diana Artemis's noggin."

Before Hiram could sufficiently collect his thought to
be able to comment on what Michael was suggesting,
the Tunstalls emerged.

The children were small, the youngest a baby in a
basket and the oldest maybe five. They were sleepy
and cooperative, though the baby cried, softly. Guy
Tunstall smiled faintly, with unfocused eyes wandering
about him. He was a tall man, thin, with a big shock

of white blond hair, parted with an uneven series of scars above his left ear. Spit dribbled from his big pink lips. He dragged a heavy steamer trunk down the front walk, generating a loud scraping noise until Hiram and Michael intervened. More spit leaked from Guy's mouth to paint his shirt in speckles. Once they had the trunk on top of the truck, they went inside to grab several more cases Diana indicated to them, and then lashed it all down in the middle of the truck's bed, creating a space between the cab and the luggage where Hiram and Guy would sit.

Guy smiled the entire time and said nothing. He continued to drool on himself, not apparently noticing.

While Michael worked to squeeze Adelaide Tunstall and her three children into the cab of the Double-A, Hiram roped Guy securely to the truck bed. He tied the man in firmly, so that he could barely move. Guy drooled again while Hiram was tying the last knot.

"You okay, Mr. Tunstall?" Hiram asked.

"Uh, yep," the big man said, eyes moving in strange circles.

Hiram took his revolver, along with the full moon loader and a handful of spare shells, and climbed into the back of the truck with Guy Tunstall.

Then he anchored himself. He couldn't leave himself much room to move and still be safe, but his harness was looser than Guy's, to allow him to slide around a bit, and pivot if he needed to. He had his clasp knife in his pocket, in case he needed to cut himself free.

If this were a more routine drive, he might have just sat on the truck bed and held on with his hands. But if Lloyd Preece's killer chased them, Michael might have to drive fast.

And if Lloyd's killer made no appearance, and Hiram rode to Provo tied into the back of his truck, there would be no harm done.

"All aboard!" Michael called. "Toot toot!"

The five-year-old, a boy with bright yellow hair, giggled from the front. "Mommy, we're on a train!"

"Uh, yep," Guy muttered.

Hiram raised a hand in farewell to Diana Artemis, and she waved back. Under the moonless sky, she was quickly a shadow, and then lost in the darkness.

And if she were the killer? Would she now get in her own car and follow Hiram and Michael, to be able to kill the Tunstalls once he had dropped them off? Or had she perhaps divined the hiding place of Lloyd Preece's money during her time watching the Tunstall children that afternoon, and would she now go back to the cabin, or the Tunstalls' house, and steal the bearer bonds?

Those things all seemed impossible. Surely, there were better explanations. Diana had liked the hat, and Adelaide had given it to her. Or Diana had known Lloyd Preece—maybe even romantically—and had recovered a hat she had left at the cabin earlier.

Or there were simply two similar hats.

But Hiram couldn't bring himself to relax.

Michael took the road north out of town. It led through a wide slalom S of a canyon past the Monument. Hiram couldn't see any of the arches, but he saw looming masses of stone to his left as they went, blocking out the light of the stars. Then they drove north across the desert toward the highway, and Hiram found himself looking at the constellation Scorpio. It stood tall on the horizon, one of the few constellations that really looked like what it was supposed to be, a scorpion with a long, J-shaped tail and a red heart. And an extra star—a new star? Hiram rubbed his eyes.

No, of course, a planet. A planet that bright had to be Jupiter, slowly making its way across Scorpio. Hiram knew his stars basically, but he hadn't spent any real time stargazing since he was a boy.

"Uh, yep. Thank you," Guy Tunstall said, without turning to face Hiram.

They turned west on the highway and kept driving. The town of Green River passed by as a swarm of lights near a bridge, and Michael didn't stop. He turned north and they passed Price, and Hiram began to wonder how much gas the Double-A had in the tank.

Michael pulled off the road at Helper and parked at a Conoco service station. Guy had fallen asleep, but Hiram untied himself to stretch his legs.

While the Conoco man filled the truck's tank and the spare can, Hiram and Michael stood at the edge of the street and looked down the gaudy midnight lights of the coal and railroad boomtown. The nearer of the town's cinema marquees announced that WEREWOLF OF LONDON was playing.

"Ah, Helper," Michael said. "Babylon of the slickrock."

"Do we put them on a train here?" Hiram asked.

"She wants to go to Provo."

"Ah, yes. Provo it is."

"Sorry I didn't tell you I went to see the movie, Pap. I guess…I guess I thought you wanted me to go to the dance, and might not approve of the film."

"It's just a movie." Hiram shrugged. "You have to make decisions for yourself. It would be okay if you told me these things." He smiled at his son. "And it's okay that you didn't."

As Hiram was tying himself back into place and Michael started the truck, Hiram saw a man standing across the street. He almost missed the fellow in the darkness, and what caught his eye was the fact that the man was naked.

A shiver went through Hiram. He blinked. Was he seeing things?

Before he could call out, Michael set the truck into motion. They drove down Helper's Main Street, past saloons, movie theaters, bordellos, and a bowling alley.

The naked man followed.

Main Street was lined with all its businesses on one side, and on the other with the railroad yard. The naked man walked in the shadow of the yard, and if the drunken revelers noticed him, they didn't shout or interfere. The man walked with his arms straight at his side, unnaturally, and leaned slightly forward with his head and shoulders.

And he stared at Hiram.

And then Hiram saw a second man. He was also naked, and he walked in the same strange fashion, not far behind the first.

Hiram took his revolver into his hands and rotated the cylinder off the empty chamber.

Nearing the end of Main Street, Michael slowed to take the left turn that would cross the railroad-tie bridge and put them back onto the highway. The brightest of the lights were behind them, and to Hiram's left rose a low hill thick with adobe bungalows, and above it a white cliff.

On the bridge, Michael abruptly stopped.

The two naked men began to run.

"Michael?" Hiram called.

Adelaide screamed.

Guy jolted upright as if he had been stabbed. He scrambled, trying to free himself of the ropes, but Hiram was a better knotsman than that, and Guy was working with his bare fingers in the dark. Hiram crouched and turned, looking through the cab of the truck—

and saw two more naked men, standing on the far bank of the river, blocking their path.

Bang! Hiram fired at the sky. He hated to attract attention, but he didn't have a choice.

"Get out of the way!" he shouted over the cab. "Right now!"

Looking over his shoulder, he saw three more naked men, running toward the truck.

The Double-A abruptly rocked. Looking forward again, Hiram saw that one of the naked men had leaped onto the hood of the truck and leaned forward, grinning.

Michael shifted into gear and hit the gas. The truck knocked aside the naked man still on the ground, but the fellow on the hood rocked to one side and then managed to keep his grip. Hiram swiveled, just in time to see the first of the naked men leap up onto the back of the Double-A.

As he landed, he was no longer a man. In the moment of his jump, antlers had sprouted from his forehead, and he opened his mouth, shrieking, with teeth big and flat like an ungulate. Hiram blinked. Was he seeing clearly?

Bang! Hiram's bullet took the man-thing in the center of his chest. The naked man sat down with a stupid expression on his antlered face, bounced once, and then fell off the back of the truck.

For a moment, Hiram felt guilt. He didn't want to shoot anyone, even naked lunatics swarming his truck in the middle of the night. Then, in the light from a house near the highway, he saw the man stand up again, saw again, more clearly now, the antlers sprouting from his head, and his guilt was washed away in a flood of fear.

Then the other two naked men leaped onto the back of the truck. They crawled forward, howling, fur sprouting from their faces and horns budding from their skulls.

Guy screamed. Adelaide screamed. At least one of the children was screaming, too.

Hiram unloaded his revolver, two shots into the chest of one man and his last bullet into the belly of the second. His heart raced and his breath came in shallow gasps, but his hand was steady, and the shots knocked the two men—monsters—to the highway.

He couldn't make out their faces clearly in the moving shadows. He heard grunts of surprise as his bullets hit the men, but not screams of pain, and no blood.

What hellish sorcery was this?

Hiram shook out the casings. They bounced away with a rattle of brass. He snapped in six new bullets with the full moon even as he turned and rose to one knee.

The naked man from the hood was climbing around the passenger side of the truck, reaching in to try to paw at Adelaide Tunstall. Despite the darkness, Hiram thought he had seen the man before. He'd been in Helper in February, and some of the coal miners, desperate for food, had tried to rob Hiram on the road. Was this more banditry?

But who ever heard of naked bandits?

Naked, bulletproof, shape-changing bandits?

Hiram pressed his revolver to the naked man's skull. "Get off now, friend."

The naked man bleated loudly, and leaped at Hiram—

Hiram pistol-whipped him across the cheek, sending him skidding along the roof of the cab and bouncing to the road.

Hiram turned back, and his heart froze in his chest. Three large deer raced behind the truck.

No, not deer—deer-monsters. They ran like men on two legs and they had enormous spreads of antlers. Their long snouts were misshapen, with eyes in the wrong places and mouths twisted at angles that seemed human. Their backs seemed elastic and snapped back and forth, so that at moments they seemed to be running with chests parallel to the ground and yet on two legs, while at other times they took long, single-legged bounds, like some kind of perverse parody of a track and field event. Even in their deerishness, they didn't resemble any deer species Hiram knew—not mule deer or white-tailed deer, but something larger and redder.

Hiram tasted bile at the back of this throat.

And then, behind the deer, he saw the men he'd just knocked from the truck rise to his feet. The naked man—old, he looked like an old man—leaped forward, not like a man jumps who expects to land on his feet, but like a good swimmer dives into water, face first, hands extended past his head—

and he hit the ground running, in the form of a shuddering deer-beast.

Hiram saw no gradual reshaping, just an instantaneous transformation.

Something was odd about the deer's head. Its ear, Hiram realized. Its ear was crumpled against the side of its head, like a plum shriveled into a prune.

And then he saw other deer-men. Seven, eight? All following the truck, and all gaining on it.

"Faster!" Hiram yelled.

"There are curves coming, Pap!" Michael's words were nearly whipped away by the wind created by the racing truck.

"Faster!"

Hiram fumbled bullets into the full moon, careful not to drop it. A couple of the bullets fell to the truck bed and spun off into the night, but he managed to get the entire clip filled and safely back into his pocket, and then the revolver into his hand.

One of the monsters coursed ahead of the others, parallel to Hiram. It was a tall man-buck with a broad forehead, majestic, though its eyes seemed to be set in the front of its skull rather than on the sides, and there was something wrong with its skin. Its brown fur was interrupted with large patches of scaly red skin.

Hiram fired three times at the deer-man, point-blank. The creature rocked back and shied briefly away, as if the bullets had pushed it or slapped it, but not penetrated its skin.

Hiram clutched at the chi-rho amulet. It felt so cold, it burned.

"Lord Divine," Hiram begged. "Give me aid."

The monster leaped forward, stabbing at Hiram with its antlers. Hiram shuffled back and the beast collided with the side of the truck, which knocked it away into the darkness. The stench of it, an excited, wet animal smell, filled Hiram's nose. The impact

knocked Hiram flat, and the antlers tore his skin in
his shoulder, his upper arm, and his thigh.

Hiram lay on the truck, feeling dazed. He heard
Guy Tunstall weeping.

The scaly deer-thing leaped into his vision again—
bang! Hiram shot it, and the deer dropped out of
his sight. The truck was accelerating, tipping slightly
up onto two wheels as Michael took a sharp turn.
Hiram knew the canyons well enough to know that if
Michael lost control of the truck, they might all fall
fifty feet to their deaths in the Price River.

Hiram hoped the lamen, the defensive written amulet,
in the door of the truck would help Michael. He needed
a charm to give the wheels stronger grip—would there
be such a piece of lore? Given Hohman's prayers that
were supposed to ward off bullets, why not a hex that
would keep a truck upright on a hairpin curve?

Hiram felt the bed of the truck rise up beneath
him at a sharp angle and he heard Guy Tunstall make
a choking sound, as if the man were vomiting. Was
this it? Was Hiram about to fall to his death?

Then the truck slammed flat to the earth again
with a loud groan of protest. Hiram heard the engine
growl an objection as Michael threw gears and pedals
all into grinding out as much speed as possible.

Finally, the deer-monstrosities began to drop back.

Hiram didn't waste any more shots on them. He
reloaded slowly, his hands now trembling, as Michael
climbed the ridge.

Deer-men. Men-deer. Men-deer-monsters. He had
seen, with his own eyes, a man change shape into
a beast. There were many stories, in the folklore of
many people, including Yas Yazzie, of people who

assumed the shapes of animals. Grandma Hettie had never given Hiram any indication that those stories were true.

But he had seen it.

Had deer-men killed Lloyd Preece? Why would men who could transform into deer want to kill a wealthy rancher, and why would they be chasing his family?

Could this possibly be about the money?

Or was this just a damned corner of the land? Hiram had defeated a demon that lived in the hills near Helper before—were the deer-men tied to the demon, or caused by the same unseen factor in the landscape?

"Thank you," Guy Tunstall said, between his tears. "Uh, yep. Thank you."

Hiram put his arm around the man to comfort him.

Chapter Seventeen

PROVO LAY IN DARKNESS WHEN MICHAEL STOPPED
the truck at the train station.

Hiram hopped down from the truck bed prepared
to encourage Adelaide Tunstall, and offer to keep
driving. He found her laughing and shaking her head.

"I'm sorry, Mrs. Tunstall," he said, unable to stop
himself from launching into the beginning of a rehearsed
speech, "but there is evil in the world."

She laughed and slapped his shoulder. "And there
are silly, silly people, too!"

Was she drunk?

Michael stood up with his feet inside the cab,
elbows spread wide on the truck's roof. "I was telling
her about my friend Porky Mullins." Michael's face
was twitching.

"I don't . . . I don't remember Porky."

Michael snorted. "Well, he remembers you! Porky
is the one who got out of his mind on reefer and got
into our barn?"

Hiram couldn't for the life of him remember the incident. "Yeah?"

"And he was convinced he could get one of our roosters to fertilize our nanny goat, so he kept standing birds up on that old goat's back, and every time he did, she complained louder, until finally you woke up and came out to the barn in your pajamas."

Hiram raised his fedora to let the cool night air dry the sweat on his skull and allow Michael to finish telling the story.

"He tried to explain what he was doing. And you said to Porky, 'Son, you got two basic problems here. One is that you're an idiot.' And Porky said, 'I'm not an idiot, I'm stoned.' And you said, 'Two is that those birds are all hens.'"

Mrs. Tunstall laughed so hard she had to gasp for breath. "Thank you both," she said when she had recovered. "Thank you for the ride, and I'm sorry some of those maniac debauchees of Helper tried to jump us. I hope the truck is all right."

"The truck is fine." Hiram untied Guy and helped him down. Would he tell his wife what he'd seen? What had he seen?

But Guy gave no indication he would say anything, and only hugged his wife, muttering, "Uh, yep. Yep. Thank you. Thank you."

"You okay with us leaving you?" Michael asked Adelaide.

"I admit I was frightened." The woman fanned her face. "But I don't think a man's going to run all the way across the mountains barefoot, even if he is smoking reefer."

"Probably true." Hiram untied the luggage and he

and Michael unloaded it. The train schedule, tacked to the wooden wall of a little shelter squatting on the platform, showed the first departure at dawn, which was about three hours away. "You have money for the fare?"

Adelaide Tunstall nodded, then sighed. "Not as much as I'd hoped, but Dad did have a little spare cash in the cabin, and I collected that. And there's the five hundred dollars I showed you."

So she *had* gone to the cabin looking for the money.

He wished she had found it. The presence of a pile of money could only complicate his efforts to solve Lloyd Preece's murder.

"What if the money shows up later?" he asked.

"I'll reach out to my father's lawyer," she said. "I know the address. There's land, in any case, and I'm the only heir, so he's going to have to sell that for me. If that falls through?" She shrugged. "My father said there's a fortune to be had in a man's good opinion of himself. I'll have that at least."

Adelaide Tunstall was going to be fine. Hiram felt the muscles of his back relax.

"We can stay until the train comes, if you like," Michael offered.

"You men get on to what you have to do," Adelaide said. "We'll catch the first train and be gone."

Hiram and Michael made a show of driving up the road north, but then, at Hiram's direction, Michael circled back. They parked out of sight, and then sat in a small grove of plum trees beside a burbling irrigation ditch, to watch the Tunstalls.

Just in case.

"This Porky Mullins sounds like a bad influence," Hiram said.

"There is no Porky Mullins."

Hiram felt like a fool. "Then why...why did you make the story up?"

"I winked at you."

"I missed it."

"I needed to comfort her," Michael said. "It's better if she thinks we ran into some kind of crazy gang of drug addicts than for us to explain what was really attacking us. I guess that's part of the job, isn't it, Pap? People who know about you come to you for help. People who don't know about you, and what you can do...part of the job is to keep them ignorant. Of the darker, nastier things that are out there."

Hiram shrugged. "Really, I just don't like that certain look people give me when they think I'm a nut. So I try to stay quiet."

"So who were those naked guys, really? I hear Europeans like to run around naked all the time. Is there a chance that maybe they really were just some Dutchmen who got a little reefer into them and went wild?"

So Michael hadn't seen the men change shape. How much should he tell his son?

Hiram put a hard brake on his old instinct. Michael was learning the craft and should know the risks.

"Did you see the deer-men?" he asked his son.

"I saw *a* deer," Michael said. "Big as an elk, and I didn't get a good look at him. I figured the naked guys must have disturbed him."

"The naked men *became* the deer," Hiram said. "Only they weren't deer, they were deer-monsters. They ran on their hind legs, and their faces looked part-man."

"Holy shit," Michael said. "Are you ser...no, of course you are. You don't joke about this kind of thing."

Hiram let the cursing go without comment. "I don't know what to make of it. I've seen men who worshipped animals before, and acted like animals, and dressed like animals to commit evil, violent acts, but this one is a first for me."

"I heard a lot of gunshots. Just tell me the deer-men didn't have rifles."

"I was the one shooting. And I hit them, but I don't think I hurt any of them. The bullets just seemed to knock them down."

"Can I say holy shit again?"

"You've said it enough."

They sat awhile in silence. Hiram felt faint. Above the mountains to the east, the sky began to bleach from its midnight indigo shade to a pale blue. Hiram found his thoughts drifting to Diana Artemis. He tried to ask himself hard questions about what she knew and what she was up to, but he kept imagining instead her throat and bosom as she leaned into the cab of his truck—

"Pap, are you wounded?" Michael asked.

Hiram touched his shoulder, and his arm. The slashes from the antlers were still bleeding.

No wonder he felt faint. And that meant that the bloodstone wasn't working; it was supposed to stanch the flow of blood from a wound.

A chaste and sober mind. He needed to recover his self-control. Hiram pinched himself.

"Yes," he said. The train was slowly arriving at the platform, and other people were beginning to appear there. "The deer-things got me. It's Sunday, or we could go to a pharmacy."

"I'll drive you home," Michael said. "We're not far. We can patch up your wounds, and you better believe we're bringing another gun back with us."

"I don't know whether that's wise."

"I don't know whether I care," Michael said. "You got smashed by a were-deer, Pap. And I had one of them jumping on the hood of the truck. If I had a gun, I could have shot him. And even if the bullets didn't break his skin, or whatever, it might have knocked him off."

Hiram took a deep breath.

"If today were Monday," Michael said, "I'd stop at a bicycle shop and buy a revolver. Since it's not, I'll settle for us bringing the shotgun and the rifle back to Moab with us."

"Back to Moab?"

"Yeah, Pap. Were-deer or not, we haven't solved the murder. We haven't even figured out the ghost, and I thought that was going to be the easy one."

The Tunstalls boarded the train. Hiram had deliberately not asked where they were going, but he hoped it was somewhere peaceful.

"Get in the truck, Pap," Michael said. "Bandages, breakfast, guns, and then one more thing before we head back."

"Church?" Hiram suggested.

"Nope," Michael said. "We have to see Mahonri."

It was nearly noon by the time they had bathed, bandaged Hiram's wounds—which finally stopped bleeding only when they were packed with gauze— eaten, slept a little, loaded the bolt-action rifle and the break-open double-barreled shotgun into the truck, along with ammunition for both, and driven back to Provo to the little chapel on 700 North where Mahonri Young attended church. Mahonri himself was one of the last people to slowly stream out when services ended.

When Mahonri saw Hiram and Michael, he smiled.

Mahonri had his great-grandfather's (or was it great-great-grandfather's?) face, the set jaw and the rugged beard along the jawline only that had made people call Brigham Young the Lion of the Lord. Mahonri looked nothing like the stone sculptures or severe oil paintings from the 1850s, though—he was animated, and the moment he saw Hiram and Michael, he leaped forward, necktie flapping back over his shoulder like a scarf.

"Wonderful!" he cried. "Jolinda has baked a cherry pie, and we've had beef simmering in the pot all morning. Come eat with us!"

He gripped Hiram by the elbow and steered him toward Mahonri's house, a blue-gray adobe brick manor large enough to accommodate the Young family's seven children.

"Ooh," Michael said. "Pie!"

Hiram resisted. "Jolinda is a generous and hospitable woman, but I wouldn't spring myself on her with so little notice."

Mahonri's face fell. "Oh, no. You're here with questions."

"It's not me." Hiram jerked a thumb at Michael. "*He* wants something."

Mahonri's face brightened. "Oh good, a science question." He rubbed his hands together gleefully. "What are you looking for, Michael? I've got the keys to the library and I can get us in this afternoon. I'll check out the book in my own name, so you have a whole year to return it."

"Good." Michael grinned, but there was a bashful note in his smile. "I'm looking for a book on astrology."

Mahonri frowned. "Astronomy?"

"No, you heard me right. *Astrology*. But not fortune-telling. I need the gnarly old stuff about talisman-making. How do I ... how does one ... make a talisman to capture the influence of Jupiter, for instance?"

"Your father has a ring." Mahonri's face darkened. "Maybe he can help you."

"He says Grandma Hettie just showed him the pattern. And besides, if it wasn't over his head, we wouldn't both be standing here."

Mahonri shook his head, looking down at polished black wing-tip shoes.

"If it helps," Michael said, "we're trying to solve a murder."

"How does that help?" Mahonri asked. "How does it improve the situation to know that you're doing something dangerous, and probably illegal, since you're doing the job of the police department?"

Michael touched Mahonri's shoulder. "Because we're helping someone who needs aid. Like you do, all the time. Like *you've* helped *me*, for years and years."

Tears formed in the corners of Mahonri's eyes, but he nodded. "Meet me at the library in twenty minutes."

"You can eat first," Hiram suggested.

Mahonri shook his head. "Pie can wait."

"Can deer get psoriasis?" Hiram asked.

Mahonri was unlocking a small side door to Brigham Young High School, a towering gothic complex that looked wholly out of place surrounded by tidy brick bungalows and fruit trees. "I don't know. You have sick deer around the farm, you're worried they might pass it to the cattle?"

A lie would have been the easiest, but Hiram resisted. "No, it's something I saw driving up here last night. What would cause a deer to get scabby, scaly skin?"

Mahonri shrugged. "You know more about animals than I do, but let me show Michael the books I have, and then I'll see what I can find for you."

They trudged up to Mahonri's office, in a tower above the library. A different key unlocked that, and then a third key unlocked a black wooden cabinet in the corner of the room, revealing three shelves of books. Their spines were all old and made of leather, and many of them didn't have visible titles at all. Hiram saw some titles but could read almost none of them, since they were in Latin, or in different alphabets entirely. He did recognize *The Discoverie of Witchcraft* and *Picatrix*, and at least he could *read* the title *New and Complete Illustration of the Occult Sciences*.

"Is this some kind of personal collection?" Michael asked.

Mahonri laughed. "Heavens, no. Well . . . sort of. These books belong to the library, but if I left them on the shelves, they'd be vandalized or destroyed."

"By students?" Hiram asked.

"Or faculty. Or administrators." Mahonri grabbed a volume with no title and looked at the frontispiece. "Here, I think this may have what you want."

"*Star-Lore*," Michael read, "*Their Signs and Influence*. Can I take it with me?"

Mahonri hesitated. "Yes. But first, why don't you sit here and read it for a bit while I take your father to look for *his* answer?"

The two men walked to the stacks. Mahonri was grinding his teeth and marching in a straight line, and in two minutes he had located a volume called *Skin Ailments of Cervidae.*

"I'll check it out to you," Mahonri said. "Don't worry about the paperwork."

"You're angry," Hiram said.

"You're involving Michael in the . . . occult . . . side of what you do."

"He involved himself," Hiram said. "He wants to know."

"He should be a scientist," Mahonri insisted. "Not a hedge-wizard."

That stung a little, but it wasn't false. Hiram nodded. "I think he'll lose interest in what I do. Farming? Performing traditional cures for hog sicknesses?"

"That isn't what you do." Mahonri jabbed a finger into Hiram's chest. "You solve murders."

Hiram nodded. "I will . . . encourage him to take up science. I already do. I'll keep doing it."

Mahonri nodded fiercely. "See that you do. You and I are friends, Hiram, but if that boy ends up hurt because of you, I will see you in hell."

Hiram hung his head. "If Michael ends up hurt because of me, I will *be* in hell."

On the drive back to Moab, Michael spouted what he had learned.

"Okay, Pap, I'm going to start with astronomy, but I'm not talking telescopes. I mean the stars from the point of view of someone standing on the earth, in the northern hemisphere."

"That's the only point of view I have."

Michael nodded. "So, there's a kind of circular track around the earth, like an equator in the sky, only it's not the equator, it intersects the celestial equator at two points, but it's a different band. And it's called the ecliptic."

"The zodiac is the twelve constellations on the ecliptic," Hiram said. "And the visible planets and the sun and moon, from our perspective, all move along the ecliptic."

"Very good, Pap. They move along it like a road. So the sun and the moon and the five visible planets are always in one of the constellations of the zodiac."

Hiram winked. He was feeling better, though it took some effort. Mahonri's words had cut him.

Michael continued. "So a planet—Jupiter, for instance—is always in one of the constellations of the zodiac. Meaning, when you look at that constellation, there's Jupiter visible inside it."

"It's in Scorpio right now," Hiram said. "I saw it last night, driving to Helper."

"Huh," Michael said. "Okay. Anyway, astral talismans are all about using objects to channel the power of the stars and planets for people to use. The stars and the planets have written symbols, and are also associated with metals, and gemstones, and colors, and days of the week, and all that stuff. You line up as many influences as you can when you're trying to draw on the strength of one of the planets."

"The ring Mahonri was talking about is my Saturn ring," Hiram said. "It's an example of what you're saying. It helps me channel the power of Saturn to have and understand prophetic dreams."

Michael nodded. "A talisman designed to harness the power of Jupiter and give it to a person would be made of silver, because that's a Jupiterian metal. Or actually, what they call it, and this is a great word, is *Jovial*. Of Jove, which is another name for Jupiter. Silver is a *Jovial* metal. It would be marked with the sign of Jupiter, and it would also be marked with a sign for that person."

"I've figured this one out. You mean the sign that Jupiter was in on the day he was born. The whole year of his birth, basically."

"Right. But not a calendar year, a year determined by the movement of Jupiter. And sometimes Jupiter moves backward for a little while, which complicates things, because it can actually move backward into the sign it has just left."

Hiram tried to wrap his mind around this and found the ideas slippery. "Tell me what the significance of this is?"

Michael was quiet for a moment. "Gudmundson and Preece both had silver knives, but they were not quite the same." He looked away briefly and cleared his throat. "I . . . I would like to be able to see and compare them, but I think the difference between them is that Gudmundson's knife had the sign of the zodiac constellation that Jupiter was in when he was born, and Preece's had the zodiac sign that held Jupiter at his birth. Aquarius and Taurus. And really, these talismans are most effective if they are made by the individual who will use them, or with that person's active cooperation, so... I don't know about that whole curio shop story."

"Channeling Jupiter, huh?" Hiram sucked at his teeth. "To what end?"

Michael thought awhile and finally shrugged. "Power and prosperity; somehow."

Hiram nodded.

"And Pap," Michael said. "The widow Artemis, too... she's full of beans, on one point at least."

Hiram felt a chill in his spine. "What's that?"

"The planet Uranus doesn't govern a *toenail*, Pap. It governs *nothing*. The old astrologers had never heard of the planet Uranus, because *it's not visible to the naked eye*. Which means that Uranus cross of hers, at the very least—"

"Is mumbo jumbo." Hiram's heart sank.

"Good thing I'm driving. You look like you might faint."

"That may answer one question, anyway," Hiram continued. "If Lloyd Preece was...uh, *seeing*...Diana Artemis, why wouldn't he give her the job of dowsing Rex Whittle's well?"

Michael nodded. "Because he knew she was a fake."

Chapter Eighteen

HIRAM AND MICHAEL PULLED BACK INTO MOAB mid-afternoon on Sunday. Hiram's throat was dry from singing hymns for most of the drive, trying to compensate, if only a little bit, for missing church.

They drove toward Diana Artemis's house so that Hiram could confront her, but they found her before they got there.

The streets were mostly empty, but there, walking, was Diana, an open parasol slung over her shoulder to keep off the sun. She wore a form-fitting dress, this one of navy blue, with small white and yellow daisies stitched onto the sleeves and collar. Her white stockings matched the daisies. She didn't limp so much as favor her false leg; she covered up her defect well.

What else was she covering up?

How much of her craft was mumbo jumbo? The fact that her Uranus cross—which Hiram had not yet had the heart to remove—was pure fiction didn't mean that the other things she did, or claimed to know, were false. But it suggested that they *might* be.

Hiram thought of the strange way Preacher Bill had moved. Could the preacher and the widow somehow be connected? But no, that was madness—what would that suggest, a conspiracy of the lame?

Diana's offending hat was tilted on her head, showing her dark hair.

"Pull over," Hiram said abruptly. "I want to talk with her, alone. You bring the truck around back, maybe park it in behind Banjo & Sons. After last night, we're marked. And be careful."

Michael pulled over and slipped his chi-rho amulet out of his shirt so it lay above the fabric. "I will, Pap. And . . . I hope there was a run of women's hats at the mercantile and this is all just a terrible misunderstanding."

"So do I, son. So do I."

"Maybe I'll do some scouting."

"Don't," Hiram said.

Hiram thought of the gossip he'd heard at the hotel concerning Diana.

"Make sure all your theories are backed up by evidence, Pap."

Hiram nodded. He was going to do just that.

He got out, the sun muted by the incoming clouds. The heat was swirling up the heavens, bringing in a storm. The desert brought out the worst in the weather, courting violent tempests that caused flashfloods and pounded the dry earth, maybe as punishment for being dry. Too little water, or too much, deserts were harsh places. Cottonwood fluff was swept along on the growing breeze.

Michael drove off and Hiram approached Diana. "Good afternoon."

"Why, Mr. Woolley, you're back from Salt Lake City already?" She gave him a half-grin. Her green eyes were a bit subdued.

"Provo, actually, or . . . Lehi, rather." He found himself stumbling. Damn, this woman had him in her grip. "Can we talk for a bit?"

"Certainly." She motioned to a little park, a bench, circling a cottonwood in a patch of beleaguered grass down a side street.

He walked with her, and there they sat, facing the empty street. The town was busy worshipping God or mourning the loss of Lloyd Preece or recovering from a Saturday drunk, or perhaps all three, and it left them alone.

Hiram didn't know where to start. Her perfume and his fatigue made thinking hard. "Thank you for yesterday and helping me keep an eye on Adelaide. I got her and her family away safely."

"It's my pleasure, Mr. Woolley." She collapsed her parasol and turned her shoulders squarely toward him.

Her body . . . he was so aware of it, every movement, every curve. He pushed into the pocket of his pants, feeling the hard lump of his heliotropius. He closed his eyes, gathered his nerve, and opened them, staring into her face. "How well *did* you know Lloyd Preece? You'd never met his daughter, is that right?"

"I knew her only casually, but it's a small town. She's lovely. She's had so much misfortune, what with the accident that hurt her husband and then her father dying." Diana paused. "And yet, the stars have brightened her life in other ways. I would imagine Mercury was strong in the eighth house when she was born. That is money accumulated through partnership or marriage. In this case, she was born to the richest man in town. Few are so lucky, with respect to money."

Hiram's bloodstone didn't pinch him. She seemed to be telling the truth, assuming his mind was sufficiently sober and chaste to permit his craft to work.

"Money," he mumbled. "Satan's best lie."

"Pardon me?" She seemed startled.

"Satan," Hiram said again. "The best lie he tells people is that they can get everything in this world for money."

"But Hiram," she said softly. "That isn't a lie at all. That's simply the truth. Education, food, shelter, safety, healthcare, influence, power, travel, beauty...you *can* buy everything in this world for money."

"Yes," Hiram agreed, "that's what makes it his best lie, and his damnedest, because it's only a lie by omission. It's only a lie in that it leaves out the fact that the best things you can possibly have cannot be purchased with money."

Diana Artemis frowned. "And what are those things, then?"

"Love," Hiram said bitterly. "The grace of God. Forgiveness. Peace. The things that a sane person should want most. And the things that are precisely not of this world."

Diana leaned back and was silent for a moment. "This conversation has taken a decidedly spiritual turn."

Hiram took a deep breath. Across the red-packed road, a jack rabbit crept between two bungalows, nervously eyeing the windows.

"Did you ever make it out to Lloyd Preece's old cabin out on the Colorado?" he asked. "Before going out yesterday with Adelaide, I mean?"

Diana harrumphed, only it came out as a chuckle. "I have to be very careful, Mr. Woolley, about where I go and whom I see. Already, people will talk about me, sitting with you, under this old tree. No, I had driven by his cabin. I'd never stopped inside."

The heliotropius didn't react to her words. Hiram, though, was sure she was lying. He felt crippled and blind, abandoned and alone.

And it was his own fault.

She touched his shoulder. "You can't believe I had anything to do with the murder."

He found himself leaning into the touch, and it felt good. Soft, yet firm. "I don't believe it. But I saw a hat in his cabin the night of the murder. It's the same hat you're wearing this moment." He'd find succor in the truth. He'd trust that the Lord Divine would bless him for his honesty.

And if he was not to have love, then maybe he could have peace, and grace, and forgiveness.

She moved her hand to his neck. Hiram stiffened, facing forward. His heart thumped in his chest, and felt as if his blood had become motor oil.

"I took the hat from Lloyd's cabin." She withdrew her hand. "But it wasn't my hat. Adelaide said I could have it. This *chapeau* is not exactly unique, you know. If you come to my home, I can show you the page of the *Sears, Roebuck* catalog from which any one of perhaps ten thousand women bought the same exact hat. Hiram, it hurts to think you might doubt me. Heaven knows, most everyone in this town has had their misgivings in my regard. That's the curse of beauty and widowhood. My sex has a bad reputation for gossip, but I have reason to know that men talk as well."

"They do," Hiram's eyes dropped to her legs, the real one and the wooden one. Did the smell of corruption that followed Preacher Bill around have something to do with his foot? Hiram didn't know what to say next. He wished Michael was with him. His son would know what to say.

"You've not talked about your wife, Mr. Woolley. You lost her, didn't you?"

"Cancer," Hiram murmured. "When the stock market went, so did she. It was bad stars back then, though I'm no expert."

"You know how lonely the nights can be, then. You've known love." She exhaled. "I came to Moab to find a place where I could rebuild myself. Henri is irreplaceable. I lost him in Baltimore, through violence. He was a banker, like our esteemed Erasmus Green. There was a robbery, and he was killed. His death slew a part of me as well."

"You're French," Hiram said. The way she pronounced her late husband's name confirmed it.

"I'm French," she said. "I try not to give myself away."

"I've known French women." Hiram blushed. "Not like . . . *that*. I fought in the Great War. I've seen Paris."

"Then you know the grandeur, the beauty, of that wonderful city." Another sigh. "After Henri was killed, I felt that I had no control over my own life. I was subject to the pressures of society, beseeching me to replace him with someone else. I had always been interested in astrology, but it wasn't until that tragedy that my studies grew intense. I wanted control, and if I could understand the movements of the universe, I thought I could gain mastery. It's laughable to say out loud, but that was my thinking."

"Why Moab?" Hiram asked.

She laughed sadly. "The American West, it is a place of new beginnings. I knew that in a small town, I could control the story, I knew what people would think, and I liked the idea I could write my narrative and make people believe it. I'm the fortune-teller, the beautiful widow in need, and still seductive and mysterious. I'm an outsider, and I play the outsider, which is why I've never remarried and never flirted with any kind of courtship."

Was she telling the truth? Her story seemed plausible. He brought to mind several Bible verses on lust, and he recited them silently while they sat. Matthew, fifth chapter, *But I tell you that anyone who looks at a woman lustfully has already committed adultery with her in his heart.* And then, the solution, Timothy, chapter two, *Flee the evil desires of youth and pursue righteousness, faith, love, and peace, along with those who call on the Lord out of a pure heart.*

He took a deep breath and felt at peace.

"So it wasn't your hat," Hiram said.

"No, I didn't leave the hat at Lloyd's cabin."

The bloodstone pinched him.

Hiram felt joy—his craft was not entirely wrecked. At the same moment, he felt sorrow—the widow Artemis was lying to him. It was her hat he had seen at Lloyd's. *Lloyd.* She referred to the dead man as *Lloyd*, not *Mr. Preece*. He thought back to dowsing for the well. Lloyd had referred to her as Diana, not the widow Artemis.

Hiram recognized the truth and the truth hurt.

But that didn't necessarily mean she had killed Lloyd Preece.

"I'm the opposite of you," Hiram said after a bit.

"How so?" Diana asked.

She put her hand on his leg, patted it, and then reached down to ease a line in her stocking.

"I struggle to let go of control," Hiram said. "I long to be God's instrument in this world. I go where He wills, and I do what He wishes me to do. If at any given moment I don't feel Him talking to me, then I do my best to follow the written instructions He left. I pray to always have a servant's heart." His own honesty surprised him. He hadn't planned on saying any of that.

"You're a man," Diana laughter was gentle and understanding. "It's easier to give up control when you've had it. I had love in Paris and Baltimore, but I never had control until I had my heart broken and I came to this empty land. Even here, I struggle against elements that are greater than me at every turn: I've danced when I was forced to dance, and I've sung beautifully when bidden. And yes, what I have had from money in this world is freedom, the freedom to say no to men and to choose my own life, so yes, I seek money and the things it can give me. Yes, we are opposites . . . and in the same breath, you and I are exactly the same."

Gus Dollar had said something similar to Hiram. It put a bad feeling in his belly. He didn't think it was true . . . and he didn't want to argue, either.

"I'm on your side, Hiram. I hope you believe that."

He wasn't sure what he believed. Her lingering touches, her delicate perfume, weren't helping him any.

He did know he'd vowed to keep Adelaide and her family safe, and that meant unraveling the mysteries in Moab as soon as possible. It was the only way to ensure the woman's future and to fulfill his oath.

Michael would have chuckled at him and his sense of duty.

Michael parked the Double-A. He wished he had his guitar, but it was back at their camp near Lloyd Preece's cabin. He'd devoured the widow's astrology book, and then the book from Mahonri Young, which had far more information, and not a few actual incantations. Spells. He was basically perusing a spell book.

And he was anxious to try one of them out.

He needed to stretch his legs; they'd driven from Provo with only one stop, at Green River to get gasoline. Michael climbed out of the truck. He'd parked in weeds behind Banjo & Sons, a big brick building in front of him. The Maxwell House Hotel was to his right across more dirt. The scent of a coming storm was heavy in the air. It wasn't humid, however, not like how it would be in Lehi, with the marshes and the lake.

Part of Michael had wanted to talk with Diana again, or at least look at her, but another part was glad his pap had decided to talk to her on his own. Something wasn't right there, and it would hurt him to think the widow Artemis might have something to do with the general chaos besieging Moab.

Low voices leaked out of the back of Banjo & Sons. He recognized a voice, Erasmus Green's, hitting the breeze.

Maybe he'd just do a little scouting, anyway.

Michael stepped quietly to the back of the building, avoiding any stick or cluster of weeds that might give him away.

He leaned up against the brick and listened. The men must be in the back room.

Banjo's husky voice said in a low voice. "Tonight is going to be tricky."

Leon couldn't keep his booming voice quiet. He'd be holding the Peteys, a habit which now seemed more sinister than it had before. "Dammit all, we have to go. Last night cost me. I was glad to do it, on account of Lloyd and all, but free drinks and food don't help my bottom line any."

Green's sigh came to Michael. "I can't believe he came back. I thought he and his Injun son would be long gone, after last night."

Injun. Michael ground his teeth. A mistake of geography made insulting by two hundred years of dispossession and a pronunciation habit that made any man sound like an imbecile. Maybe Michael could move to Palestine and say he was an Arab. That would change things, certainly. He would be a sheikh and ride a camel and no one would ever again ask him which reservation he came from.

"Do you think Addy told him anything?" Banjo asked.

"Lloyd said he raised her not knowing," Green replied.

"Bullshit," Leon cursed. "Lloyd knew the power in it."

From Green: "But he had a girl. Girls are different. There would be no reason for her to know. And you know how children are, they don't question where the money comes from."

"You have a point there," Banjo agreed. "Guy never knew. Old Tunstall didn't want him to know."

Michael didn't move, but he readied himself to run.

If the men thought he might be listening, he'd have to sprint to the truck, before they grabbed him. But would they grab him as men or as huge creatures with antlers sprouting from their heads?

"Addy is gone, and I don't expect she'll return," Green said. "You know we have to run it tonight. It's a powerful time, Jupiter crossing into the third decan, and there's the eclipse to think on. I can feel the power, and I know you boys do too."

Decan. Michael knew the word.

"The third face," Leon said in tones of awe.

"He'll be powerful, too," Banjo said. "And hankering for the power he'll gain. The odds are against us."

Michael wondered who "he" was.

From Leon: "Lloyd wouldn't care. He'd run it. He never cared what the odds were. That's why he was so rich. He'd take any chance."

"Lloyd loved the hunt, though," Green countered. "He was the best of us. It makes me sick to think he's gone. You know, things can't continue as they are. We'll have to do something eventually."

The men fell quiet.

Michael wasn't sure what he was hearing, but he was storing all the information away in his head. Thank God for his memory. *Yes, thank you, God.* It was an honest prayer of gratitude.

He had evidence now, of the occult, one more bit of proof, and yes, Davison might have doubts, but now Michael was hearing them talk. Whatever *Michael* thought, these men clearly believed in magic . . . of some strange kind that involved a hunt, and the moon, and the decans. They had to get one of the men alone, compromised, and learn more of what was going on in Moab.

Could this hunt also have to do with Jimmy Udall's death? It seemed likely.

Yet they weren't closer to finding Lloyd Preece's murderer. The three men inside didn't appear to have anything to do with it.

Green was bringing the conversation to a close. "So, tonight, at the Monument, we'll run. We'll be fleet, we'll be smart, and come tomorrow, the Tithe will bless us."

Michael heard the word *Tithe* with a capital *T*.

"You'll eat at the hotel beforehand?" Leon asked. He then mimicked the Peteys. "Bark, bark, bark."

"We'll all be there," Banjo said. "Better make the ribs good, Leon. If it's to be my final meal, I want it to be a good one. To the Tithe!"

"To the Tithe!"

Michael could imagine them lifting glasses in the toast.

The Tithe. Michael had heard one of the men mention a tithe at some point. He thought hard. It was Erasmus Green, during his story about the 1923 robbery. The insurance money helped him recoup his losses, but he'd also mentioned a tithe.

Michael moved away from the building, got into the Double-A, and drove off. He didn't want those men to know he'd eavesdropped. He and his pap had a deadline now. The men feared they might die, and they hoped they would get rich—rich like Lloyd Preece. Tonight, there would be some kind of hunt, a Tithe.

But was it a tithe of money...or of blood?

Chapter Nineteen

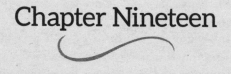

HIRAM MARCHED UP TO THE TRUCK, PARKED UNDER another cottonwood on 100 West.

Michael was inside, reading one of the astrology books. His son didn't see him right away, lost in the pages . . . which to Hiram looked like just long columns of numbers. The fact that astrology charts tended to look like complex accountants' work was one of the reasons why Hiram had never mastered this part of Grandma Hettie's craft.

Then his eye jumped from the book to Michael. Hiram had watched Michael read his entire life, from primers in elementary school to thick books on chemistry as a young man. His son read in the same position, hand on his forehead, and entangled in his thick black hair, eyes downcast on the book. Every once in a while, he'd sigh, maybe to keep himself breathing, since he was so motionless. More likely, it was a sound of utter enjoyment.

Hiram put his hand on the door and shook the Double-A.

Michael snapped to attention. "Pap! Get in. I have news. Boy, do I have news."

Hiram slid inside and Michael took off, driving south on Main. Hiram was glad his son had so much to talk about, since Hiram himself was reluctant to discuss his conversation with the widow Artemis.

After Michael finished, Hiram frowned. "I can't hardly get on you for eavesdropping, given what you've learned."

"That's what you have to say, after all that?" Michael erupted. "Those men nearly killed you! And I think they'd have killed Adelaide as well her entire family!"

"Or they were trying to scare us," Hiram said. "That wouldn't be anything new."

Michael pulled to the side of the road, on the dusty outskirts south of the city. Ramparts of a stone ridge rose up above them across a field of yellow grasses, dappled from the clouds and wind.

"Pap, the gloves are off. We're going to throw punches, bare-knuckled."

Hiram felt the frown and tried to soften his gaze, but he was equal parts afraid and frustrated. "Michael, remember, our power depends on our behavior. On keeping a chaste and sober mind." Notwithstanding his recent conversation with the widow, and his knowledge that she lied to him, the word *chaste* still brought to Hiram's mind powerful images of her. "If we allow ourselves to be . . . seduced . . . by anger, or vengeful ideas, our lore will fail."

"Pap," Michael said, "not sure I like you using the word 'seduced' around me. I understand what you are saying. This is where we are humble in the eyes of the Lord."

"Humility," Hiram agreed.

His son exhaled slowly. "So, tonight there are a variety of forces converging on our little world. I see, now, how the planets work with the constellations. I have to give it to the old astrologists. Their imaginations were first-rate. And man, to figure this stuff out, they must have been watching the sky really closely for a really long time. I mean, from before there was writing."

"Adam knew how to write," Hiram said. "Adam kept a book."

Michael took a deep breath. "Okay, fine. But look, you remember how Jupiter is in a constellation for a year, slowly moving across it?"

Hiram nodded. "We discussed that. It's in Scorpio now."

"Astronomers—excuse me, astrologers, divide that constellation into thirds, and they call each third a 'decan.'"

"*Deca*, meaning ten?"

"Yes. Because the ecliptic surrounds the earth like a circle, so it's three hundred sixty degrees, and it has twelve constellations on it, so each of them is thirty degrees, at least in the abstract."

"In the abstract?" Hiram felt a little dizzy.

"In practice, some constellations of the zodiac appear much larger than others. Virgo is very long, lying draped out across the ecliptic like she is. Cancer is tiny."

Hiram knew those constellations. "Got it."

"Each sign of the zodiac occupies thirty degrees, so each third is ten degrees. Each *decan*, or, as they're called by the astrologers, each *face*. Each sign has three faces. Except for those weird times when Jupiter appears to go backward, it takes Jupiter about four months to cross from one face to the next."

"Three faces," Hiram said. "The statue on Lloyd Preece's desk has three faces."

Michael slapped himself in the forehead. "Yes! And this is a very old way of thinking, Pap. The Egyptians had a different image and name for each decan, because they thought they were gods. But all that is just background. Look, here's the point. Jupiter entered Scorpio back on October 11, 1934. It will move from Scorpio into Sagittarius later this year. That's a total of 393 days. If you subtract a third of that, which is to say, take 131 from November 8, 1935, you get tonight."

"Even more numbers," Hiram murmured. Then suddenly he understood. "Jupiter crosses to the third decan of Scorpio tonight. The third face. There's a diary in Lloyd's office. It doesn't say much, but some of the dates are circled. I wonder what's on October 11 of last year?"

"Also, there's a solar eclipse tonight, best visible from somewhere in Russia, as far as I can tell. So we won't see the eclipse, but still, the coincidence of the eclipse just . . . I don't know, it adds to the cosmic energies that are chasing around the sky tonight." Michael snapped his fingers. "Oh, and you want to know the *really* strange thing?"

"What do you mean, '*really* strange'?"

"The weekend when we were in Helper, back in February? There was a solar eclipse then, too. We would have seen it, I guess, except for all the snow. And there's three more coming this year. Nineteen thirty-five turns out to be a year of maximum eclipses. See what I mean? *Really* strange."

"Five eclipses this year?"

"Actually, seven. Five solar and two lunar."

Hiram felt slightly sick and tried not to think about what that might suggest. Five solar eclipses? Three more this year? And could it be coincidence that both eclipses so far had coincided with Hiram finding himself in confrontation with murderous forces of darkness? "The hunt is triggered by the moment when Jupiter crosses from one decan to the next, you think?"

Michael nodded. "The hunt, or the Tithe, or whatever else you want to call it. I'm betting that Jimmy Udall died on October 11 of last year, when Jupiter transitioned from Libra to Scorpio. If Jupiter enters the sign of the hunter, Sagittarius, this November 8, it might have dramatic consequences."

"And when did Davison Rock say he was almost run over by a herd of deer on the Monument?" Hiram asked. "February?"

"That would be about four months ago. That might have been on the night Jupiter crossed from the first decan of Scorpio into the second."

"A hunt." Hiram thought. "Erasmus Green and those men know about the hunt."

"They do," Michael agreed. "And Green is in a position of real power, as the banker. He could tell us more about Lloyd Preece's bearer bonds, and why they went after Adelaide." His son swallowed. "They turned into deer . . . or deer-*things*. I'd love to hear more about that. This defies everything I know about biology at every level. And yet, I believe you. About the deer-men."

"Green is the smallest of the three," Hiram mused. "Going after Leon would be tough. Banjo is bigger, but older, and I wouldn't want to kill anyone." His ear—Banjo had a withered ear, and so had one of the deer men.

"So you're thinking what I'm thinking. This book is mostly general discussion, ideas, and tables of the motions of heavenly bodies." Michael closed the book from Diana and pulled out the book from Mahonri. "This text, Pap, is far more...uh, actionable. Yes, the stars move in a certain way, but Mahonri's book tells me how to use that energy. I say we kidnap Erasmus Green, and I have a plan to do it."

"Kidnap him. So we can interrogate him." Hiram clenched his teeth so hard, his jaw muscles ached. His conscience fought him. They were entering into a duel with the darkness, a darkness that turned men into monsters, and then drove them to evil acts. What did the deer-men hunt, on the night when Jupiter entered a new decan? But the law wouldn't see it that way, all they would see is a crazy farmer and his Navajo son kidnapping an esteemed banker in a small desert community.

Sheriff Jack Del Rose just might get off his soft backside and do something then...if he wasn't already involved in this business somehow. Did Del Rose, Gudmundson, or Clem know about the deer-men and this hunt?

"What's your plan?" Hiram asked.

Michael told him.

Hiram considered.

"Pap," Michael said, "we're close to cracking this case."

"These aren't cases," Hiram said. "These aren't your detective novels."

"Are you sure? We have a dead body, a town full of secrets, and a list of possible suspects. One of which, I'm sorry to say, is Diana Artemis. This sure feels like a detective novel." Michael was joking, but a slick sheen of sweat covered his forehead.

Hiram didn't hide his sigh. "Tonight, if things don't go as planned, you have to drive away and leave me. And if, say, Sheriff Del Rose calls you later, you say you left to check on the beet farm and you don't know a thing about the craziness your old pap might have gotten up to, back in Moab."

Michael smirked at him. "It's me, your genius son. It's my plan. Of course it's going to work. As long as our timing is right, we'll be fine."

Hiram felt a hard knot in his belly. Their timing would have to be perfect.

At the gas station, Hiram called Diana's landlady Edna. It took a few minutes, but she got Diana got on the phone, and Diana gave him Erasmus Green's birthday, hour and minute, as well as the town of his birth—Erasmus was born in Moab itself, and she had already found the latitude and longitude, which were apparently relevant. She passed on this information readily, and without asking why.

Before hanging up, she said once again, "I'm on your side, Hiram."

Hiram relayed the information on to Michael because it was Michael who would have to set up the charm.

Hiram's trust in himself was failing. Even simply talking to Diana brought back memories of the widow's low-cut dresses, and of Elmina, their bed, and their bodies, and even of Monique in France, lovely, energetic Monique. Hiram didn't trust his own craft to work, and in any case, it was Michael who had found the hex.

After the call, they drove out of Moab, looking for cultivated fields. When they stopped, Hiram bought supplies, including a bale of hay, from a local farmer growing alfalfa in irrigated fields. With the hay strapped to the back of the Double-A, they headed back into Moab.

They'd reach the Maxwell House Hotel at around five, while the restaurant was still empty of customers. Green said he and other deer men would eat before the hunt, but that the hunt wouldn't begin until night fell. With the long summer days, the sun would set at eight-thirty, but the sky wouldn't get dark until nine.

That would give them some time to talk with Erasmus Green. Only it wasn't talking, it would be an interrogation following a kidnapping. Hiram didn't see a way around it. If he went to the sheriff, nothing would happen. If he tried any other law enforcement, he couldn't exactly explain there was a ritualistic hunt involving men who became deer-monsters.

Green and the other deer-men had struck first. Hiram was simply following the next logical course of action, or at least it followed his logic. Michael had found the charm in the book for a reason, otherwise, they wouldn't have had it nor their plan.

Michael parked the truck. Hiram led the way up the steps and into the restaurant lobby of the Maxwell House.

The place was empty. But for how long?

Even the front desk was empty. From up the stairs, noises—they'd have to hurry.

Michael didn't pause. He marched over to a table, the very table they'd seen Erasmus Green sit at before, both times they'd come in, near the back, with a view of the room. Michael had a piece of chalk in his hands, taken from the toolbox.

"Hurry," Hiram hissed.

Michael crouched, then lay flat on his back, under the table, and began to scribble the signs underneath. He'd showed Hiram the book, and the complicated symbols, including Erasmus Green's birthday: February 21, 1883. That meant Green was fifty-two years old. He was still strangely spry.

"Bark! Bark!" Leon came traipsing down the stairs, holding his dog-bottle monstrosity and smiling, in an obvious good mood. Was it the eclipse giving him power in some way? Or was it Jupiter, moving through Scorpio?

Hiram quickly walked forward and got in Leon's way, keeping him at the bottom of the steps and obstructing his view so he wouldn't see Michael. "Oh, Sorry, Mr. Björnsson." Hiram pretended to be surprised. "Are you open? My son and I have so enjoyed your food. We'd like to take an early dinner before going up to our camp."

Leon let out a laugh. "You should get a room here with us, Mr. Woolley. And aren't we beyond last names? We're old friends now, I daresay. Yes, Hiram, we can get you and your son some food. Where is he?"

Hiram waved back to the dining area. "At a table already. May I pet Petey... Peteys?"

Leon laughed more. He shoved the conjoined dogs into Hiram's face. "Bark! Bark! Give me some petting, Hiram!"

Hiram grinned, though he didn't feel it. The border collie's hair was soft, all right, but the skin underneath had wrinkled. The chihuahua's head felt like a hard rubber ball.

"Good boy," Hiram said.

Leon pushed past him.

Hiram's heart went to this throat. He followed the hotelier, and there, sitting at the table that was now chalked on its underside, was Michael, who waved. "What's the special tonight, Mr. Björnsson?"

"We have local trout," Leon said, "caught right out of the Colorado."

"Sounds delicious!" Michael seemed genuinely enthusiastic.

Leon scowled. "Yeah, it is. It is." Then he found a grin, threw Michael a bark from Petey, and waltzed back into the kitchen.

Hiram sat down, careful not to brush his knees underneath the table. One smear of the sigils might ruin their power.

Michael wiped sweat from his forehead. "Thirty seconds earlier, our plan would've been undone."

"Your plan," Hiram said. "Your charms. How are you feeling?"

"Chaste and sober mind," Michael affirmed. "Got it. Which, I gotta tell you, is tough when you're a seventeen-year-old boy. But my heart's beating fast, and it's not because there are any ginchy girls around. That man's stuffed dogs give me the heebie-jeebies."

"What of your faith?" Hiram asked.

Michael frowned and squinted. "Faith in God? I . . . I always had faith in the beauty of the stars, the complexity of the systems, the divine mathematics of the galaxy's dance. And God...you know what, Pap, maybe I do. Maybe I believe. And I'm excited to *try*."

"It will be enough." Hiram smiled. If he had faith, and Michael had a chaste and sober mind, maybe between the two of them, it would be enough.

The trout came with rice, green beans braised in bacon, and some cheese biscuits Leon had made himself. Hot out of the oven, they were crumbly and rich.

Hiram fell into the meal, eating his fill but careful not to overeat.

Michael picked at his food, and soon gave up.

"Too nervous to eat?" Hiram asked.

"I am," Michael said. "We'll call it fasting. God willing, it's close enough."

"God willing." Hiram liked how that sounded. "When I find myself forced to break the laws of man, I... sometimes...try to ask God that His will be done. If my cause is not righteous, I beseech Him to let my charms fail."

"That's so weird," Michael said. "But I guess I understand it."

After paying for their meal, Michael and Hiram walked out. They rehearsed the plan and then Michael drove away in the truck while Hiram took a short stroll. Michael's scheme would either work or it wouldn't, but it shouldn't put anyone at risk, other than the two of them. As long as Main Street didn't get too crowded.

Hiram found a bench to sit on. He held a small gray candle in his pocket, marked with a symbol that he'd been told was the Sixth Pentacle of the Sun, or the Key of Solomon. He'd anointed the candle in oil, said a prayer over it, and put it in his toolbox over a year ago, but it ought to work still.

This was not craft he'd learned from Grandma Hettie. He'd learned it from an old colored man in France, who'd had to explain it through another doughboy, one who spoke French and who couldn't believe that Hiram was taking it seriously. But Hiram had not only taken it seriously, he'd used it in the war, burning one of the three candles the old man had sold him. Just once, but once was enough to know that it worked.

Hiram waited, Michael cruised slowly past in the Double-A.

Men began to drift into the hotel at around six-thirty.

They had agreed that Hiram would set his hat on the wooden slats of the sidewalk once Erasmus Green sat at his normal table in the restaurant. Hiram hoped that really was the man's regular table—otherwise, Hiram would have to try to lure him into switching seats.

The banker walked up the street at seven and entered the hotel.

Michael passed again.

Hiram casually sauntered up the steps and peeped in. The Solomon candle, once lit, should hide him. It wouldn't exactly make him invisible, but it would cast a shroud over him, turning him into someone you needn't pay attention to. *Comme un fantôme*, the old man had said, and those were the only words of his explanation that Hiram specifically remembered. Hiram's heart leapt. Yes, Green was at his table at the back, along with Banjo Johansson, and Howard Balsley, whiskey glasses in front of them.

Good, the liquor would help.

Hiram stepped to the corner, dropped his hat, and then walked quickly past Banjo & Sons Mercantile, and around the block. He had to act quickly now, before Michael did.

Hiram stopped beside the back door of the hotel. Placing the Solomon candle on a brick window sill, he lit it with his Zippo, murmuring a short prayer. His unnoticeability would last only as long as the candle did, so he was alarmed at the speed with which the flame immediately began to devour the wax.

Then Hiram hurried through the back door, down a long corridor, past the kitchen, and he emerged at the corridor by the front desk—on the far side of the lobby from the front doors.

Erasmus Green drank his whiskey, grinning at his friends, his eyes growing heavy.

Michael had turned their normal table into a sleeping table, marking the bottom with the astrological signs identifying Erasmus Green's birth moment. Hiram had understood only that Green was born when the sun was in Pisces, but the information from Diana had made perfect sense to Michael. Hiram was impressed by Michael's quick learning, and also anxious to see whether this hex worked. Hiram himself knew a sleep prayer, but it was really to help someone who had trouble sleeping, or to keep someone asleep who was already asleep—he didn't think it would knock a man unconscious at the dinner table, surrounded by his friends.

Leon's boy, Arnie, passed Hiram, carrying a tray. Hiram pushed himself up against the wall to let him by. Leon paid him no notice.

The kid was overworked, focused on doing his job, and didn't even nod at Hiram. Or perhaps the Solomon candle had hidden him.

Arnie returned.

Any minute now. Hiram hoped Michael would have the presence of mind to grab his fedora. It would be a shame to lose a good hat.

Hiram glanced at Erasmus Green. His meal was in front of him, and his head bobbed up and down, eyelids dragging. Banjo Johansson and Howard Balsley were in some kind of deep conversation. Was Balsley part of the deer-men's cult? He hadn't been at the secret meeting at the mercantile that afternoon, and he wasn't easily recognizable as one of the deer-monsters Hiram had seen the night before.

Honks outside, from the Double-A—that horn was as familiar as the laughter of his son.

"Hey!" a man shouted. "Something's on fire out there!"

That would be the bale of hay, soaked in gasoline.

Tables emptied instantly, men rushing to the windows and door to look out onto Main Street. Erasmus Green fell forward at the same instant, head making a dull thud as it struck the table beside his plate. His scabby scalp glistened in the brass light, taunting Hiram with the reminder that he'd seen Green transformed into a beast.

Hiram was impressed; Michael's sleep-table astrological hex worked. He hoisted the banker and slung him over his shoulders.

Arnie stomped past them, not giving Hiram a look. Hiram's charm was working. His heart pounded, but he felt light and free.

Hiram thanked the Lord Divine for his physical strength and walked with Green back down the hallway and out the back door, to where Michael had parked the truck. Hiram gently laid the banker in the back and then clambered in, picking his hat up from the truck's seat and resettling it on his head.

Michael took a back road, a simple dirt track, out to another street and then back on Main Street, headed out of town. Behind them, Hiram saw a small bucket brigade of men watering the bale and stamping its flames into submission.

Hiram and his son had the banker. Now, to make him talk. Hiram felt bad for a moment for capturing the man, for casting sorcery on him, but then he remembered the frightened faces of Adelaide Tunstall and her children.

Hiram's heart hardened. The Lord Divine had delivered the banker to them. Their cause was righteous. They hadn't failed.

Chapter Twenty

BY THE TIME THE BANKER CAME TO, RATTLING along in the cab of the Double-A, Hiram had tied his hands behind him with a length of cord. Hiram had also blindfolded the man with an old blue bandana from the upper section of his toolbox. From the lower section, he had removed a small dried frog, completely dissected and wrapped in a square of deer leather, soft with age, and tucked it into his own pocket.

Deer leather. The irony wasn't lost on Hiram.

Michael turned up to Frenchie's Canyon and parked in a thick stand of junipers along the Colorado River, where they would be hidden from the view of the road.

Michael helped Hiram lower Green to the ground. Hiram had his revolver in his pocket and the rest of the rope coiled on his shoulder. He prodded the banker from behind, forcing the man across the road and up the rocky trail to Preacher Bill's amphitheater. A back trail blind canyon should be a good enough place to keep themselves out of sight and the banker out of the hunt. Whatever the hunt was.

And whatever the deer-beasts' role was in the hunt.

It was getting harder to see, with the sun gone from the bottoms of the canyons. They sat the banker down on a flat rock. Hiram checked the dugout, including its hidden chimney. The place was deserted.

Green chuckled. "Hiram, you can remove the blindfold. I know it's you. You shouldn't have come back."

"I won't lie," Hiram said, "but what makes you guess it's me, Erasmus? Why not, say, a bank robber, wanting your help in opening a safe?"

"I fell asleep at my table and whiskey wasn't involved. How would a bank robber accomplish that?"

Michael shot Hiram a panicked glance. Hiram jerked his head, wanting Michael back in the shadows, while Hiram interrogated their prisoner. Michael moved himself behind Erasmus.

"Drug your food, maybe?" Hiram undid the blindfold and stuck the bandana in his pocket. "Remember that you came after us first, Erasmus."

"That would result in me falling asleep *after* the meal, rather than *before* it." The banker grunted laughter. "We didn't really come after you. We wanted to get to Preece's daughter. Why was she leaving town all of the sudden? What does she know about the *Blót*?"

Hiram stood in front of the man. "What's the *Blót*?"

Erasmus grinned, and rattled off a string of foreign words.

Hiram let the rope drop in loops. "Let's stick to English."

"Hiram, what are you doing, kidnapping me?"

"I promised Addy I'd keep her safe from you, and to do that, I need to know the nature of your hunt . . . or *tithe* or *Blót*. It's all the same thing, isn't it?"

Green didn't answer.

Michael was quiet.

"I want to know more about Jimmy Udall and Lloyd Preece," Hiram said. "I want to know whether you and your friends were involved in their deaths, and what the connection is to your hunt."

"And if I don't tell you a word?" Green asked.

"That's what the rope is for." Hiram walked behind Green, caught him up in a lasso, and then pulled him back, dragging him to the dirt. At the same time, he looped an end around a knob of rock on the lower part of the canyon wall. Green lay on his back, pulled down, facing the darkness of the fading blue sky.

Michael stepped back farther into the shadows.

"And I will also seek help from the Lord Divine." Hiram loosened and unclasped the banker's shoe-string tie. He then undid the buttons on Green's shirt to expose pale skin.

"What is the meaning of this?" Green asked nervously. "Hurting me won't get you anything."

"All I want is the truth." From out of Hiram's pocket, he took the square of deer leather, and unfolded it on the sandstone table next to Green. He picked up a frog's tongue, thoroughly dried, about an inch in length. He laid the tongue on Green's chest.

To add power to the charm, Hiram whispered Ephesians, chapter four, verse twenty-five: "Therefore each of you must put off falsehood and speak truthfully to your neighbor, for we are all members of one body."

Green twisted. "What are you doing? What is this?"

"You're going to tell me everything you know," Hiram said.

"Ha, damn you, Hiram. I won't. And even if I did tell you, you couldn't possibly understand. You're not prepared for the knowledge, so it would simply bounce off your forehead."

"I'd understand more than you think." Hiram himself had said uncomfortably similar things to Michael, quite recently. "Tell me about the *Blót*."

"Go to hell!"

Hiram took his hat off and ran his fingers through his thinning hair. The frog's tongue should compel the man to speak the truth—why wasn't it working? Did Erasmus Green have a countercharm? Did the power that transformed him also protect him?

Was Hiram still weakened by his thoughts of the widow? Having his craft work sometimes-yes and sometimes-no was worse than it never working it all.

"We know that tonight, Jupiter enters the third face of Scorpio," Michael said.

Hiram felt stricken. He wanted to keep Michael out of this.

Green laughed meanly. "Oh, is the Injun going to work his savagery on me? You gonna do a rain dance, boy?"

Hiram wanted to shut the man up, but he didn't move.

Michael picked up the frog's tongue from the banker's bare chest and examined it. "Pap, this business of ours involves a lot of tongues. Dried dog's tongue to keep other dogs from barking. Dried frog's tongue to get people to tell the truth. I wonder what a dried 'Injun' tongue would do?" Michael snickered. "Or a dried deer-man's tongue?"

"I don't know," Green said, "but I do know my

wet tongue still rooted firmly in my head isn't going to tell you a thing."

"We'll see about that." Michael laid the tongue back down on Green's chest, and he repeated the Bible verse Hiram had quoted. Michael had never really learned his Bible, but he had a quick memory.

The minute Michael was done, Green writhed, trying to dislodge the frog's tongue from his skin. Despite his movements, the dried piece of leather stuck in place, as if glued.

"Tell us about the *Blót*," Michael commanded.

"It is ancient. It comes from Iceland, where my mother's people come from." Sweat trickled down Erasmus Green's forehead. "We haven't always been Mormons, you know. The missionaries only found my people in the 1870s. My parents, my father, they came to Utah, settled in Spanish Fork, for a bit, but they didn't fit in. They came south, to Moab, or really this valley before it was a town. They came here in 1877, crossed the Colorado, floating one piece of furniture across it at a time. That's how the story goes. I was born here in 1883, to Cornelius Green and my mother, Hekla Jónsdóttir. My father wasn't Icelandic nor was he Mormon, but his closest friends were both. My father raised me to be Mormon out of respect for his wife, and my father's friends raised me with the *Blót*. I ran my first Tithe when I was sixteen."

Michael's eyes flicked up to Hiram. "So it gets him to talk, but the charm doesn't really compel him to focus on the question."

"He's resisting," Hiram murmured.

"Hell yes, I'm resisting!" Green was sweating, his face pinched, his teeth clenched. "That frog's tongue is not going to overcome my own good sense. I won't tell this Injun shit! Let me go, or you'll have the whole herd down on you!"

Michael poked the man's arm. "My father isn't doing the interrogating. I am. And luckily, I'm a righteous man, a humble man, with a forgiving spirit. I'm going to turn the other cheek, but don't call me an Injun again."

Hiram smiled, proud for a moment, until a thought made him frown. Would Michael ever be able to work at any ordinary profession, after experiences like this one?

"Okay, Erasmus," Michael said. "You can turn into a deer, can't you?"

"You know the answer to that," Green snapped. Then he grinned. "I have to talk. And I have to tell the truth. But I don't have to *keep* talking."

"Do you know who killed Jimmy Udall?" Michael asked.

"I don't."

"Who killed Lloyd Preece?" Michael asked.

"I don't know."

"Do you have your suspicions?"

Green twisted, exhaled, and blinked against his sweat. "I do."

"Whom do you suspect?" Michael's question was clear.

"The hunters." Green grinned, but there was pain in his eyes. "The pack killed him."

"Lloyd was one of you?" Michael asked. "He ran the Tithe?"

Green laughed. "Of course, you idiot! He was First of Hoof! How do you think he got so rich?"

Michael frowned, thinking. "Who is in the pack?"

Green spewed more of the harsh syllables, which must be Icelandic. Green was strong and he was clever—was he clever enough to outwit Michael?

Michael didn't appear nervous. He stood, arms straight on the sandstone, leaning hard against it. His legs were behind him. "Well, we know that tonight there's going to be a hunt. And we know the hunt is connected to the Tithe, or maybe it *is* the Tithe. And we know that you get money from the hunt, because you admitted it yourself when you threw out that little inside joke, during your story of the 1923 robbery. You got your money back through insurance, and the Tithe."

"I'm not going to say a word on any of that in English. How is your Icelandic, boy?" Green asked.

"We'll see." Michael didn't seem upset. "Yes or no, is Leon Björnsson part of the hunt?"

Green grimaced, but out of his mouth popped, "*Já.*"

Michael chuckled. "That's a yes. It's close enough to the German. Yes or no, is Howard Balsley part of the hunt?"

"*Nei!*" popped out of Green's mouth.

Michael gave Hiram a sweaty smile. "*Já* and *nei* helps us out. It's kind of like the lantern game we did with the ghost that first night. Twenty questions! I've already asked him about Jimmy Udall and Preece, and he doesn't know." His son thought again, and then asked, "Yes or no, if we let you go, will you try to kill us?"

Green didn't even try to answer it in Icelandic. "No, not if you can keep what you know a secret. And why would you tell anyone? Who would believe you? There might be movies about werewolves, but there aren't movies about deer men."

"Yes or no, do you hunt during the *Blót*?" Michael asked.

"No." Green scowled.

Hiram felt a shiver run up his spine. Then what was the hunt, exactly?

Michael's face was thoughtful. "Who hunts *you* during the *Blót*?"

"The pack. Do you really want to keep playing this game? I can play all night." Green laughed. "I won't tell you anything useful."

"You're telling us immensely useful things," Michael said.

Erasmus Green hissed.

"Yes or no, is the widow Artemis part of the *Blót*?" Michael asked.

"No. Women can't be a part of the *Blót*. But Diana is involved."

Hiram felt as if he wasn't breathing.

"How's that?" Michael asked.

"Oh, I don't mind talking about this. Let's just say, the widow Artemis has a definite open mind when it comes to anything that brings her money. She was at Preece's when he was killed."

"Yes or no, do you think she killed him?"

"Yes and no," Green answered. "How do you like *that* answer? Ha!"

Michael's face darkened. "And how do you know Diana was at Preece's when he died?"

"Because someone told me!"

"Was it Diana?" Michael pressed.

"Of course not!"

"Who told you she was there, then?" Michael frowned.

A long stream of Icelandic ensued.

Hiram felt compassion for his son. And Hiram had wanted to protect his son, but this was the result of Hiram bringing his son into the very real world where men and women did desperate things. Would Michael turn to cynicism? It seemed to be in his nature. Intelligent, complicated men often turned to cynicism as a shield against the world and its pain.

Hiram wished for a servant's heart.

How could Hiram best serve Michael, or the man tied to the rock?

Perhaps they'd learned enough from Green. Perhaps they'd learned enough to be able to try some of Grandma Hettie's divination techniques.

"Anything else do you want to ask him?" Hiram asked.

"We could go through the entire town, to figure out who is part of this Tithe thing," Michael suggested. "He says he can do this all night, let's give it a try."

Michael spent the next several minutes going through everyone in town he and Hiram could name. Sheriff Jack Del Rose, Bishop Gudmund Gudmundson, Deputy Russ Pickens, and the ranch hand Clem were all part of the *Blót*, according to Erasmus Green. Mormons and Catholics, it didn't seem to matter. Icelandic ancestry or not, didn't seem to matter, either. Rex Whittle, Hiram was pleased to hear, was not part of it. Ernie and Bobette Smothers, Jeff Webb, Orville Peterson, and Don Pout were not. Leon Björnsson was.

"Surprise," Michael said. "The guy who stuffs dogs inside of other dogs is part of the crazy."

When asked whether the individuals were deer-men

or hunters, Green laughed and spewed long Icelandic speeches.

"Is the *Blót* a plot to commit murder?" Michael asked.

Hiram expected an answer not in English.

Green though, surprised him. His laughter evaporated abruptly. "Absolutely not. We don't want to hurt anyone, and if others do, well, there's an old maxim of the law that says *volenti non fit iniuria.*"

"Great," Michael said. "Latin?"

Green smiled. "It means, if the victim is willing, there is no crime."

"There's something else I want to try," Hiram said.

"I hope it involves letting me go." Green looked at Hiram.

"Not tonight," Hiram answered. "I do have a salve for your scalp. I'm assuming your psoriasis doesn't have anything to do with your two-formed nature or the hunt."

Green smiled. "That would be nice of you, Hiram. See? We'll get past this. The hunter and his victim can be friends."

Hiram imagined he and Michael would let Green go, and then flee back to Lehi. Once Hiram got his head in order, he'd have his craft to protect him.

Until then, he had another charm to show Michael. Hopefully, it would tell them the killer and maybe get Green to talk a little more.

"Let's take him back to the truck," Hiram said. "We'll finish this up by the river."

Chapter Twenty-One

THE SUN HAD SET BUT THE SKY GLOWED RED BY the time they had returned to their camp, close to the river. Hiram lit their kerosene lantern to keep the coming gloom at bay.

"You guys are idiots," Erasmus Green called from the back of the Double-A. The banker flailed around, pulling at the ropes with which Hiram had tied him down. "Seriously. What do you think is going to happen next? You're going to solve the murder of Lloyd Preece and be heroes? What, you think there's some kind of reward for doing the sheriff's job? Ha!"

Hiram and Michael leaned closed together.

"The problem is this," Hiram said. "The stone I carry in my pocket?"

"The bloodstone."

Hiram nodded. "I don't think it's working. Yes and no, hit and miss, but not consistently. And it's a bigger problem; my craft has become unreliable for me."

A look washed across Michael's face and disappeared.

It flashed for only a brief moment, but that was enough for Hiram to recognize it and be wounded; it was an expression that was part disappointment, part glee at being proven right, and part pity. The pity wounded Hiram the most.

But the expression passed, and Michael regained control of his face. "That's why I had to take over with the dried frog's tongue. Okay, so your magic isn't working?"

"I don't love the word *magic*, son."

Michael looked at him as if he were avoiding the question. "It doesn't work."

"It *does* work," Hiram said. "It's just not working for me right *now*."

Michael frowned. Hiram knew what he was thinking.

"The bloodstone works," Hiram said. The stone worked. It had worked for Hiram innumerable times, except when it was interfered with by the working of other influences, or when Hiram himself was not a worthy instrument. "Listen, you know what I tell you about the state of mind you need to have to be able to work any of Grandma Hettie's lore."

"No cussing."

"No, not that. I mean yes that, but, more basically . . ."

Michael nodded. "A chaste and sober mind."

Hiram breathed a sigh of relief. "That."

Michael stared blankly for a moment. "Wait, are you saying . . . Pap?"

"Yes." Hiram hung his head.

"Who . . . ? It's Diana Artemis, isn't it? Ho ho ho, Pap, what did you do?"

"No, nothing. I—look, you don't have to do anything.

Jesus says in Matthew 5 that if you look upon a woman with lust in your heart, you've already committed adultery."

"That's a pretty high bar, Pap."

"It's the highest bar, son." Hiram felt his cheeks coloring. "It's the judgment bar."

"So you're telling me," Michael said slowly, "that you didn't do anything with Diana Artemis. Didn't kiss, snuggle, hold hands, touch, say naughty words."

"Nothing."

"And yet you feel like an adulterer."

"No!" What Hiram *felt* was mortification. "Look, all I'm saying is, I don't have the kind of concentration to be able to make the charms work for me right now. I'm pretty sure that's why the heliotropius has been . . . somewhat not working."

"Look, Pap, this is totally normal, I promise you. As a fellow who has felt lust in his heart while looking upon a girl or two in his own time, I can assure you that the feelings are thoroughly natural. And if you didn't do anything to act on those feelings, Pap, really, that's the best you can do. I promise. Mom couldn't ask anything more from you. You can't ask anything more from yourself."

"I'm going to ask something from *you*."

Michael stopped his rapid-fire reassurances. "Sure, Pap. What do you need?"

"I want you to try another charm. I know this is three in a row—the sleeping table, the frog's tongue, and now this—and I know it's a lot to ask, but I'm not very . . . cunning . . . right now."

Michael's face froze, then shifted into a slightly uncomfortable grin. "I'm not so sure I have a chaste and sober mind. I mean, a couple of hours ago I said I did, but now that I've heard your standards..."

"I think you have what it takes, son. In any case, I know that I do not."

Michael took a deep breath and nodded. "Okay. Give me the bloodstone."

Hiram handed the stone over to his son. They turned back to face Green.

"What's the charm?" Michael asked.

"I have a divination in mind," Hiram said. "I think we've got all we could get out of Erasmus Green, but at least he's given us a list of suspects. And with that, we can begin to test." He grinned a crooked grin. "Science, you know."

"Which one?" Michael's face lit up. "I mean yes, of course, but which one? Sheep's entrails?"

"That's old Greek stuff," Hiram told him. "You know I don't do that."

"Divining rod? Sieve and shears?"

"I was thinking clay balls," Hiram said. "And we do it in front of Mr. Green here."

"Because sometimes a guilty man will reveal himself, independently of the magic?"

"The charm. Yes. There's clay down on the riverbank we can use."

"I'll fetch some clay," Michael said. "You can show me what to do."

Michael took the tin bowl from his mess kit and headed down to the water. Hiram grabbed his toolbox from the back of the truck. Erasmus Green craned his neck to see what Hiram was doing, but finally grumbled, "Torture won't get you anything."

"Agreed," Hiram said.

On the end of the truck bed, Hiram spread out what Michael would need: virgin paper, the finest ink Hiram could buy, Hiram's ritual knife, the big tin bucket in which he washed dishes, now full of clean water.

Michael returned with a heaping pile of thick brown clay in his bowl, and, at Hiram's directions, washed his hands.

"First," Hiram said, "take this pen and ink and write out on this virgin sheet of paper the names of our murder suspects. Each name on a separate line. As you write, keep a prayer in your heart."

"How do I keep a prayer in my heart?"

Hiram considered. "Try remembering the pity you have for Lloyd Preece, and think the words *please, Lord,* as you work."

Michael nodded. "Who are our suspects?"

Hiram sighed. "Diana Artemis."

Erasmus Green cackled.

Michael wrote the name.

"Davison Rock. Earl Bill Clay." Hiram looked up at Mr. Green. "Erasmus Green."

Michael wrote out the names. Green laughed, snorted, and spit.

"You know you're going to go to prison for this," Green said meanly. "That's what you call irony. You all think you're hunting down a criminal, but the criminals are you. Kidnapping! That's a trip to Sugar House for both of you!"

Hiram fixed Erasmus Green with a steady eye, looking for any signs of flinching in the man. He saw none. There was manic energy there, and conviction, and anger, but no uncertainty or hesitation.

He was certain Green had attacked him on the road to Provo, in the form of the deer-beast with the skin affliction. Was it possible that wasn't connected to the murder of Lloyd Price, who had been a member—the head—of Green's were-deer herd?

Was this just about the money after all?

"Anyone else, Pap?" Michael asked.

"Adelaide Tunstall," Hiram suggested. "She knew there was money. We have no reason to think it was her, but let's see what the clay says. Jack Del Rose."

"He's certainly been useless enough in the investigation." Michael wrote the two names.

"Any others you can think of?" Hiram asked.

Michael shook his head.

"Okay, son, take the ritual knife and cut those names from the virgin sheet in long strips, from one side of the paper to the other." Hiram indicated what he meant with a finger. "Make the strips equal in size."

"Ritual knife?" Michael asked.

"It's a knife I use for no other purposes," Hiram said. "And it's been blessed to the purpose."

Michael looked·as if he wanted to say something, but then shook off the thought to focus on the matter at hand. He cut the names off in careful strips.

"Now roll those strips up as tight as you can," Hiram said. "Keep the prayer in your heart and be sure not to play favorites. Roll them equally tightly."

Green chuckled. "This is rich, watching you magicians. Under other circumstances, we could charge a nickel for such a show."

While his son worked, Hiram put away the paper and his knife.

"Now roll each piece of paper into a clay ball,"

Hiram continued, when Michael was ready. "Make the balls equal in size. Keep praying."

Michael wiped sweat from his forehead with the back of his arm. The night was cool—Michael was concentrating so hard, it was making him sweat.

He would make a good scientist. He was methodical and precise, and he was the smartest person Hiram had ever known. Hiram resolved to tell Michael all those things, at a moment when the information would be less distracting.

"Now what, Pap?" Michael asked.

The neat stack of brown clay balls sat beside the basin of still water.

"You think this is going to be admissible in court, do you?" Erasmus Green howled. "Hell, I might even wish we still lived in a world where you could tell a judge you wrote the names of suspects on sheets of paper and a bowl of water told you which one was guilty, but we don't, and you know it!"

"In a moment," Hiram told his son, "you're going to place all the balls into the water. Once they're all in, there's a charm that you're going to pronounce. I don't have it written down, so I will whisper the words into your ear. At various points, while you are reciting, you must cross yourself. Do you know how to make the sign of the cross?"

Michael crossed himself, sloppily.

Hiram nodded to encourage him. "Forehead, chest, left shoulder, right shoulder. Make the movements slowly and deliberately, at a consistent speed. Touch your head or your chest with two fingers at each of the four spots."

"Even if you do find out I'm guilty," Erasmus Green

shouted, "all you can do with that information is kill me! Are you prepared to do that, Woolley?"

Hiram stood beside Michael, placing his left hand on Michael's left shoulder. "Place the clay into the water. One ball at a time, careful not to damage them. Set them in a ring around the bottom of the bucket, equidistant from each other."

Michael followed his instructions.

"I will say the charm now," Hiram said. "Repeat it after me, and every time I squeeze your shoulder, make a good, slow, deliberate cross. I'll cross myself, too, if you want to follow my timing." He smiled. "I've done this before. And keep a prayer in your heart."

Michael smiled. It was the gentlest smile Hiram could ever remember seeing on his face.

"I conjure thou earth and clay," Hiram began, with Michael following, and both of them making the multiple crosses required by the charm. "By the Father, the Son, and the Holy Ghost, amen, and by all the holy names of God: Messias, Soter, Emanuel, Sabaoth, Adonay, Panthon, Kraton, Anefeto, Theos, Otheas, Eley, Eloy. And by all the names of God, by heaven and earth and by the sea and all that be in them and by our blessed virgin Mary, the mother of our savior Jesus Christ, and by his humility, and by the holy company of heaven, and by all that God created in heaven, in earth, and in the sea or other places, and by the virtues and merits of all the saints, that amongst those names hidden within the clay, his name or her name which hath murdered Lloyd Preece may be known by him who liveth and reigneth, world without end, amen."

The words left Hiram deep in thought. Sabaoth, Grandma Hettie had once told him, was the host of heaven, which meant the stars. She had wanted Hiram to read the almanac as she did, and know the stars, but he had fallen far short. Perhaps Michael would now master that lore that Hiram hadn't been able to. Was the holy company of heaven also the stars? The stars tonight were scuffed by a web of clouds, but still mostly visible. Standing beneath a moonless sky dominated by Hercules and the Summer Triangle, with the reigning star Jupiter in Scorpio low on the southern horizon, it felt to Hiram that it was. His craft seemed, for a moment, of a piece with Lloyd Preece's and Grandma Hettie's and Michael's.

And what were the "other places" in which God might have created things, that were not in earth, heaven, or the sea? In outer space? Even Michael's hero Buck Rogers seemed to be part of the field of energy in which Hiram felt himself floating.

Erasmus Green snorted. "Horseshit."

Michael hissed out a breath. "Kind of a silly answer, from a man who takes his clothes off and turns into a deer for fun."

"Not for fun, son. Never for mere fun."

"Now what?" Michael asked.

"We stay here and watch." Hiram clapped him on the shoulder. "You did well. If the divination works, the name of the guilty party will unfold first."

"If?"

"You have a chaste and sober mind. It'll work."

"Pap, you're the best man I know."

Michael's words took Hiram by surprise, and he found he had to clear his throat. "You're a better man than I am, son. Smarter and braver, and you have a lion's heart."

"Dad, you help the poor. You're like the Shadow, only not creepy, and you hate to hurt people, even bad guys."

"Son . . ."

"No, listen. I have a hard time believing the charms wouldn't work for you just because you have completely ordinary feelings of attraction for a woman. I mean, if you were a liar, or a violent man, or greedy, and you said those reasons stopped the craft from working, I'd understand, but . . . finding a girl attractive? Man, we *all* fail *that* test."

Green was silent, sitting tied in the bed of the truck. He'd stopped his jeers, and Hiram felt relief.

Hiram's eyes stung slightly. He pointed at the water, where the first of the clay balls was just beginning to open.

"Are you rooting for anyone?" Michael asked.

"I'm rooting for God to do justice," Hiram said, "and for us to receive mercy."

Michael threw an arm around Hiram's shoulders and squeezed him in a sideways hug. "That's my Pap."

The first of the names was free of the clay and unrolling. It was considerably in advance of the other names.

"As soon as you can read it, do so," Hiram said.

Michael leaned in. "Diana Artemis."

Hiram felt as if he had been clubbed in the head.

Erasmus Green exhaled loudly. "Well, hell, I told you so." His whole demeanor had changed.

"It was the money," Michael said. "All this weirdness going on, and in the end, he was just killed for the money."

Hiram closed his eyes, a bit of his heart broken. "Love of money is the root of all evil, Paul says."

Bang! A loud shot echoed through the wide river canyon. Boots crunched in the dirt. Sheriff Jack Del Rose's voice called out, "Nobody move! You're under arrest!"

Hiram charged forward and kicked the lantern across the dirt, snuffing out the light. "Michael, run!"

Chapter Twenty-Two

MEN SURGED FORWARD, FLASHLIGHTS LICKING LIGHT across Hiram, the truck, Green, and the wash basin. Hiram heard his son break through the brush; he was following orders. Thank the Lord Divine for that.

Jack Del Rose sauntered into the streams of light, a pump-action shotgun in hand. "Where'd your boy go?"

Hiram shrugged.

Del Rose raised one hand and made a circular gesture. Men broke free to search the weeds, willows, and junipers of the riverbank.

"You have to let me go, Del Rose," Erasmus Green said.

"Oh? I *have* to?"

"It's the Tithe." Green looked southward, toward Scorpio. "You know it is."

Hiram's blood ran cold. The clay balls had seemed to vindicate Del Rose, but now the sheriff and the banker were talking as if they were in cahoots. Had Hiram's lustful thoughts corrupted Michael's attempt at divination?

"I know what day it is," Del Rose said. "On the other hand, there's some criminal activity going on here."

"I've been kidnapped." Green's face twisted into a skeptical curl. "Are you suggesting I'm a party to my own kidnapping?"

"I've been sitting out there listening for a spell," Del Rose said. "I heard more than just about kidnapping."

Two deputies, including Russ Pickens, emerged from the brush, holding shotguns and flashlights. One shook his head at the sheriff. Jack Del Rose tucked his shotgun into the crook of his elbow and slowly lit a cigarette.

"Whatever you heard, Del Rose," Green said, "you know I'm the victim here."

Del Rose squinted, if it was possible, even tighter. "What I know is that you and your prongheads took it upon yourself to try to run down Lloyd Preece's daughter. What was it, Erasmus? Your own wealth not enough for you, so you had to try to get Preece's? Or was it that you weren't satisfied taking his leadership position in the herd, you had to take his daughter, too?"

Green hesitated. "We shouldn't talk about this in front of Woolley."

Sheriff Del Rose raised his shotgun to point it at Hiram's chest, and laughed. "Him? He don't matter. Couple hours, he won't know anything ever again."

Hiram's breath caught in his chest.

Should he flee? But he didn't know where Michael had run off to. If the sheriff found Michael, he and his men might take their anger out on his son. He wished his charms were working—on a better day, he'd trust his chi-rho medallion to protect him from the shotgun.

"All I ever did was to try to help people who needed it," Hiram said softly. "Adelaide Tunstall asked for a ride out of town, and Erasmus Green and his . . . creatures . . . attacked us."

"Creatures, huh?" Del Rose took a draw on his cigarette. "You see, the problem with helping the victims of the world is that there's always someone who made 'em the victims. And you go around doing good works, you're going to step on *that* fellow's toes."

"We didn't want her to leave!" Green kicked uselessly with his heel at the bed of the truck. "Once we knew Lloyd was dead, we didn't know how much she knew, and we didn't want her running off to San Francisco or El Paso and writing a book or something."

Del Rose grunted laughter. "*My Life Among the Shapechangers of Grand County*, huh? I guess I can understand not wanting that kind of thing getting out."

Green was staring at the southern sky. "So let me go!"

"The problem, though, is that I don't think you really see how this works." The sheriff took a drag on his cigarette. "You see, Green, you're the prey. Always have been. Always will be."

"No." Green stared. "It's not like that."

"Yeah, it is." Del Rose shrugged. "You get something out of being the prey, I know. You're rich and fat, and you get the joy of the Tithe and all, and most of you survive the experience. And you know, I think that must be the most exciting thing, isn't it?"

"Surviving?" Green asked.

"Surviving while the man next to you dies. You run in a herd, knowing that someone's going down, someone's going to get eaten, and then when it isn't you, that's a thrill. Isn't it? Come on, you can admit it."

Green said nothing. His lip trembled.

"I was in the war," Del Rose said. "Best day in the damn affair was the day I was going over the trench between two of my buddies. Andy on the left and Lemuel on the right, I'd known 'em both for months, and we charged at the same time as some Jerry on the other side let loose with his machinegun. Andy's head exploded. Lemuel took so many rounds through his gut, it sawed him right in half. Me, I was untouched."

Hiram felt sick.

"When I sat down to mess that night," Del Rose continued, "you might guess the loss of my buddies had put me off my feed, but it hadn't. I had appetite. I was the one who had *lived*. I ate for all three of us, and I was so excited, I couldn't sleep a wink." He dropped his cigarette butt to the sand and ground it underneath his heel. "So I think I know how you feel."

"I was in the war," Hiram said, "and I fought alongside a buddy named Yas. The day Yas died was one of the worst days of my life."

Del Rose shrugged. "Sounds like you might be prey, too."

"I need to run tonight," Green begged. "Please."

Del Rose nodded. "The prey runs. But the prey doesn't decide." He nodded to one of the deputies, who stepped forward and cut Green free. The banker, shirt undone, pants dust-stained, wobbled to the edge of the Double-A's bed and dropped to his feet on the ground. Del Rose handed his shotgun off to one of his men. He also gave the man his hat. "The mistake you made, you moron, was to take matters into your own hands by going after Preece's daughter. You understand who decides now, don't you?"

Green chafed at his wrists, restoring circulation. "The pack."

"Correct." The sheriff leapt on Green, throwing the smaller man to the ground.

Hiram bit his lip. The sheriff's hands and face changed, becoming hairier, longer, more powerful.

Del Rose shoved Green's head into the dirt with his left paw while he ripped through the man's pants with the claws of his right. The banker struggled. Del Rose growled.

The beast-sheriff then sank his fangs into Green's leg. The banker shrieked in pain.

Hiram blinked, and a second later, Del Rose was drawing back, standing up, wiping blood from his sneering, human face. His hands had fingers again, and ordinary nails, with no sign that they had ever been different.

Green staggered back to his feet, pants torn to shreds. His face radiated pain and fear, but mostly surprise.

Del Rose retrieved his hat and shotgun. "You know which deer the pack hunters usually cull out, don't you, Green?"

Bent over, clutching his leg, Green hyperventilated too hard to answer.

Hiram answered for him. "The old. The sick. The wounded."

Jack Del Rose laughed, showing bloody teeth. "The beet farmer from Lehi finally puts a point on the board. Good luck with the Tithe tonight, Green."

Erasmus Green stumbled into the darkness. It was too dark to see, but Hiram heard the clack of hooves on rock, and a long shape brushed through the greenery. Green might have staggered away as a man, but was he fleeing now in a more monstrous shape?

"Now you," the sheriff said, turning to Hiram. "You heard how sensitive we are to information about our . . . local culture . . . getting out."

"You're not arresting me."

"An arrested man gets free, eventually. Maybe wins at trial, maybe does his time and then gets released. So you can understand that it's nothing personal when I tell you that I have to kill you now."

Hiram took a step backward reflexively, and felt the hard barrel of a firearm in his lower back. A shotgun, probably. A hand reached into his pocket and took his revolver.

"Just toss that," Del Rose said.

Hiram heard a grunt and then the soft, distant thump of his weapon falling to the sand.

He might have to rely on the chi-rho medallion, whether he liked it or not.

"Aw, look." Del Rose leaned over the bucket and began to pull out strips of paper. "Davison Rock. Earl Bill Clay." He looked up to meet Hiram's gaze. "Two of my favorite people. I like 'em both so much, we rounded them up this evening. Worried about what they might know too, you understand. Adelaide, I know her. And look, here I am in your little mud puddle!"

Hiram said nothing.

"I couldn't make out everything you said to your boy," Del Rose continued. "I guess that was by design. But do you seriously think this tub of water was going to tell you who killed Lloyd Preece?"

Del Rose's tone was one of challenge. Did Del Rose know who the killer was? Was it him, and the divination had failed? Was that why he had failed to investigate the crime? Another mystery: the sheriff hadn't read Diana Artemis's name—did that mean he hadn't seen the slip? Did Michael have it?

"It *did* tell me," Hiram said.

"Uh huh. And what did you plan to do about it?"

"I *had* planned to turn the killer in to you," Hiram said. "I see now that that wouldn't have worked out so well."

"Not for you."

Hiram was about to leap into action—

"Wait!" The voice belonged to the bishop, Gudmund Gudmundson. He walked into the light, hands up to show that they were empty. Light from flashlights glinted on the silver knife at his belt.

"Why, Bishop," Sheriff Del Rose said slowly, "I don't think you want to interfere in a sheriff department investigation, do you?"

For a brief moment, Hiram imagined that the bishop had come to rescue him. But then the sheriff laughed, the bishop laughed, and the deputies laughed hardest of all.

Bishop Gudmundson was with the sheriff.

Hiram tried to think. Had the clay balls failed? Could the sheriff have killed Lloyd Preece? He certainly could have been at the cabin that night. Would the bishop want Preece's money—Gudmundson was a handyman, and the thought of thousands or tens of thousands of dollars in a neat stack of bearer bonds might be irresistible to him. But Gudmundson and Preece had been friends.

How did the knives connect the two men? They were Jupiter knives. What did that mean about the

Tithe, and the chase that seemed poised to happen tonight?

The clay balls had identified Diana Artemis as Lloyd Preece's killer. What would they have said if Michael had rolled the name Gudmund Gudmundson into a ball?

"You don't need to die, Brother Woolley," the bishop said.

Hiram swallowed, finding his throat very dry. "Are you offering me a chance to join you? Become a were-deer?" He couldn't imagine how else these men could possibly let him live.

Gudmundson laughed. "The sheriff and I do not transform into deer. But you are not totally wrong; I will let you run with the Tithe. If you run, you may escape and survive. On the other hand, I think it's likely the pack will be trying to kill *you* in particular. I know *I* will be."

"You're a wolf," Hiram said.

Gudmundson nodded. "All men, in their hearts, are either predator or prey."

"Not all," Hiram countered. "Some men are servants."

That made the Bishop laugh. "Servant? Prey? That's the same thing."

Hiram felt ill at the bishop's words. "Why kill me in the Tithe? Is it more fun?"

"A hunter may kill at any time," Gudmundson said. "But a kill on the Tithe gives power. And the more powerful the prey, the more power the predator gains."

"Eat the heart of your enemy to become brave like him?" Hiram shook his head. "I think you've read too many cheap novels."

The bishop smiled. "I would very much like to eat your heart, Hiram Woolley."

Hiram looked away south, at Scorpio, with its second blue heart of Jupiter. Michael's explanation of the astrology came back to him. "The Tithe occurs on a night when Jupiter crosses into a new decan. About three times a year, you run out onto the Monument and chase someone down?"

"About," the bishop said. "Jupiter is sometimes in retrograde, and the timing isn't strictly regular."

"And how do you reconcile that with holding the pulpit in your ward?" Hiram asked. "How do you reconcile this astrology and paganism with going to church on Sunday and telling people not to cuss, drink, or cheat on their taxes?" He realized that, on some level, he was asking *himself* the question, so he tried to focus. "How do you hunt for power, and then tell people to turn the other cheek?"

Gudmundson chuckled. "You have been listening to the antlered prey, I see. I do not hunt for power, Brother Woolley. I kill in the Tithe, and that act of killing brings me power. I bear the Jupiter Knife because I am First of Fang, as Lloyd Preece was First of Hoof, and the power of Jupiter flows through me on the Tithe, empowering all those who hunt. I am very good at killing, Brother Woolley. I killed many men, in deer-form and out of it, before I became First and it fell to me to have a Jupiter Knife forged. Jupiter is my god, and he makes me strong. He gives me command, over the hunters, and over others."

Hiram shook his head. "You think Jupiter made you bishop?"

Gudmundson stepped closer, his smile widening and a queer light coming to his eye. "The *kill* made me bishop. There is no power in the act of running.

There is power in life, for those who retain it, and wealth. There is power in death, for those who master it, and command. And besides ... Jacob says that it's okay to seek *riches*, if you seek with the intent to do good. As long as I intend to do good, shouldn't I be able to seek *power*? Power to organize a new well for Rex Whittle, or help those hobos in their truck, or plan a move for Bobette Smothers?"

Still no sign of Michael. Hiram hoped his son had escaped. Michael was resourceful and smart, and as long as the sheriff's men didn't capture him right away, the young man would easily make it home.

And would they follow him there?

"I've heard some sick perversions of what priesthood office is supposed to be." Hiram felt the weight of his clasp knife in his pocket. "That's about the sickest. You're going to spend eternity in a deep, dark hell, Gudmundson, and I think you know it."

"I know that's what *your* god would say," Gudmundson answered, his voice light. "*My* god says something different."

Hiram struck quickly. Snatching his knife out of his pocket, he leaped at the bishop. He was no wrestler, and would much rather punch a man in the jaw than come to any closer quarters than that, but if he was going to get out of this bind, he was going to need a shield. First of Fang sounded like a good shield to have, so Hiram grabbed the bishop's wrist and yanked the man close toward him, spinning him around and slapping his blade to the bishop's neck.

The sheriff's men stopped, shotguns raised. Looking at their faces, Hiram saw the two deputies, Russ Pickens and other one, as well as the ranch hand

Clem. All poor men, but all strong. Through the bishop's shirt, too, Hiram felt the muscles of a hard worker, or a warrior.

"You ever seen a man chewed to bits by shotguns before, Woolley?" Del Rose asked.

"Yes." Hiram backed slowly away, pulling the bishop with him. He had been unable to wound the deer-men while in deer-form or even when they appeared as naked humans—would these men be invulnerable as well? He had a brief vision of Gudmundson shrugging off Hiram's blade, and then laughing while the sheriff and his men blasted Hiram into oblivion with their pump-actions. *Please, Lord Divine, however this plays out, let Michael be far away from this camp.* "I've seen such things and worse."

"Mr. Woolley," the bishop said, "I look forward to this Tithe very much. Please promise me you'll fight this hard on the hunt, to protect your life and the life of your son."

"You don't have my son," Hiram said.

"We will, though," the bishop told him.

Hiram pressed the knife harder into Gudmundson's throat. "Unlikely. You and I are going to get into that car and drive away." He called his words in a loud voice, so that Michael might be able to hear him, and join him in a getaway car. "But first, you tell me why you killed Lloyd Preece. It wasn't the Tithe yet, so you didn't kill him for the hunt. You murdered him for something else."

It was a guess, based mostly on how much pride Gudmundson exhibited in being a killer, and the fact that they had failed to include his name in the clay balls, but all Hiram's investigation had consisted of nothing but guesses.

Gudmundson laughed softly. "Yes, I killed him. While he was strong as a deer, he was weak as a man. He thought we were going too far with the *Blót*, though we weren't doing anything that hadn't been done before. Preece lost his nerve, that's all, and he wanted to leave. The man was never sentimental about his daughter, but something about having three grandchildren made him decide it was time to take his money and get out."

"And you didn't like that?" Hiram stepped slowly to the driver's side of the truck. How was he going to keep Gudmundson prisoner and drive at the same time? He had a hard time imagining keeping a driver in line with his clasp knife.

"Erasmus Green and his friends should have consulted with us first, but you're right, I didn't like it. No one . . . ever . . . leaves."

"Pretty brazen of you to run your hunt out of Wolfe Ranch," Hiram said. It was a guess. "Was it just too irresistible? Did you just want to put your presence right onto the map, announce what you were doing to everyone in the world with eyes to see?"

Gudmundson laughed. "The Wolfe who owned Wolfe Ranch had nothing to do with us. Pure coincidence. The Turnbows are even more ignorant of what we do—they only know that every few months, wild beasts eat some of their cattle."

Abruptly, the bishop grabbed Hiram's hands and pulled, forcing Hiram's knife, hard, into the flesh of the bishop's own neck. In the same motion, far too fast for Hiram to react, he spun and hurled Hiram against the side of the Double-A. Hiram hit the truck with his forehead and fell to the ground.

In the dancing flashlights and through spinning vision, Hiram saw the bishop toss the clasp knife away. His flesh was unmarked, and the bishop walked away.

Hiram tried to rise, but men crowded around him, boots kicked him in the chest and gut, and shotgun butts slammed over and over into his face.

Chapter Twenty-Three

MICHAEL HATED LEAVING HIS PAP IN THE HANDS of their enemies, but better one person get away than both get caught. Slipping between two men who were looking the wrong way at the wrong time, he dove into the Colorado, letting the dark water whisk him away.

The water was cold and fast, but Michael was a good swimmer. After a couple of minutes of riding the brisk current, he crawled out into a stand of willows, squeezed the worst of the water out of his clothing, and then crept back up to where the sheriff and his men held his pap.

Squatting in thick bushes that smelled like evergreen, Michael heard Gudmund Gudmundson confess to the murder. That seemed like good news for Diana, though she was apparently involved in the crime somehow. Or had the clay balls been simply hocus pocus?

Michael ground his teeth and bit back angry cries as the men attacked his father and beat him until he lay still.

"Do we just tie the farmer up at the Bloomers?" Sheriff Del Rose asked.

"The farmer runs the Tithe tonight," Gudmund Gudmundson said. "Don't worry, we'll kill him at the arch, but there's no power in it if he doesn't run."

When the men drove off, taking his pap with them, Michael crept out of the brush. He was cold and wet and shaken.

Michael picked up the fallen lantern. He didn't have much time. The *Blót* was happening that night. And his pap was going to be an unwilling participant.

"We figured you'd come back," a voice whispered from the darkness. That voice, Michael knew it. It was the crossword deputy, Pickens.

Another man chuckled. "You was right. Looks like it's gonna be a full hunt tonight. Lots of prey. Lots of meat."

Michael didn't pause. Turning and seeing the two men, he hurled the lantern into the deputy's face. Pickens cursed.

Michael charged to the truck, started it—fortunately, the engine was still reasonably warm—and then ground gears to get her moving. He tried to get the truck into second, but the clutch was sticking. He glanced into the rearview mirror and saw, lit by the red of his taillights, two faces from a nightmare.

The shaggy hair of the hunched creatures looked like blood in the lights. The long faces of wolves hung over the huge, muscular bodies, and they reached out with human hands tipped with vicious nails.

A third figure leapt out of the darkness and onto the side of the truck. Michael had the window rolled down, and the stink of the thing washed over him.

It was the musk and bestial stench of something not animal and not human, but a mixture of both.

A werewolf. Michael was looking into the face of something that should only exist in movies. There was no fossil record. There was no science to this thing. It shouldn't exist.

But it did.

The wolf man snapped its head into the truck. Michael threw himself forward, accidentally jerking the wheel to the right. The truck plunged into the reeds and water plants growing on the embankment.

Michael was forced to slam on the brakes. That whipped the wolf man off the car, and it rolled across the ground, in a swirl of dust motes and shredded grasses that floated in the Double-A's headlights. From behind, howls and growls from the two werewolves running toward him.

Michael slammed the gas pedal to the floor. He shot forward, and the werewolf dodged aside. Its nails screeched down the side of the truck before it leapt back up on the running boards, on the right side of the car.

"The lamen!" Michael called out. He wasn't shouting to the wolf-monster, but to himself. "I have a lamen, in the side door, and it's going to protect me. I know it!"

The wolf man grabbed hold of the door with a furry hand tipped with yellow claws.

Michael swiveled in his seat and slammed his right foot into the door. Just as the wolf-man pulled the door open, Michael kicked it wide, and the monster swung out away from the car, yelping, and struck a tree, bouncing to the ground.

"Take that for empirical evidence!" Michael bellowed.

Michael stomped on the pedal again, and the engine screamed. He shifted into second, then third, bouncing over the rough dirt, and jarring himself and the truck, as it rumbled over washboard in the road.

His wheels spun in the gravel, he felt the backside fishtail, and again, he found himself riding the edge of the road, reeds thwacking the grill, and the murky smell of the water crowding in. He tried to steer back on the road, but something was wrong, one of his wheels felt flat, or something was weighting down the back.

Instead of driving faster on the bad tire, Michael applied the brakes until he stopped. A cloud of road dust rolled into his headlights.

Michael turned, grabbed the shotgun, and exited the cab. He left the engine going, and it ticked, running hot, in the hot night.

Lightning flashed above, and the air was electrified, all that energy in the clouds, but not a single drop of rain falling. The wind gusted.

There was a flashlight in the toolbox. He could get it and check the tires, but what would he do if he had a flat? He couldn't very well try and fix it with werewolves prowling in the night. Hunting him. Was this the hunt? He didn't know for sure, but they didn't talk about the Tithe, or the *Blót*, happening alongside the Colorado River. It was definitely up in the Monument, near the arch, near where Jimmy Udall had been killed.

The river gurgled below, a rush of water, he could hear over the sound of the Double-A's engine.

A growl from the back. A lupine face rose above the truck bed, over massive, bunched shoulders. One half of the monster was lit indirectly by the headlights, glowing yellow, and half was lit by the taillights, glowing red.

One of the wolves had gotten in the back. That must have been the weight Michael had felt.

He raised the muzzle of the shotgun. "I know you're human. I know you can understand me. And I know I can fill you full of buckshot before you can spring. There's only one reason you're still alive right now."

The wolf growled harder, a line of saliva dropping from its exposed fangs.

"Your people have my pap," Michael said. "And I have you. If you move, I'll blow your damn head off."

Michael winced. He couldn't keep cussing. He didn't want the magic to stop working for him.

The werewolf leaped toward him.

Michael squeezed both triggers. Fire erupted from the weapon in long lines of light that instantly disappeared but left impressions on Michael's eyes. The gunpowder stink followed.

The wolf-man went rolling backward, whining like a beaten dog. He'd hurt the thing. Or had he? Did he need silver? Pap said he'd shot the deer-men and the bullets hadn't done much. But even if the shot didn't pierce the wolf-man's skin, that was a lot of kinetic energy for a creature to absorb.

Michael wheeled. Opening the door, he grabbed two new shells, expecting to be torn to pieces from moment to moment.

He spun, broke open the action, and burned his fingers on the used shells. He shoved fresh ammunition in and snapped the shotgun closed.

The werewolf was up, near the darkness of the river, snarling and slavering.

Michael wasn't going to outrun this thing. And he wasn't going to be able to kill him with the shotgun. But he could still take care of the beast. He hurried forward, getting as close as he could to the beast, ready to spring.

The beast-man rose.

Michael, still advancing, took aim and squeezed both triggers. The shot sent the wolf-man into the river, and the current snatched him away.

Michael hurried back to the truck to reload it. The night had become suddenly still, the only sounds the tick of the engine and the burble of the river. He loaded the shotgun and then circled the truck to check the tires, and they were all full. He must have simply lost his nerve driving across the reeds at the very edge of the road.

Back in the cab, he drove off, got into second gear, and stayed there, avoiding potholes and ruts as best he could.

He felt shaky and overexcited—that was the adrenaline in his system. His mind racing, he blinked the sweat from his eyes. "Okay, let's go through where we're at." He tittered, sounding hysterical.

"This is what crazy people do . . . they talk to themselves. But talking is better than stewing in silence. Pap is in trouble, all right, but they want him for the hunt. Then again, Gudmundson cut Lloyd Preece's throat. No, that was a murder, not a hunt. Not the Tithe. Aren't the werewolves supposed to be in London? Why must you lie to me, Hollywood?"

He laughed again. Crazy or not, his soliloquy was helping him.

"So, they're going to take Pap up to the Monument

for the hunt, which is probably going to happen any time now. The arch. They were going to kill him at the Bloomers, the bishop said. Only, he won't be running alone. Davison Rock and Preacher Bill will be with him. The wolves hunt the prey, and that's the *Blót*. And why?"

This was an old ritual hunt, from Iceland. Hunting was a powerful and terrifying thing, it brought food to families, but a lot of a hunter's success depended on luck. How did people try and control their lives, when luck could save them or kill them? They added ritual to give that luck meaning. In a ritual hunt, they acted out the best possible circumstances, and so, they used the fantasy to help with their uncertain reality. They pretended to catch the deer, so they could catch real deer. Or they re-enacted the stories of their greatest hunters, so they could have the luck of those great hunters.

Didn't they?

"But why do the deer run?" In an ordinary hunt, the deer ran because they were chased. They had no choice. But these deer-men, Erasmus Green's herd, seemed to be choosing to participate.

Green, at the hotel, had said that the Tithe brought him money.

That didn't feel right.

How does one win the hunt? By surviving, if you were a deer-man, and by slaughtering, if you were one of the wolves. The deer-men he could name—Erasmus Green, Leon Björnsson, Banjo Johansson—all were wealthy business owners. Banjo's mercantile was doing well, unlike the Moab Co-op. The ones who knew ran the race and prospered. Like Lloyd Preece, who was the wealthiest man in the area.

Michael checked for more wolves following him. None were, or at least not that he could see.

"So I survived the *Blót*. Does that mean I'm going to be lucky and rich? Let's hope so. Michael, my friend, you need help."

Here was the crux of the problem. "The Sheriff is a wolf, as are his deputies. So I can't go to the local police. Gudmund and Clem are wolves too, and Gudmund is the son of a bitch in charge. Sorry, God. Go easy on me. I meant it literally."

Michael's mind continued to work. "If I drove up to Green River, not much there in the way of policemen, and my best bet is Price. I know Carbon County has a sheriff." Michael knew at least one friendly policeman in Helper, too, and likely some miners who would help. But that was what, a couple hours up, and a couple hours back? By that time, his pap might wind up inside a werewolf's belly.

"No, this is happening tonight, the eclipse, Jupiter moving into the third decan of Scorpio. Which brings us to those knives, I bet Gudmund's knife is going to be full of power tonight. Green said that one of the hunters was going to be damn near impossible to avoid during this Tithe. Yeah, that would be Gudmundson, the First of Fang."

Michael had Lloyd Preece's knife, the murder weapon. He'd picked it up when Preacher Bill had dropped it, wanting to examine it, and he'd tucked it up inside the seat of the Double-A. He hadn't told his father because he didn't want to implicate his pap in obstruction of justice, which sounded very serious.

The knives were supposed to channel power, but not just to anyone. They worked for someone born

at the right time. Gudmundson's knife was inscribed
with the sign of Aquarius. Michael knew from reading
the tables of star-data that Jupiter would next enter
Aquarius in December 1937. Since Jupiter was in a
constellation for roughly a year, he could count back
twelve years at a time and see if he, Michael, was
born when Jupiter was in Aquarius. He could do this
rough math while driving, no problem, and if he got
a near hit, he could confirm the precise dates when
he stopped.

Subtract twelve and you got 1925, when Michael
was already seven. Which made the next year of
Aquarius before that about five years before Michael's
birth. Nuts.

What about Preece's knife? Preece had the sign
of Taurus on his knife, and Michael started to feel
excited. Jupiter entered Taurus next in 1940, didn't it?
Which meant that maybe it was in Taurus in 1918,
when Michael was born, so the dead man's knife
would be good for Michael?

Michael stopped the truck. With the engine trembling beneath him, parked by the side of the road,
he leafed through the widow's astrology book by the
glow of a flashlight.

And found that, on his birthday, Jupiter had been in
the constellation Gemini. A near miss, only a couple
of months away from Taurus, but still a miss.

The knives were going to be of no use.

He needed an ally.

He put the truck in gear again. "Okay, Michael,
who do you know in Moab who could help, and who
isn't already a prisoner?"

It was a short list. Almost every one of the men he'd

met was part of the *Blót*. Howard Balsley wasn't, but how could Michael find him? And would Balsley help him? And what could he do? Rex Whittle was way out in Spanish Valley, and didn't seem especially formidable.

"The Udalls might want justice for the men who killed their kid," Michael said. Of course, they might not. He and his pap hadn't thrown Moses Udall's name into the clay balls—what if he was out running in the Tithe? And even if he wasn't, Michael wasn't sure Moses could be much help.

Michael was left with only one person, and that person definitely wasn't part of the hunt. Because Diana Artemis might have helped kill Lloyd Preece, but she was a woman, and according to Erasmus Green, that meant that she couldn't participate.

She was a flimflam artist, no doubt. On the other hand, she had useful books, and, as Pap had said, just because she had lied about the falling-sickness cure, it didn't follow that she had *no* craft. And what had Erasmus Green said about her—that she'd do anything for money?

Would she help rescue Pap for money?

Michael hit the intersection and stopped. To the right was the road to the Monument. To his left was the dirt strip that led into town.

A plan formed in his head. He turned left. In the end, he would only need Diana to drive. Surely, she could drive. If she knew any actual magical spells, so much the better.

Sudden summer rain slashed across the truck's windshield, and lightning cracked over Moab.

And if she turned into a wolf? Well, he had the shotgun and the bolt-action rifle. He'd shoot her and run.

Chapter Twenty-Four

HIRAM REGAINED CONSCIOUSNESS IN A SPLASH OF cold water. His vision swam. His cheek was chafed by sandpaper.

"You can call it Jupiter all you like," a man's voice snarled. "I know Satan when I see him! An asshole is an asshole is an asshole! Tell your master, Kaiser Roosevelt, that I said hello!"

"Surely, this is some kind of practical joke," a second voice said. This voice, too, belonged to a man, but it had a refined, vaguely English sound to it. "I pledged at university, I understand. What do you need me to do, run a mile naked or drink a gallon of milk or something?"

Not sandpaper, but sand.

Hiram raised his head and then dropped it again from the sheer weight. His temples throbbed.

Rain battered him.

He knew the voices. He tried to focus and think through what he was hearing. He saw blurred charcoal smudges moving against deeper darkness.

"This is no joke." This voice was definitely Gudmund

Gudmundson's. Who had killed Lloyd Preece, and was now going to kill Hiram. "You are not being hazed. This is a hunt, in deadly earnest, and I do not think that you, Mr. Rock, are going to survive."

Rock. Davison Rock. The uranium prospector. With the fancy accent.

And the other voice belonged to the Reverend Majestic, Earl Bill Clay.

Boots. Hiram saw the toes of boots, pointed at him and barely visible in dim light. He was outside, and lying on sand. On the Monument somewhere? Was this how the Tithe began?

It was raining. Lightning flashed, illuminating a distant red ridge.

Hiram hoped that Michael was still at large. He didn't want Michael to rescue him, he wanted Michael to run far away. To Harvard or Stanford, or some other magical place where smart young women would talk to Michael, and he would become a geologist or a botanist or lawyer or spaceship pilot or whatever he wanted. Where no one would ever threaten Michael's life, by means natural or supernatural.

If Hiram lived through the night, Mahonri Young was going to kill him.

Means natural and supernatural. Gudmundson had killed Lloyd Preece with his own knife. That struck Hiram now as a curious detail, as grays and silver began to bleed into his vision and the men about him slowly took visible form. Why with Preece's own knife? It seemed too specific to be a coincidence.

Was it a symbolic act? Was Gudmundson showing that the First of Fang was superior to the First of Hoof by using Preece's own talisman?

Or, more likely, was it a tactical choice? Had Preece been vulnerable to his own weapon, in a way that he wasn't vulnerable to others? Hiram hadn't been able to pierce the bishop's skin with his clasp knife—maybe the Jupiter knife overcame the wolf-man's thick hide?

Or by surprising him and taking his weapon away, had Gudmundson removed from Preece the power effectively to strike back?

The knives channeled the strength of Jupiter into the men for whom they were made. They were not unlike Hiram's ring in that regard, which channeled the power of Saturn. But where Saturn gave dreams and insight and melancholy, Jupiter gave wealth and rule.

Wealth to the deer-men.

Rule to the werewolves.

Had Lloyd Preece's Jupiter knife made him wealthy? Was the possession of a Jupiter dagger what made Gudmundson as strong as he was? Hiram was well-muscled from his farming work, but Gudmundson had flung him about like a rag doll.

"My name's not really Rock," the prospector said. "I call myself that to avoid attracting attention, especially when I'm out here on the Monument all by myself, but my name is Rockefeller."

A round of raucous laughter. Lightning flashed. The rain was already letting up, brief summer storm that it had been. Hiram saw men's legs in a circle, surrounding him, Rock, and the Reverend Majestic.

"As in John D. Rockefeller?" Rock pressed.

More laughter.

"Listen," Rock continued, "I don't understand the game here, but what I'm telling you is that my family has money. A lot of money. I have cousins who could pay for Moab with the cash they have lying around the house. They'll bluster, and you'll have to duck a P.I. or two, but I'm confident they'll ransom me. I can give you an address, just have one of your number here send a telegraph from Salt Lake—"

"Shut up," Jack Del Rose said.

"I don't think this one is hardly even worth the eating." That voice belonged to Clem.

"Any man is worth the eating," Bishop Gudmundson said. "Some men are merely appetizers, and others are a main course."

"You Satanic bastards!" the Reverend Majestic yelled. "I've eaten bigger shits than you for breakfast!"

"Yeah," Del Rose said. "From the smell, I'm guessing you eat shit for breakfast on a regular basis."

Hiram tried to stand, had a hard time balancing, and was hauled roughly to his feet by hands he couldn't see. He patted down his pockets—he had the bogus Uranus cross, the chi-rho medallion, and his Zippo lighter, but that was all. His revolver and even his clasp knife lay on the desert floor.

It took him a moment to remember that he had given the bloodstone to Michael.

How far was he from his truck?

"You're remembering now that we threw your gun away," Del Rose told him. Was it the starlight, or were the man's teeth elongating?

There were perhaps fifteen men surrounding Hiram. He saw Clem and Russ and the sheriff, and other faces he knew but couldn't connect to a name. Was this the entire . . . Fang? Pack? Or might there be more of them? Hiram took a deep breath to steady himself and found Gudmundson in the circle.

"It's not too late to repent," Hiram said. "God is still ready to extend His mercy to you."

"God-Yahweh is ready." The bishop smiled. "And God-Hiram Woolley. But God-Jupiter and God-Gudmund Gudmundson have something entirely different from mercy on their minds."

"Satan!" Clay punched Russ Pickens in the jaw. It took the man by surprise and knocked him down, but then the others pushed Clay back and filled in their ranks.

Hiram nodded. "You were warned."

"So were you," Gudmundson said.

The crowd parted at one end and Hiram saw that he stood atop a knuckle of stone that looked dark brown in the light, but was probably a shade of red. A steep, sandy path now firmed up by the brief squall led down through the parted men to a flat-bottomed canyon, spotted with dark blotches that might be prickly pear. On the far side of the canyon rose a ridge of stone, and standing on that ridge, Hiram saw a herd of deer-men. They were tall and man-shaped, and antlers rose above their heads they turned toward the men. Was he fooling himself, or did he see a crumpled ear on one of the beasts?

"The hunt begins when your feet touch the stone of that ridge," Gudmundson said.

"Where are we?" Hiram asked.

"We're on the Monument," Davison Rock said. "I've seen this rock before." He pointed toward the horizon with both hands, in two different directions. "My campsite is that way. The Schoolmarm's Bloomers, if you know the Monument at all, are over there." The Bloomers were beyond the ridge full of deer-monsters.

Gudmundson was quiet.

"If we refuse to go, you'll just kill us here," Hiram guessed.

He heard the *snicker-snack* of a bolt action. "Damn straight," Jack Del Rose said.

"You'll lose the magic of the hunt," Hiram pointed out.

"The magic of the kill," Gudmundson corrected him. "And you will lose the chance, however slim, of escape."

"The deer are faster than we are," Hiram said.

"Hard to be the slow ones in the herd." Gudmundson shrugged.

"There's poor little Erasmus Green." Clem laughed, a guttural, ugly sound. "He'll be slowed a bit on account of his leg."

"And Jimmy Udall?" Hiram asked. The boy had died eight months earlier, which would have been about the time of a hunt. "Did you have to hobble him, too, or were you able to run down a ten-year-old boy without that advantage?"

Gudmundson nodded. "An accident. Jimmy was taken in the Tithe. It happens. The Fang takes not only from the Hoof, but from all the animals that live on the Monument, including man. Jimmy should have been home earlier that night."

"Is that what you said at this funeral?" And was this why Jimmy was a ghost—his own trusted bishop had murdered him, and then presided over his graveside service.

"Angering me will not make me go any easier on you, cunning man." Gudmund Gudmundson shrugged out of his shirt, pulling his arms through the sleeves. Starlight glinted off a hard wall of chest muscles.

Other men kicked off their boots and began unbuckling belts.

Hiram started walking. Reverend Clay followed with him immediately, stumping from his good foot to his bad with surprising alacrity, and then Davison Rock—Rockefeller—jogged to catch up.

Behind them, Hiram heard the sound of chanting. It was a chant unlike any he'd heard before, part wail and part rhythmic surge, the two parts seeming to intersect modally at some impossible, inaudible point, and then blend to give the impression of hungry hunting beasts, surging forward in a pack.

He shuddered. Sweat chilled on his lower back.

"This is all pantomime, right?" the prospector asked. "Play-acting? They're letting us go, but now we're supposed to have . . . learned a lesson or something. Received a warning. What was it, did I trespass on someone's land? This isn't about that child, is it? No one thinks I killed Jimmy Udall, or Lloyd Preece?"

"No one thinks you killed anyone," Hiram said. "I'm betting the cult thinks you know more than you do. Maybe because you were out here in February, or perhaps from just talking to me."

Which would make Davison Rock's death Hiram's fault.

"False words and shallow comfort," the Reverend grumbled. "He isn't innocent. We're all murderers, every man jack of us. I was born a murderer and a whoremonger and a cheater at cards, and so were you two. The only path to redemption is the spiritual and saving grace of money! O Benjamin Franklin, rain down thy grace upon us!"

"Cult?" Rock bellowed. "Cult?"

"Cult," Hiram said. "Human sacrifice cult. Cannibals, I think, or at least, sort of cannibals. Who did you believe we were dealing with, the Kiwanis?"

He regretted that jibe immediately. It was the sort of thing Michael would say, but it wasn't really Hiram's style of wit.

He hoped Michael was safe.

Rockefeller snorted several times, high pitched sounds that reminded Hiram of a horse. "Don't these people realize what my family is capable of? The Pinkertons will be down here by tomorrow morning!"

Hiram looked back over his shoulder and saw the silhouettes of the hunters standing on the knuckle of rock. "We need to locate weapons as soon as we can," he said. "And we need to stake out a defensible position. I'd love to find a high overhang, or a ledge with only one entrance, or better still a cave, but I don't know this place and it's dark. How about it, Mr. Rock . . . Rockefeller, that is? You've been prospecting around here for months. Do you know any good places to hunker down and defend ourselves?"

"Hunker down?" Rockefeller squeaked. "Are you serious? This is a nightmare. This can't be happening."

Preacher Bill laughed heartily. "We shall prevail, my friends, for a 'Sceptre shall rise out of Israel, and shall smite the corners of Moab, and destroy all the children of Sheth.'"

An actual Bible verse coming from the Reverend Majestic made Hiram smile, but he couldn't let himself get sidetracked. "Davison, Bill, come on, is there a cave where we can hide?"

"Who do you think I am?" Rockefeller squealed.

Hiram, slightly ahead of the other two, was just

about to step onto the sandstone of the ridge. Above him, he saw deer antlers tremble in anticipation. He wished he had a gun, but if the hunters were as hard to injure as the deer-men...a few bullets might not make a difference.

"If we can block ourselves in somewhere, find some dry wood, maybe we can get a fire started," Hiram suggested. "Fire is a good basic countermagic, most dark and evil things are afraid of fire." But had the hunters left him the Zippo because they had no fear of the power of fire? Hiram climbed the ridge, and the Revered Majestic climbed with him. "I don't suppose you have a stashed gasoline can anywhere near here? I'd give a lot for a gallon of gasoline."

Rockefeller stopped. "No. I'm calling this bluff. I stop right here, this is all nonsense, and I'm not going to budge. They can ransom me and I'm sure my family will pay, but I'm not going to give into this ridiculous story, because you're only saying these terrible things to make me afraid. You're one of them, Mr. Woolley."

Hiram looked down at Rockefeller's feet; the man was standing on stone.

He looked up again, at the men on the knuckle of rock. They were all naked now, and they swayed back and forth and shuddered, the gesture reminding Hiram uncomfortably of the seizures he sometimes experienced. Then one of them leaped forward—was it Clem? hard to tell in the poor light—and when he hit the ground, streaking down the rock, he was no longer a man. A wolf-like head sprouted above massive, shaggy shoulders, and long limbs ending in claws. From a distance, he seemed as large as a pony.

"Run!" Hiram shouted.

Earl Bill Clay burst into a shuffling lope, sometimes touching the stone with his hands as he stooped to rush up the rock.

"No!" Rockefeller spread his arms defiantly. "What are they going to do to me, really?"

The single wolf-man slammed into Davison Rock from behind, dragging the prospector instantly to the ground and then falling on his throat. Rockefeller screamed once and then fell silent, but jets of blood squirted up and his booted feet kicked at the sand repeatedly.

"Asshole should've been paying more attention!" Preacher Bill shouted.

He and Hiram ran.

Fear put steel rods into Hiram's legs and stoked a fire in his tinder. He charged up the hill, cresting the top of the stone just in time to see large deer-monsters bolting away in various directions. One of the slowest, and the last to vanish from his sight, was red-skinned and scabby, and bled from a wound in its hindquarters.

Hiram shot a glance back, not to see Rockefeller's remains, but to look at the werewolves. They were leaping off the knuckle of rock now, one at a time, each leap beginning in the shape of a man but hitting the base of the boulder in monstrous form.

"Satan!" Reverend Clay roared. "Get thee behind me!"

Hiram was inclined to agree, but he wasn't willing to waste his breath.

He ran.

He tried to stick to the ridge, because it would be harder to follow them, and he tried to get out of sight immediately. How good was the wolves' sense of smell? If it was as good as the smell of a natural wolf, then maybe any effort to hide tracks was a complete waste. He also tried to aim for the Bloomers, as Davison Rock had indicated the way. If nothing else, once he got there, he would have some ability to orient himself. Also, the arch itself stood on high ground, and might be at least somewhat defensible.

At the end of the ridge, one deer-man, startled by Hiram and Earl Bill Clay crashing into its hiding space, leaped away. Hiram turned up a crack between two cliff faces, struggling to step over a thicket of prickly pear in the dark without spearing himself. Clay made the same climb and then stopped, panting.

"Need...drink," he huffed, and then produced a fifth of some spirituous alcohol from inside his ragged coat.

At the same moment, leaping down off the ridge forty feet away, came two of the wolf-beasts. They were bigger than ponies, they were the size of small horses, and though they were shaped like men, they ran on all fours. The one in front threw back his head and howled.

Hiram snatched the bottle from the Reverend.

"Satan!" Clay objected.

The wolves leaped forward.

Hiram sloshed alcohol across the bed of cactus, and all the dried foliage packed in around it, and then touched his Zippo to it.

Fire burst up in a thin line. The wolves hesitated, back slightly away, and Hiram shouted a Biblical fire verse.

The fire vamped higher, and one wolf whined.

"This way!" Hiram grabbed Clay's sleeve and dragged him up the narrow crack.

They climbed a stair built of choking boulders and flash flood jetsam, up toward the top of the mesa. Looking down, Hiram saw five or six of the wolves, pacing anxiously as they waited for the fire to die down.

He wasn't going to be able to do that all night. He had enough spirits in the bottle, he guessed, to light one more fire. Memories of Helper came back to him. Fire had saved them then. It could save them again, but he'd have to be clever.

Emerging at the height of the crack, he ran along the top of a cliff. He wasn't looking for ways down, but for holes to hide in. A cave or a dead-end canyon, preferably with wood he could use to start a real defensive fire.

How would the hunt end? Did the pack transform back into men at dawn, and slink away home? Would the law of this bloody hunt somehow guarantee that, in the future, Fang and Hoof would leave Hiram alone?

A strange little thought tickled him: did the fact that Hiram was participating as the hunted mean that his survival would bring prosperity to his farm? Or was that only true for herders, and not for farmers?

It was after all, Fang and Hoof, and not Fang and Beet.

"There." Hiram stopped and pointed.

"Give me back my liquor." Clay was out of breath, and leaned over onto his knees to spit stringy saliva onto the rocks.

"No."

"You're as bad as one of them children of Sheth."

Hiram grinned. "You know that's not right."

Preacher Bill smiled back. "Naw, probably just a Mormon."

Hiram saw a canyon that looked as if it dead-ended. The walls were steep; he couldn't be certain in the darkness, but he thought he was seeing a narrow box canyon. But what he knew for sure was that there were trees. Wood for a fire.

"I'm going down there," Hiram said. "You want to come with me, do. We'll use your spirits and start a bonfire."

"That'll attract the monsters." Ironic that the insane preacher was more clear-eyed about the nature of what chased them than the scientist had been.

"And be a weapon." A stand of cottonwoods grew close enough to the cliff at this point that Hiram could touch them. He reached out, grabbed a trunk, and began to shimmy down.

"Satan, you can kiss my ass," the Reverend Majestic Earl Bill Clay grumbled again, and jumped.

Chapter Twenty-Five

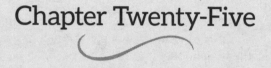

MICHAEL PULLED UNDER THE COTTONWOOD IN front of Edna's house and parked. The rain had stopped, though lightning still flashed out over the Colorado River and thunder rolled across the valley. He took the shotgun with him, just in case. The spread of the shot would be more effective than the single round of the rifle, if one of the wolf-beasts showed up. Had the wolf-man he'd knocked into the Colorado drowned? Probably wishful thinking.

Could they die by drowning, or fire?

He also tucked Lloyd Preece's Jupiter knife into the pocket of his pants.

With the gun in his hand, he crunched across the gravel. He'd go right to Diana, see if she attacked him, and then try and get her to help. Maybe the clay balls had been wrong. More wishful thinking.

He knocked quietly on her door. He knew it wouldn't look good to the neighbors for the widow to have men showing up on her doorstep late on a Sunday

night. There were already enough rumors about her
floating through town. Only, they weren't rumors,
apparently. But Michael couldn't very well accuse her
of prostitution—or murder—when he needed her help.
First things first.

Michael knocked louder.

Diana opened the door in a silk gown, covering
what could only be her night-time outfit. A word
slithered through Michael's head, a silken word he'd
never actually had occasion to say out loud. *Lingerie.*
He was looking at her lingerie.

She gave him a crooked grin. "It's kind of late to
drop by, Michael. Where is your father? Or should
I not ask?"

"We're in trouble," Michael said. "I need your help,
desperately."

She stepped aside.

She was barefoot. One foot had toenails painted red.
The other was a wooden foot, or the approximation
of one; the white wood, maybe pine, met the white
flesh of her stump below her knee. A strap connected
the false leg to her real one.

Michael went in, and suddenly felt silly carrying
the shotgun.

"I like a man who comes to my house prepared to
do battle," the widow quipped.

"Sorry about this. Like I said, there's trouble. I
feel terrible coming this late, but there's no one else
I can trust."

"I'm certainly glad you feel you can trust me." She
motioned to the couch where his father had sat the
other times they'd visited the widow.

Diana took her chair. As she sat, the lingerie moved

around her body in interesting ways. "Tell me what's going on. Does it have anything to do with Adelaide's abrupt departure?"

"It's all connected."

Diana held a wine glass, half full. A bottle stood on the table. "Would you like a drink?"

He was thirsty beyond belief, and there was no plumbing in her little house ... and suddenly, he found himself asking what Hiram Woolley would do, if he were here. He wouldn't drink the wine. Would he ask the widow to put more clothes on? But maybe that would be impolite. Plus, the sight of Diana Artemis in this state of near-undress would probably have knocked Hiram Woolley unconscious immediately. Or if not, it certainly would have left him unable to speak. "No, I'm fine. Diana, how much do you know about this town and the men in it?"

She smiled wryly. "I know a great deal about the men." Her eyes seemed a bit fuzzy, and there was a bit of a slur to her speech. Was she drunk?

"There's a cult. There's a hunt." Michael swallowed, and told her what he knew, about the deer-men, the wolf-men, and the *Blót*.

That smile grew even wider on her face with every word. "This sounds like the movie showing at the Ides. Are you sure you aren't trying to pull my leg?" She lifted her left leg and flexed her toes. "You'll want to pull this one. The other one would come off, *tout suite*."

She hit those last words hard, with a full seductive French accent. Hearing the language of *ooh la la* wasn't going to help Michael keep a chaste and sober mind. Neither would the smooth skin of her leg.

Michael looked at the floor. "I wish I was."

"And so you and I will charge out into the desert to save your father from this hunt?" she asked with a laugh.

Michael felt the situation coming unraveled. "I don't have anywhere else to turn. I can't go to the sheriff. He's one of them."

She swirled the wine in her glass. "Yes, it would be hard to trust anyone, once you learn that everyone is wearing a mask. I too wear a mask." She gestured to her candles, the bookshelves, and the rest of her room. "This is all a mask. But people believe. They want to believe."

"I was skeptical for a long time," Michael admitted. "But I have proof. Or at least, reasons to believe." He set the shotgun to the side and retrieved the Jupiter knife he'd stolen from the Reverend Majestic. "This has power."

She raised her eyebrows at him. "This knife has given you reasons to believe?"

Michael shook his head, feeling confused. "Things I've seen have given me reason. This may give me power, but I can't use it. I'm born the wrong year. I don't suppose you were born the same year as Lloyd Preece, were you?"

She laughed out loud.

"Or twelve or twenty-four years later," Michael added, feeling himself blush. "Or thirty-six. Approximately. When Jupiter was in Taurus."

She chuckled at his befuddlement. "Why should I help you on this dangerous mission, with *loups-garous* rampaging the countryside?" She paused. "I heard a legend like this before, the Beast of Gévaudan. As a young girl, I might have shivered at the tale. But now, I am no longer a child. But you, you are young. The world has its mysteries for you still."

Michael frowned. "I need to know if you'll help. If not, I have to leave."

More laughter. "Because time is of the essence. That is what they would say in a novel or a movie. Yes, a grand rescue. But surely, you don't expect me to dress and help you."

"You helped before," Michael said. "You helped Addy Tunstall when Pap asked you to."

"That?" Diana waved a hand. "That served my interests. I've been interested in the Preeces' fortune for a long time now. I came to Moab in the first place because I met Lloyd Preece and learned that he was single and wealthy. He and I have been good friends for a long time."

She kept her gaze on him.

Michael couldn't meet those smoky green eyes. It felt as if he'd been punched in the gut. He was afraid of how it would go, but he only had one last card to play. "You were there, at the cabin, the night Mr. Preece was murdered." The clay balls had said she was involved.

The widow sighed. "I'm not going to confess to you, Michael. As I told your father, I do things because I'm paid to do them, and I find that an entirely reasonable approach to living my life."

"So Mr. Preece paid you to be there?" Michael asked.

"Oh, he paid me. Many of the men in this town do. But no, there was another gentleman involved in that transaction." She shrugged. "You're a smart boy. You can piece it together, I think."

Michael's mind whirled. This encounter was not going the way he'd expected. "Bishop Gudmundson. He paid you to make sure you were there, at the Preece homestead, with Preece. You were the bait. In that way, you helped kill him."

She looked at him, eyes glittering.

"But why would you do that, if Lloyd was your... uh, source of money?" Michael felt his own eyes widened. "You learned Lloyd was planning to leave. That source of cash had dried up, so at least you could get paid one last time for helping kill him. Wow, that's... you're... cold."

Was she unburdening her soul before she killed Michael? Or was she now planning to leave town, and negotiating for one last payment on the way out?

But the confession, or hint of confession, seemed to have come to an end. "Would you like to know how I lost my leg?" she asked.

Michael was a little afraid to find out. He nodded anyway.

She continued in the quiet. "I met a man, this was in Denver, a few years back. He said he loved me, but they all say that. They love me. I'm beautiful. I have grown accustomed to the game, and I could recite the encounters, line for line, before they happen. There are monsters in this world, Michael, but they don't need to sprout fangs or horns. Men are monsters enough in their own skin."

Michael moved his hand to the shotgun.

"This man in Denver wasn't the only gentleman in my life. My occupation, my trade, requires I see many men. He grew jealous. He chased me, on a night like this, when the moon was new and hidden. I hid in a barn, while he raged, looking for me. I got away, but stepped on a rusty nail in the process. They had to take the leg." She paused to sip her wine. "At first I thought that would be end of my trade, but fortunately I was mistaken. Men's interest in me generally lapses about mid-thigh. As long as I was complete, from mid-thigh to my forehead, I could continue my occupation unimpaired."

Michael felt sick.

"If I were to go with you," Diana said, "there is a chance I would lose more than a leg. Almost certainly, I would have to leave town and never come back again. I do things for money, Michael. Do you have money to pay me for my services?"

He didn't. "I guess you must be even more disappointed than the rest of them that there was no stolen bank silver hidden in Lloyd's cabin."

Mercifully, now that Diana had revealed her true colors, his lust was abating. She was bad news.

Diana shrugged. "Lloyd had money, it just wasn't from a bank robbery, it was from ranching. And it wasn't in a pot of silver."

"It was in bearer bonds," Michael said. "I saw one. Addy had it. We figured that she went back to her dad's cabin to look for the rest."

"*I* went to his cabin to look for them, and couldn't find them. Not with the little clue Adelaide had. What was it her father said all the time? *Oui*. There's a fortune to be had in a man's good opinion of himself. I don't know what that means. Do you? Or maybe it wasn't a clue it all. Maybe it was the desperate plea of a man who wanted to be admired, disguised as self-deprecating humor."

Michael stood, shotgun in hand. "It was a mistake coming here."

"Probably, but you did get to see me in my nightie." She touched the wine glass to her lips, rubbing it there.

The sick feeling in his stomach deepened. "I'm going."

He left the house, walked to the truck, and stowed the shotgun in the front seat. The houses were all dark, the town fast asleep.

Her perfume lingered on his clothes, and Michael wished he could take a shower. Diana didn't kill Preece, but she'd been instrumental in his death. And she'd done it for money. If only they'd added Gudmund Gudmundson's name to the clay balls. He bet both bits of clay would have melted away simultaneously. Gudmundson paid her to make sure Preece was in his cabin. She'd left, and Gudmundson had probably walked right in.

Diana was Preece's mistress, and Gudmundson was his best friend. They were in the bishopric together. Lloyd Preece had never had a chance.

Michael looked up at the stars. Constellations peeped bright and visible around the edges of storm clouds. He found Scorpio, the scorpion, a troublesome sign, full of passion and power. It was a water sign, and it flowed into open spaces, and filled cracks.

Diana was like that, flowing into Moab, providing false insight into the mysteries of the universe for the women, providing other services for the men. But even those were false, counterfeit, temporary, mercenary.

She was a fake, through and through.

Michael missed his father.

"God," Michael started. "I'm in a mess. Me and Pap

are. I know you're probably surprised to be hearing from me. *Thou* art probably surprised. I'm not a very prayerful fellow, but that . . . maybe it will change. Thou have . . . you've protected me, and you've protected Pap, over and over. We're out here, trying to do your work."

That was true, no matter how odd it seemed. Helping the poor, they did that all the time, but their true calling was to deal with the evil outside the scope of normal human affairs. Michael was a part of that now.

Michael could go alone to the Monument, but the thought frightened him. He'd survived one encounter alone with the werewolves, but he didn't think he'd get that lucky again. He wanted someone else to drive, leaving his hands free to shoot. And he didn't think anyone else in town would even begin to take his story seriously.

Michael gripped his chi-rho amulet. "I don't know the Bible as well as my father, and I'm learning the stars, but they aren't telling me much. I need a burning bush. Can you give a poor Navajo boy a break? You haven't been very kind to the Navajo in general, Lord, but maybe you can make an exception for me?"

What did he expect? One of the roses in Edna Whatever's lawn to burst into flames? Or a mysterious voice to come booming out of the night sky? Michael wasn't certain, but he waited.

He felt himself wanting to curse this God and his sky. He wished he had told Diana what he really thought of her and her cynicism. He could go back, but that wouldn't do any good, and time was slipping away from him.

He'd been inside Lloyd Preece's cabin. Was that where the bearer bonds were? It seemed likely. Putting them in Erasmus Green's bank wouldn't be a good way to keep them secret from the rest of the herd.

There's a fortune to be had in a man's good opinion of himself.

What did that mean? Did it mean anything at all? Preece had loved the hunt. Had he stuffed the bearer bonds inside one of the mounted animal heads in his cabin? Up the big elk's nose? But surely, Addy and Diana would have looked there.

But still . . . Addy knew that her father had bearer bonds, and she thought he would have hidden them at his cabin. She hadn't found them herself, but that didn't make her wrong.

Michael threw himself into the Double-A and drove away, fast.

Chapter Twenty-Six

HIRAM SCRAMBLED DOWN THE COTTONWOOD QUICKLY and reached the ground shortly after the Revered Majestic stood up again.

"That didn't hurt your feet?" Hiram asked.

"The left foot, yes." Earl Bill Clay's voice was calm, and his face, at least what Hiram could see of it in the darkness, was relatively sane. "I haven't felt anything in my right foot for some time."

Hiram pushed himself into a fast lope, heading up the wash toward where he'd seen the trees. The sand under his feet was dry, and the cloud cover overhead was nearly gone, though he still saw the play of lightning on the horizon. He couldn't shake the feeling that he'd seen this place before, but southeastern Utah had ten thousand arroyos, and in the dark, they all looked the same. "What does 'some time' mean? A week? A month?"

"Forty years in the wilderness," Clay mumbled. "So am I Joshua, about to cross into the promised land?

Or Moses, to be buried on the sacred mountain? Or Jesus, to be crucified?"

"Or Earl Bill Clay," Hiram said, "who should probably have a doctor look at his foot."

"I don't look at it myself. Why should I? It doesn't bother me."

"You don't look at your foot?"

"I last took my boots off in nineteen hundred and thirty. What year is this?"

Hiram shook his head, thinking of the smell of rot that surrounded the desert preacher. "When you do take the boots off, I don't want to be present. But after you've given both your feet a good wash, maybe in rubbing alcohol, you might need to show them to a doctor."

"Satan!" Clay shouted. "Get thee behind me, Satan!"

"I'm just worried about your health," Hiram said.

"Sataaaaaaaan!"

Hiram looked where Clay was pointing, and saw two wolf-beasts down the canyon behind them. A thicket of scrub brush bunched around the base of a living cottonwood tree and along a fallen cottonwood trunk lay nearby—it would do. Fortunately, thanks to a sandstone overhang above, the wood was dry as paper. It was also split by age and weather into a bouquet of shavings and sheets that would make great natural tinder.

Hiram sloshed the remaining spirits onto the fallen tree and hit it with his Zippo. Flame sprang up from the wood.

"Noooo!" Preacher Bill wailed.

Hiram wheeled, expecting to see the wolves falling upon him, and instead saw the Revered Majestic staring bleakly at the flames.

"The liquor," he whimpered.

The wolves had moved only slightly closer. Where there had been two of them, there were now six.

The wood of the tree had taken fire, but only barely. Hiram tried to force Diana Artemis from his mind, and the very effort made her seem more important and central than ever. It wasn't that she was beautiful, it was that she was...alive. Energetic. Responsive. She stimulated his imagination, despite the fact that he knew she was at least in part a fraud.

Or possibly *because* of that fact?

She had helped kill Lloyd Preece in some way. For all Hiram knew, she had slit his throat herself.

The thought was a bucket of cold water on Hiram's burning desire, and his thoughts snapped into focus again.

"If I be a man of God," he shouted, quoting Elijah in the Book of Kings, "then let fire come down from heaven!"

Fire didn't drop from the sky, but the fire that had already taken root in the fallen wood exploded in volume and intensity.

"Amen, Brother Hiram!" Clay shouted.

"Throw more wood on!" Hiram yelled to him.

The preacher stumbled to obey, and Hiram seized a branch of the fallen tree. The end of it connected to the trunk was in flames, but the tapering length of it was still free of fire. It looked something like a flaming baseball bat, if slightly curved.

Hiram wrenched the branch from the trunk and turned to face the wolves.

The canyon was narrow in this stretch, only fifteen feet across. With the fallen tree on fire, about half the canyon was blocked by flame. A bold man might run and jump over the fire, so Hiram could only hope that the men in half-wolf form had enough animal instinct to be held back. If Hiram himself could then defend the remaining seven feet of open canyon with a brand, he could keep wolf-men from coming around and attacking him from behind.

Assuming he was right to think he was in a box canyon, since he hadn't had the time to thoroughly confirm that perception.

And how long did he have to hold out? Hiram looked at the sky, hoping to get a sense of how much time had passed since sunset, and saw something surprising.

The Schoolmarm's Bloomers.

He'd been trying to reach this place, but he'd had no idea he was so close. He *had* been in this wash before; this was where he had come looking for the ghost of Jimmy Udall. Jimmy who had been killed in the Tithe eight months earlier. The Tithe was a recurring hunt that took place on the Monument—did it always take place around the Bloomers?

Six wolf-men crept toward Hiram on their hind legs, muzzles nosing at the air and claws groping before them. He stood in the gap, flaming tree to his right and stone wall to his left, and raised the brand in his fist. Hiram prayed in his heart that both fires would last long enough. What he said out loud was, "I will send a fire on Magog, and among them that dwell carelessly in the isles."

The flame in his hand burned brighter, but it definitely meant that the wood was being consumed. And that he was in his right mind again.

Two of the man-wolves slunk ahead, attempting to dash between Hiram and the canyon wall. Hiram stepped forward to meet them, swinging the flaming brand to close the space. The burning tip struck one of the wolves on the snout, sending up a shower of sparks. The monsters yelped and piled on top of each other trying to back away, but that gave Hiram not a moment's rest—two of the remaining wolf-men threw themselves at the other corner, close to the fire.

Hiram swung again, and struck one of the beasts in the chest. It was the second wolf-man, though, and not the foremost.

The monster in front got through.

Hiram spun. Was the end here already? He tried to back against the stone wall, but he could already hear the wolves charging him from behind, even as he committed with the impetus of his body's motion to trying to keep the one that had slipped through from killing Preacher Bill.

The Revered Majestic cowered, dropped a branch that he had been dragging to throw onto the fire. The wolf leaped—

Hiram expected to feel teeth dig into the back of his neck—

he swung his burning club and struck the wolf in his ribs with all his might. The beast missed his attack, flew a yard to the side, and landed in the fire. With a howl that seemed to be an animal noise wrapped around a high-pitched human cuss-word, the wolf-man rolled out of the fire, on the far side, and fled into the night.

The skin on the back of Hiram's neck prickled. How had he not been killed by the other werewolves?

He spun about, still expecting a fanged wall of hairy death to take him at any second, and saw the five monsters, standing at bay beyond the fire in a loose semicircle. They whimpered, and looked at a figure standing between them and Hiram.

A boy in a frayed and oversized jacket, who held his arms up to the sky, revealing rows of circular bite marks.

Jimmy Udall.

The wolf-men whined.

Hiram stepped forward, holding his torch away from the specter; not that he thought the fire would harm the ghost, but he didn't want it to feel threatened or insulted.

"You're Jimmy Udall," Hiram said. "I know who killed you. I'll see that justice is done."

The boy nodded without smiling, then slowly faded from view.

But what justice could Hiram possibly bring to the Fang when it was about to tear him to pieces?

Preacher Bill dumped an armload of wood at Hiram's feet. "More!" Hiram barked. "And more on the burning log, and connect them! We need the fire to spread, and block off the canyon entirely!"

How much trouble would Hiram be in if he lit fire to the Monument? Lighting fires in mid-summer in such a dry place was not the best idea. He imagined Bishop Smith overriding John Wells and going straight to excommunication and prison for Hiram Woolley.

Hiram wished he had a better option.

He kicked some of the wood into place, shouting more fire verses and willing the fire to spread faster.

The wolf-beasts had disappeared into the canyons, which Hiram didn't find reassuring. The flames licked along the new branches, and in a few short minutes, the wall of fire stretched entirely across the canyon. Hiram dragged more brush wood out onto the fire— the nearest grove was entirely stripped of usable wood now, short of having an ax to chop down the living cottonwood, and Hiram eyed the trembling dark masses farther up the canyon that represented more trees, junipers and cottonwoods.

Preacher Bill panted, leaning with one hand against the canyon's rock wall.

"Can you get more wood?" Hiram asked.

"Acacia wood, five cubits long and five cubits wide?" Clay snapped. "Not that I know what a goddamn cubit is. Satan can kiss my ass, regardless, him and the rest of the National Recovery Administration with him!"

Hiram would get the wood, then. But could he keep the fire burning until dawn? And if he did, would that matter?

Howling in the canyon on the other side of the fire stopped him. Seconds later, a deer-man came leaping into view. It was moving slower than Hiram would have expected, and its bounds were wobbly, as if one of its legs were injured. Only when it drew close enough to be lit by the fire, and then reared back in panic at the flames themselves, did Hiram see the monster's scabby red skin.

Erasmus Green.

The banker-turned-deer-beast stopped on the other side of the fire, shying back and rearing up. He scrabbled with large hooves at the red rock on the side of the canyon, looking for purchase, and couldn't find any.

Werewolves appeared in the depths of the canyon.

"Green!" Hiram called out. "Jump the fire!"

The deer-monster made a desperate shrieking noise and reared back again. The man-wolves rushed forward, roaring and snapping at the air with slavering jaws.

The fire worked on the pack, and it worked on the

herd, too, and now it meant that Erasmus Green was trapped. Hiram struggled with this realization in his heart. Erasmus Green might deserve punishment—he had certainly tried to attack Adelaide Tunstall and her family, for instance. And more broadly, he was a member of a single cult, the Fang and Hoof, that killed. And Green had kept the secrets of that cult.

On the other hand, Green himself hadn't killed anyone. Not Lloyd Preece, not Jimmy Udall.

And it was Hiram who had captured and inter-rogated him, and because Hiram had done so, Jack Del Rose had wounded the banker in the leg. And probably because the banker had been injured, he was now cornered against Hiram's fire.

Erasmus Green had made his own bed to some degree, but he didn't deserve to die.

And if he died now, it would be Hiram's fault. Like Davison Rockefeller.

Hiram touched his chi-rho amulet. "Lo, I see four men loose, walking in the midst of the fire, and they have no hurt." He leaped across the flames himself, feeling a wave of heat strike his face and wrists as he did so.

The werewolves raced soundlessly toward him, and toward Green. Hiram had no time; he stepped away from the panicked beast-man to get a better angle, and then he charged it. He waved his flaming branch and yelled, "They have no hurt!"

He slapped the brand against the deer's flank.

Erasmus Green burst across the line of the fire, kicking the flaming wood in all directions.

Hiram stared at the deer's hindquarters as he bounded up the box canyon. Hiram had saved the banker, but he had destroyed his own defensive wall.

Hiram slipped and fell to his knees. He dropped the brand, which lay beside him on the sand. He struggled to regain his footing and stand, but the sand was soft and deep, and yielded to his Redwing Harvesters so that he had a hard time getting any purchase.

"Roosevelt!"

The Reverend Majestic Earl Bill Clay lurched past Hiram. He held his own flaming brand above his head, and he swung it in a full circle like a bullroarer. The trail of sparks and the imprint of the light on Hiram's eyes made the preacher seem to have a halo of fire and he charged the wolves.

"Sataaaaaaaaan!"

Hiram finally got his fingers wrapped around his torch and kicked himself to his feet. He turned in time to see two wolves tear the preacher down to the ground. One had its jaws clamped on Clay's throat, which cut his screaming short. The other tore at his boot, and as the preacher hit the sand, silenced forever, the wolf tore the boot from his foot—

revealing bones.

In the light of his shattered wall of fire, Hiram saw a mass of black rot that was the preacher's ankle. The rot swarmed with maggots, which must be the only reason Earl Bill Clay hadn't died weeks or maybe months ago, because naked bones protruded from that swollen, festering stump, ending in further black gobbets that had once been toes.

Satan, indeed.

Hiram was alone, his defensive wall broken, but at least for the moment, the wolves were distracted. He turned and ran.

His legs hurt and his breath hammered in his lungs.

The canyon he was in was not a box canyon, after all; at his first sight of the Schoolmarm's Bloomers, he should have remembered that the Bloomers were approachable from below, from the arroyo that Hiram was in. Rounding the corner, cringing at every shadow, Hiram came to the steep but scalable slickrock slope that ascended to the stone arch.

He began to climb, holding his torch.

The other side of the arch, he was certain, was not an impassable cliff. If they had wanted to, why couldn't the pack have come at Hiram from this angle, and attacked him from behind?

Had they been busy chasing the herd instead?

Hiram's leg muscles burned.

Above and to his left, he saw a stone ridge that ran to the base of the promontory on which the Bloomers stood. It was hard to be certain in the darkness—they could be branches instead—but he thought he saw antlers silhouetted against the stars on the height of the ridge. Maybe that was a good sign—maybe it meant that Hiram had stumbled into a passage that was free of the wolf-men, or safe from them.

As he climbed onto the knob of stone on which the Bloomers stood, Hiram heard howling behind him. Turning, he saw half a dozen werewolves slink from the sandy canyon floor onto the lower reaches of the slickrock, and then come padding toward him. They spread out as they came, forming into a fanged horseshoe of menace.

Turning again, Hiram stepped up his pace. His brand began to burn low, and though he muttered more Bible verses at the wood, there was simply nothing left for the fire to burn.

He looked left, seeking a route past and away from the arch, toward where the deer-men stood in apparent impunity. He saw instead two werewolves, blocking off that route.

Through the arch itself, he spotted distant Scorpio, in the south, and within it, the planet Jupiter, staring coldly.

Hiram raced up into the arch—was there a way down the other side?

But beyond the enormous red pillars that were apparently the ankles of the schoolmarm, he saw a short curve before a steep fall, and standing on the curve were more wolves.

He was surrounded.

He had been herded here. Here, where Jimmy Udall had been killed.

Here, under the Monument's great arch.

It was an altar, and he was the intended sacrifice.

His torch sputtered and died.

Chapter Twenty-Seven

MICHAEL DROVE BY HIS AND PAP'S CAMPSITE IN THE hope that his father might be there, cleaning up after the attack, and all the wolf-men and deer-men up in the Monument, chasing each other around. The werewolves were gone, all right, but there was no sign of Hiram.

The headlights showed him the scuffed dirt, the ripped tarpaulins, the shattered lantern, and the sandy blankets, all strewn about along the black water of the Colorado River. His heart hurt, but he had no time to grieve or be afraid.

Dust smoked in his headlights as he pulled into the wide patch of ground in front of the Preece cabin. Carrying the shotgun, Michael climbed onto the back to the truck, opened the toolbox, and fished out the flashlight from on top. Below, from the secret tray, he took a Y-shaped length of witch hazel.

He stuck the rod in his back pocket. Then he started forward, shotgun in his right hand, balanced on the crook of his left arm, flashlight in his left hand.

A shotgun was a nice weapon: not a lot of aiming, just point it in the general direction of what you wanted to shoot and pull the trigger. If something came for him, he'd unload one barrel, then the other. The bolt-action rifle held more bullets in the magazine, but re-loading took longer. With the shotgun, he had two tries before he had to reach for the extra ammo he had poured into his pocket.

The shotgun only knocked the wolf-men and the deer-men down. Maybe that was why Lloyd Preece had been killed with a silver dagger.

Michael opened the screen a crack and then pulled it the rest of the way open with the shotgun's nose.

He didn't rush in. No, in detective novels, you had to slowly work your way into a room, especially a crime scene. The movies might not have the details on the supernatural right, but he trusted his detective novels: *Grey Mask* by Patricia Wentworth, or *Murder Must Advertise* by Dorothy L. Sayers, wouldn't steer him wrong.

Michael didn't call out, though he wanted to. He slowly walked into the cabin, ready for anything.

He could imagine some specter, maybe the ghost of Lloyd Preece, with blood dribbling down his lips, begging for help. No shade rose to harass Michael. No creature of darkness leapt for him. Once inside, he pushed his back against the rough logs of the low-ceilinged structure.

His flashlight threw a circle against the rocks of the fireplace, the logs, glued together with mud plaster, and the rough thicket of the ceiling. A deer pelt on the wall, something else that looked like a wolf belt. An antlered head.

He couldn't think too much of the widow Artemis. He had to get to work, and he had to keep his focus intact. Michael set the flashlight on the windowsill on his right. He aimed the light across to the far wall, to illuminate the front room of the cabin, and send light into the bedroom and the study as well.

Michael felt the sweat drip off his nose. Inside the cabin, it was stifling.

Did Diana sweat with Preece? Did he sweat on her?

"Dammit!" Michael cursed his traitor mind. Then he regretted the profanity. "Lord Divine, help a young man in his hour of need. Take from me these impure thoughts."

That seemed to help.

Michael left the shotgun tilted against the wall beside the window. "There's a fortune to be had in a man's good opinion of himself." It wasn't much of a clue.

It probably wasn't a clue at all.

Michael would have to use craft to find the money.

Michael took out his pocketknife, took the Y-shaped branch, and carefully peeled off all the bark. Then he cut three crosses into the green wood. He then carved the name *Lloyd Preece* into the wood and the word "fortune" followed by three more crosses. He didn't want to find Preece, nor his corpse or his ghost, but only his riches. Depending on the denomination of the bearer bonds, they might only be a few pieces of paper. Or one. Could you have a million-dollar bearer bond? Michael thought it was possible. In any case, you didn't need a big space to hide paper. A loose floorboard? A chunk of adobe? Maybe a rock in the fireplace?

Or Preece might have hidden it somewhere out in the desert, and if so, finding it might take all night.

Michael took the forks of the rod in his hands. "Lord Divine, which prayer should I use? Go easy on me. I'm not a great biblical scholar like my pap."

No verses came to him, but he did think of a hymn. It felt right that he should say some sort of godly words, so he went ahead and sang.

> *God moves in a mysterious way His wonders*
> *   to perform;*
> *He plants His footsteps in the sea and rides*
> *   upon the storm.*

He wasn't sure there was an obvious connection between the song and his need to find Lloyd Preece's hidden treasure. However, in the incantations he'd heard his father recite, the words often seemed to have only an indirect connection with the effect desired.

He only remembered the one verse. Singing it, he liked it, and thought he should learn the other verses and maybe the chords on a guitar. But his more urgent task at hand was to test the divining rod. "Did Germany win the Great War?"

The rod was motionless in his hand. He kept a light hold on it, not clutching it, but letting it nearly dangle, so he could feel any movement. He'd done this with Pap, so doing it without Pap should work just as well.

And this would be his . . . what, fourth? . . . act of magic in the last two days. Michael Yazzie Woolley was becoming a regular magician.

"Did Lloyd Preece keep his money in this room?"

Nothing.

This room, that bed, that was where he and Diana

did it, the evil act, and with how...hot it was, yes, there had been sweat. A lot of it.

Michael felt his eyes burn from his own perspiration. He remembered Diana lifting her leg to show him her painted toes. And that robe, which hardly covered her, and that black lace on her pale skin. Her smoky green eyes. The tumble of her long dark hair. And boy, when she'd unchained that French, it had really been something.

"God, this is not helping me. You created the entire universe, if the Bible has anything to say about it, and took only seven days to do it. Surely, you can help me with my lust."

Michael blew out a breath, sang his verse again, and asked a different question: "Did Lloyd Preece keep his bearer bonds in this room?"

Another thought struck him. He'd been alone with Diana, in her room, that very night. Just the two of them. She'd let him in, had him sit, and she'd sat, drinking her wine which would have lowered her inhibitions.

Nothing from the rod.

Michael squeezed his eyes shut. "Come on, head. I know I'm a mess of hormones, and I'm young, and my urges are strong. But come on, Pap's life is involved."

Again, he reset himself, said the psalm, and was determined to be filled with the pure grace of God. God's saving grace. He didn't ask about silver, that was just town gossip. And it wasn't exactly money. No, it was bearer bonds, and yet the dowsing hadn't worked. He'd try it again. "Did Lloyd Preece keep the fortune meant for his daughter in this room?"

A fortune. Money. If Michael had money, Diana

would've done things with him. He'd been a simple paying customer after all. And he knew she liked him. At least a part of her did. She was an outcast, and so was he, a Navajo with a Mormon father, not your normal joe.

The witch hazel remained still.

Michael was failing when he needed this magic stuff to work. "Well, this is terribly inconvenient. I'm making a poor instrument." He lifted the rod. "Or are you the problem, witch hazel? Is it Witch? Or Miss Hazel?"

Michael walked across to the middle of the room, holding the rod. He waved the rod around with a flourish. "Abracadabra!"

It wasn't just a vaudeville word. According to pap, that word had power, and you could draw a chart using the letters, which could do all sorts of things if you had a chaste and sober mind.

Michael was going to have to give up on that.

"God helps those who help themselves." He tapped the rod against this thigh. "I've done pretty well so far with the magic stuff, but then, I wasn't in an extreme situation, and I wasn't dealing with a beautiful prostitute. I wonder if Mary Magdalene was ginchy like that."

He frowned at himself. "Come on, Michael, enough jokes. This is not a laughing matter."

He'd have to give up and go by himself, his grand plan undone by his untamed mind, and the seductive powers of Diana Artemis. She'd searched the cabin and hadn't found anything. Maybe the money simply wasn't here.

He thought of the clue and said it out loud. "There's

a fortune to be had in a man's good opinion of himself." His mind raced, as he tried to think of what it might mean. And wasn't there where his real power lay? His intellect was a marvelous thing, it helped him remember, it was a tool he could use to deduce the truth, and to solve problems. Someday, and maybe soon, human intellect would launch human bodies off the planet and into the stars.

Already, the human mind was exploring the nature of reality itself, the atomic nature of what seemed so solid. In his musings, he turned.

The witch hazel rod jumped out of his hand and clattered to the floor.

A shiver tickled up the back of Michael's hair.

He stooped and picked up the rod. Rather than asking it questions, should he be dowsing for the money? As he and his father had dowsed for water? Holding the rod loose in his palms again, he turned.

And the rod dipped.

He swung it back the other way—and it dipped in the same place.

It was indicating the study. Michael following the rod, walking into the shadowed study, turning to face each dip as it happened—

and bumped against a wall.

Looking up, he saw a monster and jumped.

But the monster was him, in the study's tall mirror. He saw himself, but where his head should be, he saw the head of a beast, a monster with three faces. Stepping slightly to one side, he realized that a crack in the mirror had caused the effect; by standing in exactly the right spot, he could see his body, with his head replaced by the stone statue on Lloyd Preece's shelf.

He turned and looked at the statue for a moment. Three faces, there it was, in front of them from the start. The three decans of any sign of the zodiac, embodied in a sly bit of art on the rancher's shelf.

His pap had mentioned a diary. There had been dates that were circled but had nothing marked on them. Michael quickly found the diary and flipped it open. October 11, 1934, was circled—that was the night on which Jupiter had entered Scorpio. There would have been a Tithe, and that would have been the night Jimmy Udall died.

Michael felt ill. He should test one more date. What date fell halfway between October 11 and today, June 30? That should be the day when Jupiter entered Scorpio's second face and should also be the day of a hunt.

Michael did some quick math: February 19.

He checked the diary: circled.

Which might have been the date when, according to Davison Rock, the prospector had nearly been run over by a herd of deer on the Monument.

Lloyd Preece had noted the days of the hunt in his calendar. He must have known about Jimmy Udall's death. He might have watched it.

Suddenly, Michael felt a lot less sympathy for the dead rancher, however much the man had wanted to get out.

He needed to get his pap out now, though. The money.

Michael turned and looked at the mirror to which the dowsing rod had led him.

"A man's good opinion of himself." The grin on his face turned into a full-blown smile. Then a memory came to him, standing with Preece, Gudmundson, and Clem, dowsing Rex Whittle's well. Preece had been joking, and he'd said, *You'd be surprised how much time a man like me spends looking into the mirror.*

Michael stuck the hazel rod in his back pocket and retrieved the shotgun. This was probably some kind of crime. What was it Pap said he did, again?

"Dear God," he said out loud, "if I'm barking up the wrong tree, please make the mirror resist my shotgun."

He smashed that mirror into bits with a single blow of the shotgun butt. Inside, tucked between the frame and the backing, was a long, thin leather wallet.

He plucked the wallet out, then hurried back to the flashlight, unlashing the leather thong tying it shut. This was a cowboy's wallet, fifty years old at least. Within the cracked leather sheath were bearer bonds, each worth five hundred dollars. Michael did a quick count: sixty slips of paper, each worth five hundred dollars in cash. Thirty thousand dollars in bearer bonds. Lloyd Preece's fortune.

Michael didn't pause. He tried to put the wallet in his back pocket. It was too thick. He held it pressed up against the shotgun as he snatched up the flashlight and jogged to the Double-A, not even bothering closing the door to Preece's cabin. Michael tossed the hazel rod into the back of the truck before getting into the driver's seat.

Back on the road, Michael took in a deep breath. "Now, I would like to say, for the record, I figured out where the money was. The clue's pretty obvious in hindsight. But yes, God, you get some of the credit. Let's say, twenty percent. Okay, I can go as a high as thirty, but what can you do for me?"

He laughed at that. If God didn't appreciate his sense of humor, Michael was sunk. He patted the wallet on the front seat.

Should he keep some of the money? Set it aside, maybe pay down the mortgage on the farm with it, or buy a second car? Michael was worldly enough to ask himself the question, but he had enough Hiram Woolley in him to know immediately that he couldn't keep any of the cash.

The harder question was: could he spend the money rescuing his father? Didn't the bearer bonds really belong to Addy Tunstall? Michael immediately saw options for rationalization: the money had an occult origin, and came from the death of innocent people, so it was fair game; Hiram and Michael had saved Addy's life by getting her out of town before the deer-men got to her, so she was only returning the favor.

But to hell with that. He was going to rescue his pap, and figure out what he owed Addy Tunstall later.

Michael drove on.

He didn't have to worry about the local police pulling him over for driving too fast. The local police were currently up in the hills, trying to murder his father. He raced at nearly sixty miles per hour through town, which was quiet.

He turned hard and skidded onto the lawn of Edna Whatever's house. God might want Michael to have a chaste and sober mind, but Pap had never said anything about his magic depending on good driving habits.

The sky overhead was clear; a moist wind tried to wrap itself around his neck as Michael hurried up to Diana's bungalow, wallet gripped tightly in both hands. He knocked on the door and called out in a loud voice, "Diana, it's important."

The lights went on in Edna's house, in an upper

room, and the window was thrown open. "What is it? What's the meaning of this?"

Diana came to the door, scowling.

"You want money," Michael said, "and I have it." He lowered his voice and raised Lloyd Preece's wallet, but kept it close to his body so Edna couldn't see it. "I will pay you thirty thousand dollars for your help, but you do what I say, when I say it, and you get the pay day when we're done." The words made him feel magnificent and powerful.

Her scowl turned into a skeptical half-smile. "You know I'll need proof."

Michael took a step back, opened the wallet, and then flicked through the bonds. "I'm not going to let you count it yet. We don't have time. Get in the truck."

"What is it, Diana?" Edna wailed. "What's the meaning of this?"

Diana answered her. "The stars are in an uproar tonight, Edna. Jupiter is expanding all of our horizons." Then to Michael. "Give me five minutes."

"Two minutes. Then I start docking your pay."

Michael walked back to the truck. The crisp night air stung his nose and ears. He got his jacket out from behind the seat, put it on, and slipped the wallet into his inside pocket. He'd imagined thirty thousand dollars would weigh more.

He had the truck backed up and parked neatly on the street when Diana hurried out. She got in and they drove off. She looked as if she were going to ride in the Kentucky Derby; she wore canvas pants, high leather boots, and a tight coat with a vest, which seemed to make her bosom both rise and expand. He wondered how she could breathe.

And he found, to his relief, that he didn't wonder anything else. She sat beside him in the truck, as alluring as ever, and Michael's mind was entirely on the rescue operation.

He smelled a hint of wine beneath the wafting perfume. "How sober are you?" he asked.

"Sober enough to drive. What's your plan?"

He told her.

"Where did you find Preece's money?"

"In the mirror." He cast her a glance. "It seems pretty obvious, in hindsight. A man's good opinion of himself begins in the mirror."

"Damn," she said. "I considered breaking open the mirror, but couldn't really do it with Adelaide there."

"Uh huh," Michael said. "You are the smart one. You know all the things." He passed the turn to Lloyd Preece's cabin and Frenchie's Canyon, then drove over the bridge spanning the Colorado River. "No wonder you outwit all the men." The entrance to the Monument lay on Michael's right, and he took it.

"Not all of them," she said.

"I must admit, I'm not sure what to make of you," Michael said. "You know, I had this idea of, uh, fallen women, and you're not exactly it. You're more . . . uh, complicated. Don't take this the wrong way, but more interesting."

"Jesus liked to spend time with fallen women." Diana Artemis laughed. "There must be *something* interesting about us."

Michael took the roads fast, sliding across the dirt, bouncing over ridges, and then careening down the other side. When he got to the Turnbow Cabin, he didn't stop, but drove up a rough cattle path.

Diana braced herself against the dashboard. "I heard from Lloyd that they used to call this the Wolfe Ranch, before the Turnbow family took it over. I always took *Wolfe* for a family name, but after the revelations of tonight, I'm beginning to think...maybe not."

No point telling her that Gudmundson had already denied that exact connection. Michael kept shifting back and forth between first gear and second as the truck rattled up and down low ridges. "Do you at all feel good about going to rescue my father? I mean, even though it took a big cash reward, do you have some feeling of virtue?"

"Feelings of virtue, like feelings of remorse, are dangerous before the fact," Diana said. "I indulge in both, but I do it afterward, when the men have paid and left. That way, the feelings don't interfere with wise decision-making."

Michael ground his teeth. He'd made a similar calculation about Lloyd Preece's money. "There's some truth in that. But also, I think kindness is what makes us human."

An expanse of slickrock appeared out of the sand, the incline too sharp for the Double-A. Michael stopped the truck.

"I do not know a single mother who would not steal, or prostitute herself, or even kill, if that was the only way to keep her children alive," Diana said. "Kindness is for the rich, Michael Woolley. If you rely on people's greed in this world, you'll get farther."

"Which is what I am doing tonight," he said. "I don't like it."

"You don't have to like life, *mon enfant*. You only have to get through it." She exited the truck.

He directed her to a stone, which they lifted, though she had trouble with her false leg in the sand. She had to go slowly, working her legs in such a way she didn't fall over. They stacked the rocks until they'd fashioned a rough ramp onto the slickrock.

Michael's hands were sweating. On the way back to the truck, he had to joke. "*Mon enfant*? I thought you'd refer to me as *mon ami*."

She laughed and grabbed his hand. "You have a good heart, Michael, if one that's a bit naïve. We can be friends." She hugged him.

"Thanks," he said.

"I'm glad you have money so I can help you, Michael. I do honestly enjoy you. You have a good mind, and that is as rare in this world as kindness." She stepped away and continued to the passenger seat. "I know I'll take the wheel eventually, but I'll let you drive this next part."

He gave the engine gas. The truck tipped up on the ramp, the rocks shifted but didn't spill, and they bounced and jounced and wrestled their way up onto the slickrock. The stone plane was smooth as far as they could see, though they'd have to avoid water traps and sand pits as well as thickets of grasses growing where the desert had collected enough dirt.

Finally, he stopped. He got out, raced around the back, just as she went around the front. In the cab, she released the handbrake and started forward, driving fast. Faster than Michael had.

"You really want to save him," Michael said.

"Of course, I do. I like to earn my pay." She gave him a sizzling smile.

They drove past a blazing stand of trees. The night was too dark for Michael to the see the arch, but he knew they must be close. This was the wash where he and his pap had communicated with the ghost of Jimmy Udall.

Michael gave Diana her orders. "This is it. That fire means pap has to be close. Honk the horn. Flash the lights. Pap will hear the horn, see the lights, and come right to us. I'll go out to guide him in and give him some cover. And if any of the hunters try for you, I'll shoot them. Once Pap comes, we'll jump into the back, and you'll drive off. Deal?"

"Deal."

He climbed out of the truck with a flashlight in one hand and the shotgun in the other. He tried hard not to think about the fact that, at best, firearms seemed to be able to knock the wolf-men down, without injuring them. He carried the bolt-action rifle over his back with the strap across his chest, and he stepped into one of the darkest nights of his life.

Why did they call it a new moon when there wasn't a moon at all?

Chapter Twenty-Eight

"I WILL CONCEDE THIS MUCH TO YOUR WEAKNESS, and to your god of mercy." Gudmund Gudmundson stepped into view. He had been standing outside the arch, on the steep rock slope, and now stood directly beneath it, squarely facing Hiram. Faintly visible in the starlight, his face and expression seemed wolfish to Hiram. He was naked, except for a belt from which hung an empty knife sheath. "I will give you a moment to compose your soul."

In his hand, Gudmundson held his silver dagger.

Behind him, in rings of jagged shadows, came the other wolf-men, shaggy and monstrous.

They were visible because the clouds had all dissipated and the stars shone down on the Monument. In particular—could it possibly be an illusion, or a trick of Hiram's imagination?—Jupiter flooded the Bloomers with its light. Scorpio faded to invisibility in the cool, white, pulsating light of the planet Jupiter, cast horizontally like a web across the red rock.

Hiram shuddered.

A breeze cooled Hiram's head, and he realized that his hat was gone. Somewhere in the chase he had led across the Monument, it must have blown off.

Hiram dropped the useless bit of charcoal that had once been his torch. "Not worried I'll cast a spell, or pull a secret holdout pistol and shoot you?"

Gudmundson shook his head. "That's not your kind of magic, Woolley. And I'll believe you carry a holdout gun when I see it."

A cold wind blew across the Monument. In the wash below, Hiram saw the trace of a red glow—the remains of his fire. Farther away, beyond the Monument, a yellow halo on the horizon hinted at the location of Moab.

The only escape route he saw involved jumping down off the promontory of rock that the Bloomers stood on. But even if the wolves didn't catch him, that was a route that would no doubt end in broken legs, which would then mean being torn to death by Gudmundson and his men.

Unless maybe the chi-rho medallion would save his legs from breaking.

But Hiram didn't want to test it, not even with the sense he had been freed from his lust. The fire charms had worked well. He didn't want to press his luck.

"I've seen bullets bounce off the hides of Erasmus Green and his fellows," he said. "I guess I figured that meant you had to be in animal form to get the special bulletproof hide. But then I dulled my blade on your neck, too."

"Our hides are not always bulletproof." Gudmundson

stood with the planet Jupiter shining directly behind his ear. It gave him a cold halo. The breeze that blew over Hiram's face seemed to blow directly *out of* Gudmundson, and the bishop's eyes were bottomless wells. "The stars strengthen us. God-Jupiter sustains God-Gudmundson."

"And he was supposed to sustain Lloyd Preece." Hiram nodded. "But you killed him with his own knife because it was the best way to be sure he wasn't holding it himself. But he still should have had an impervious hide, because his knife in your hands was an ordinary weapon. Or no . . . you killed him with *your* knife, but you took his from him first, because if he wasn't holding it, Jupiter would do him no good."

Gudmundson shrugged.

"What did you do?" Hiram asked. "You must have surprised him. Did he think that you and he had a truce, because of the Hoof and Fang, or did he simply believe you were a friend? Did you violate your own cult laws as well as the laws of human hospitality when you disarmed and attacked him?"

"He was leaving," Gudmundson said. "The breaking of laws was not on my conscience."

"And who is your lawgiver, then?" Hiram asked. "What repulsive monster do you worship as a god, who gives you power in exchange for killing? Does it have a real name, this demon you love? Or do you only know him by his Jovial mask?"

"As much fun as I think it would be to debate theology with you," Bishop Gudmundson said, "it's not what I'm here for."

"Did you sneak up on Lloyd? Was he relaxed, maybe drinking, an old fellow living alone, and so you sneaked up on a defenseless man and slit his throat in his own home?"

"He was never defenseless," Gudmundson said, "and he was a traitor."

"Because he wanted a better life for his grand-children?"

"There is no better life." Gudmundson's voice was fierce. "There is only the Hoof and the Fang, the pack and the herd, there is only this life. Children of the Hoof die, when they are eaten by the pack or when their herd cannot bring them enough to eat. Children of the Fang must also feed. This is true when the wolves run on all four feet, and it is equally true when they stand on their hind legs and wear neckties."

"So now what?" Hiram asked. "Will one of the other members of the Hoof get himself forged a Jupiter dagger? Will they lock horns over who has the right? Will the demon of the Hoof tell them all who gets to be the new boss? Do *you* get a say?"

"The herd will choose its leader," Gudmundson said. "And once it does, I will hunt that man, and all his herd-mates with him."

"Green knows you killed Preece," Hiram pointed out. "By now, I'd think the whole herd knows it. You don't think that's a problem for you?"

None of the wolf men made a sound. They looked at their leader with bright eyes, waiting.

As for Hiram, he was asking questions, buying time, but what for? The dawn? The cavalry? But there was no cavalry coming.

The bishop's lips curled into a smirk. "I told Green that I had killed the First of Hoof. That fact only tells them something that they should have known from the beginning, which is that no one leaves the herd, just as no one leaves the pack. That knowledge will only make them fear me more."

Fear...was that the ultimate weapon or power that the wolves gained? Maybe both sides gained a kind of power. The deer-men gained the power of wealth, which could ward off hunger and climate and want, and buy influence. The werewolves gained the power to make their enemies fear them.

He would never join such a cult, but Hiram realized that he had a preference. If given a choice between the Hoof and the Fang, he would choose the Hoof.

In the short term, the Fang could win.

In the long term, it must always be the Hoof. For starters, because if the Hoof disappeared entirely, the Fang went with it, while the reverse was not true.

Or did Hiram feel that way merely because herding was reasonably close to farming, and because he kept a little livestock himself?

"If you want to become more powerful, you might try killing someone more impressive than me," Hiram said. "Frankly, Erasmus Green is a more noteworthy man than I am by almost any account. If you take on the power of the people you sacrifice, killing me is only going to make you a beet farmer."

"I saw you dowse, Hiram Woolley." Gudmundson circled slowly about him, like a rattler looking for an opening. The eyes of the other werewolves glimmered. "You were talented and precise, and also moderate and wise in how you interpreted the information. And you fought off Green and his men hand to hand, which makes you brave. And you stuck around town to try to resolve problems that weren't any of your business, for Adelaide Preece and for the Udalls—that shows that you have a compassionate heart. I admire all those traits of yours."

"You admire me," Hiram said, "and therefore you're going to kill me."

"And eat you." Gudmundson grinned.

Behind him, the members of the Fang howled.

The bishop attacked. He darted forward like a rattlesnake, silver knife flashing gray in the gloom. Hiram threw himself right, and Gudmundson pounced sideways, like a spider that could leap in any direction that it wanted. With his left fist, he punched Hiram in the midriff, sending him staggering backward and crashing into the base of the stone arch.

Gudmundson was younger than Hiram by a decade or so, and he was muscular from his work. Still, he was moving way too fast.

Gudmundson punched again, hitting Hiram in the shoulder this time. Hiram hit the rock behind him hard and bounced—as much by force of will as by any native elasticity of his flesh—then ducked, managing to get beneath Gudmundson's next swing and plant his shoulder in the bishop's solar plexus.

The air rushed out of Gudmundson's lungs. In any normal brawl, that blow should have ended the fight, leaving Gudmundson panting in a heap on the floor. But instead of collapsing helpless, Gudmundson gripped Hiram by the back of his overalls, slashed the Jupiter knife at Hiram's throat, and then threw Hiram over his shoulder.

The slashing attack could easily have killed Hiram, but by a good piece of luck, he got his arms both up in front of his face at just the right moment. The knife slashed through Hiram's sleeves and cut across his left forearm. The wound burned. Hiram tumbled across the stone.

Only it wasn't luck that had saved him, but his chi-rho amulet that had put his arm into the right place at the right time to parry the blow.

The chi-rho was working again, and yet Hiram was losing the fight.

He landed on his back, and immediately one of the werewolves pounced upon him. The beast snapped and snarled on all fours almost like a real wolf, teeth cracking together inches from Hiram's nose. Hiram felt his chi-rho amulet bounce hard into his Adam's apple—or was it the widow's bogus Uranus cross, that he had never removed?—and he thrust his wounded left forearm forward, into the beast's maw.

Foam-flecked slobber spattered into Hiram's face and the monster sank its teeth into his flesh. He heard screaming far away, and the pounding of feet. Gudmundson was swooping in for the kill.

No, not screaming far away. Hiram himself was screaming.

He ground his teeth against the pain. Two enemies were attacking him at once, which meant he was moments from death if he didn't act immediately. Reaching up with his free hand, Hiram curled his fingers tightly into the fur on the wolf's belly—

then heaved.

He meant to pull the beast-man forward and throw it, but he underestimated the size and weight of the monster, which didn't budge. Still, the force of his muscles contracting dragged Hiram himself beneath the wolf-man, and made him collide with the legs on the monster's left side. The wolf-man slipped, snarling in anger and surprise, and then howled in pain.

Hot blood spattered Hiram's hands and neck and the beast collapsed. Hiram tried to haul himself from underneath the mound of fur and destroyed flesh, but it was too heavy—

until suddenly it wasn't.

Abruptly, Hiram lay beneath the twitching, stark naked body of the ranch hand Clem, spraying blood from his head. Gudmund Gudmundson leaned over the corpse, his hand on the hilt of the dagger sunk into the dead man's skull.

"You deserve this, Clem," Gudmundson said.

Hiram rolled from underneath the corpse and dragged himself to his feet. His left arm was torn, but the bleeding wasn't severe. His entire body, though, shook with pain and exhaustion. The night air of the Monument felt like ice cubes on his skin. He spat, tasting blood—his, or Clem's?

"You knew he was mine to kill," Gudmundson said to the body. "Your fool ambition betrayed you. What did you think to gain?"

Clem shuddered one last time and lay still. Gudmundson withdrew the knife. Hiram stared at the sliver of silver in the bishop's hand—how could he get that weapon away from Gudmundson? It might not do any good for Hiram, but for Gudmundson it cut through the hide of a creature that was impervious to bullets.

"Hunt happily, my pack brother," Gudmundson said. "You made a mistake, but it was the mistake of a brave man and a true wolf."

The sound of an automobile horn blared in the

wash below the arch. Electric lights flashed, shining on the slickrock slope, suggesting that someone was driving a car up the rock slope. *Honk, honk!*

How had Hiram missed the sound of an automobile engine approaching?

Whoever it was, they couldn't possibly be worse than the Fang. Hiram threw himself past Gudmundson and raced down the stone.

Honk!

And then Hiram recognized the horn; it belonged to his own Double-A.

The cavalry had arrived, after all.

Wolves snarled behind Hiram and a howl arose from somewhere on the ridge. Hiram ran straight for the truck, but he heard wolf-men coming up fast behind him.

Boom! Boom!

The sound was louder than Hiram's revolver—the hunting rifle? A wolf-man sprang past Hiram on his right, bounding toward the truck—*Boom!* The beast was knocked to the ground, yelping in surprise and annoyance. It wasn't dead or even wounded, though— like the deer-men the night before, it had been knocked down and maybe stunned at most.

Still, the barking seemed to recede into the distance behind Hiram. He stumbled and fell, rolled and skidded down the rock, and then regained his feet with a helping hand.

The hand was Michael's, and Michael was pressing the shotgun into Hiram's grip.

"I couldn't find your pistol, Pap," he said. "We might have to go back and look for it. Maybe dowse for it. Can you dowse for a pistol?"

"You can sure try," Hiram told his son. "Who's driving the truck?"

"Don't lose your grip on me if I tell you," Michael said.

"Mahonri?"

"Diana."

Hiram could hardly believe it.

The headlights pulled back and turned as the driver backed the truck sideways, preparing to drive away. Before he lost the light, Hiram raised the shotgun to take aim at one of the oncoming wolves. *Boom!* Knocked backward two steps, the monster darted sideways and out of Hiram's view.

"I didn't hear it coming."

Michael fired at a wolf and then worked the rifle's action to eject the casing and slide in a new shell. "Maybe you were distracted."

"How did you know how to find me?"

They both backed toward the truck, watching for wolf-men. Hiram saw the silhouettes of the deer-men, man-shaped, but with racks of antlers sprouting from their elongated skulls. They watched from the heights of the rock ridge to his left. He wanted the deer to rebel and attack the wolves, but that would never happen. That wasn't the nature of the herd.

Hiram felt a little kinship for the Hoof, but that herd felt nothing for him in return.

Michael snorted. "Because I'm a genius, that's why. Where else would the *Blót* be? And, this was where Jimmy Udall was killed by the hunt."

The truck engine roared.

"Are you in gear?" Michael called, stepping back toward the truck, but Diana was definitely in gear—the

Double-A shot away from Hiram and Michael, bounding over humps of sand and through thickets to rattle away down the canyon.

"Hey!" Hiram almost fired at his own truck, to take out one of the wheels, but held back—with a flat tire, the Double-A wouldn't carry anybody out of the Monument. Instead, he watched as the glow of the headlights whipped down the wash, past the dying embers of Hiram's barrier fire and then on into deeper canyons.

"Shit!" Michael yelled and slapped at the inside pocket of his jacket. "Dammit!"

"Michael," Hiram said, "you can still run away. They're after me."

Michael shook his head and dropped his voice to a whisper. "No, Pap, listen. You have to get your hands on Gudmundson's knife. Whatever it does for him, it will do for you."

Hiram was tired and battered, and didn't entirely follow. "No, those knives are made for specific people. It will only work for the owner."

Michael shook his head again. "No, it will work for anyone born while Jupiter was in the same sign as it was when Gudmundson was born."

"But he's a younger man..." Hiram trailed off as he started to understand.

"Yeah. About twelve years younger, right? I looked at his chart. Listen, do you know where his knife is?"

Hiram nodded.

"Keep an eye on his knife, and grab it the instant you can. I have a plan."

Hiram nodded.

"A *close* eye," Michael said. "Watch *the bishop's knife*. Don't watch me."

Footsteps walked down the slickrock toward them. "I would have preferred to kill you under the arch," Gudmund Gudmundson said. "That is the sacred site, and the true slaughterhouse. But I can kill you just as easily here."

Hiram fired his shotgun into the center of Gudmundson's chest. *Boom!*

The bishop fell to the ground. He promptly stood again. Powder darkened his pale chest, but his flesh remained whole.

Hiram's heart fell.

"More shells?" Hiram asked Michael.

"In the truck," Michael said.

Gudmundson leaped forward, and Hiram prepared to dodge—

but the bishop wrenched the rifle from Michael's hands and tossed it aside, down into the wash.

"I'm going to offer you another act of mercy, Brother Woolley," Gudmund Gudmundson said. "I'm going to kill you first."

Chapter Twenty-Nine

HIRAM DROPPED THE EMPTY SHOTGUN. THE CLATTER of its fall echoed back at him from the amphitheater of rock.

"Good," Gudmundson said. He looked strange, naked save the belt that held his sheathed Jupiter knife. "We'll fight with bare hands, like the animals we are."

"Like God intended?"

"Like members of the Pack."

Hiram threw a punch. Fear that his blow would be futile might blunt the attack, so Hiram willed himself to believe that he could knock Gudmundson unconscious. He snapped with his hips and shoulders, putting all the impetus he could into the motion of his fist.

He connected with Gudmundson's jaw, and rocked the man's chin slightly to one side.

Gudmundson smiled. Hiram hadn't left a mark.

The bishop then stepped in close to Hiram, punching him in the stomach. The air left Hiram's lungs and the blow hurt. The sheer force of the attack raised

Hiram off the ground—surely, without the protective force of his chi-rho amulet, that single punch would have snapped Hiram's spine.

Hiram staggered back a step and raised his fists defensively. Around him and Gudmundson, a ring of werewolves prowled. They made music as they slunk in a circle, their throats emitting melodic whines and low, guttural yips. Michael stood within the ring, but the wolves ignored him; he had his hand inside his shirt—probably touching his own chi-rho medallion.

Hiram wished Michael hadn't come to rescue him. It only meant that Michael would die here along with Hiram.

Only...what was the plan that Michael had almost told Hiram?

Hiram had to keep his eye on the bishop's dagger and grab it when he could. That was Michael's plan.

Perhaps Gudmundson's strength came from the Jupiter knife. Perhaps that was what had saved him from the shotgun blast. All the more reason to get the blade away from him.

Was Michael going to distract Gudmundson?

Images of the Reverend Majestic's death flooded Hiram's mind—his last charge, his howl of "Satan!", the rotting, skeletal foot emerging from his boot, the fire scattered, and Hiram's life saved...but at a high cost.

Did Michael intend to sacrifice himself as well?

Hiram felt sick.

Farther up on the ridge, Hiram still saw the silhouettes of antlers that told him that the Hoof was participating in this ceremony just as much as the Fang was.

The bishop swooped in again, swinging blows at Hiram's belly and face. Hiram backed away, catching most of the flurry of blows on his forearms. That shot lightning bolts of agony up Hiram's shoulders, since the flesh was already torn by Clem's bite; the few attacks that got past Hiram's guard hurt worse, rocking him at every contact, and a final blow to the shoulder, glancing as it was, sent Hiram staggering back up the slope and almost knocked him down.

Hiram's retreat had been uphill, though not intentionally. Michael and the wolf-men had kept pace with his march backward—unfortunately. Michael watched Hiram and the bishop intently, a referee watching an unevenly matched pair of boxers, ready to step in to save the weaker man the minute he hit the canvas.

But there was no canvas here; only hard rock.

And no sign of dawn.

Jupiter was at Hiram's back, beyond the School-marm's Bloomers. He felt the presence of both the planet and the rock formation like a pair of malevolent giants, intent on doing Hiram harm. The Jovial lantern spilled milky light all down the rock slope on which he stood, elongating Hiram's shadow.

"No more witty banter?" Gudmundson closed in again.

Hiram jabbed with his left, then again, and both times drawing a block as Gudmundson hunkered behind his balled fists. He didn't need to block, Hiram thought, so why was he doing it? Habit? He hadn't always been—apparently—impervious to attack.

Perhaps it was only on this night, during the Tithe, that the Jupiter knife made the First of Fang invulnerable. Would Hiram ever know?

He launched a right across the bishop's face, and connected on the man's temple. Hiram knew his own strength—an ordinary fighter would have been stunned, and maybe knocked out of the fight.

Gudmund Gudmundson smiled, and stepped in to attack again.

Michael lunged in.

"Leave my Pap alone!" he yelled.

The young man's charge was awkward; he still had one hand inside his shirt. He rushed forward as if he were going to try to wrestle Gudmundson, and the bishop responded as if he were being molested by an inconvenient fly.

Without even looking, he swatted Michael with a backhanded blow to the face. The blow lifted Michael off the ground and sent him flying among the werewolves, who howled their approval.

Something clattered to the ground behind Gudmund Gudmundson.

The bishop turned, poised on the balls of his feet, and he and Hiram both looked down at the source of the sound—

and saw a silver dagger lying on the rock.

A *close eye*, Michael had said. *Close*. On *the bishop's knife*.

Hiram looked back to Gudmundson's hip and saw the man's sheath and dagger there.

The knife on the slickrock was Preece's.

Gudmundson bent at the waist, hands swooping in to grab the dagger on the ground, which left his own knife exposed, on a hip facing Hiram—

Hiram grabbed the bishop's dagger.

Both men leaped away from each other, each holding his blade low, point upward. A puzzled growl arose among the pack, and their circling stopped.

Michael scrambled to his feet. He hadn't been holding his chi-rho amulet, after all, but Lloyd Preece's dagger. When had he acquired it?

Hiram shook his head—this was no time to be distracted.

The knife would work for him, Michael had been earnestly certain. Could that be true? It could, Hiram thought, if he was in fact twelve years older than Bishop Gudmundson, and born with Jupiter in the same sign.

But maybe Hiram misunderstood how the knife worked.

This fight, with his life as the stakes, would be the test.

In any case, he was happier with the dagger in his hand than in Gudmundson's.

The bishop laughed. "Oh, Michael, you're a clever young man. You've done to me what I did to Lloyd Preece—taken away some of my power. After I'm done killing and eating your father, I'm going to kill and eat you. Every member of the pack will come away braver tonight, for having eaten the flesh of Hiram Woolley, and smarter, for having eaten the flesh of his son Michael. But your deaths are mine, and mine will be the greatest glory and the greatest gain."

"Go to hell," Michael said.

Gudmundson attacked. He moved slower now, without his Jupiter dagger, but he was still a younger and stronger man than Hiram, with quicker reflexes. Gudmundson feinted, slashed, feinted again, and then swung at Hiram's belly, and Hiram, who had never been a knife fighter, was hard pressed to avoid the blows. He blocked the first attack by catching Gudmundson's forearm with his own, and avoided the second by leaping backward—

landing underneath the Bloomers.

The footing here was even, a small natural cockpit for a close fight to the death. It *felt* like a place where a hunter would want to trap and finally kill his quarry. Michael crept beneath the stone formation and pressed himself against the rock, lips moving and his hand again inside his shirt.

Michael had been faithful, and smart, and right.

Except about Diana Artemis. He had thought she was a charming distraction, that Hiram's reaction to her was natural and harmless. Instead, she had turned out to be a wicked criminal, and the fire she had kindled in Hiram's loins had generated so much smoke that it had blinded him, and nearly choked him to death.

Was Michael right about the dagger? He must be. If not . . . what other chance did Hiram have?

"I'm still willing to negotiate," he said. "Let my son go."

Gudmundson chuckled. "The pot roast promises to be delicious, as long as we agree to let the cake go free. No deal."

Hiram attacked. He *did* feel faster, and he pushed himself. Some part of him relaxed, and restraints that held his muscles back seemed to disappear. He struck like a snake, cutting at the bishop's face and arms, stabbing toward the large veins of his thigh. He managed to scratch Gudmundson along the back of a forearm, and to nick his shoulder. Gudmundson remained quick, and he had much more skill with his knife, so Hiram's attacks quickly melted into parries and dodges, trying to keep the counterattacks from his face and chest.

The song of the wolves returned, and rose in volume and pitch.

Beyond the wolves, shadowy presences told Hiram that the were-deer had closed in to see the kill. They rotated around the fight in the opposite direction from the wolves, and raised a bleating, rhythmic song that lay underneath the cry of the wolves. It was eerily beautiful, the combined liturgical hymn of the Fang and the Hoof.

It was not music that Hiram wanted to die to.

Hiram realized that he didn't feel winded. The aches he had felt in his muscles had disappeared, too. He felt strong, young, and vital. Even his chewed-up left arm felt better.

But still, he couldn't get through Gudmundson's defenses to land a decisive blow.

How long until the wolf-men tired of watching Hiram and Gudmundson dance, and closed in to help their leader?

Indeed, if Hiram defeated the bishop, would he then have to face the entire pack, swarming him together? Or worse, the Fang and the Hoof at the same time?

As if in response to his thoughts, the pack's circle tightened. There was barely room to maneuver beneath the arch, penned in as they were by a curtain of gray fur.

If the bishop was worried about the Jupiter knife, Hiram could attack in other ways. He feinted with the knife, and when Gudmundson blocked him, forearm to forearm, Hiram jumped in close to attack, not with the knife—but with his head.

Hiram slammed his own head into Gudmundson's face. Hiram was the taller man, so he didn't break the bishop's nose, but instead landed a ringing hammer blow, forehead to forehead.

The bishop staggered back, blood spraying from split skin in the man's face, and Hiram pressed the attack. He lowered his shoulder and charged. Before, that had resulted in his being tossed to the stone. Now he managed to smash Gudmundson up against the red rock, and with satisfaction he heard air whoosh from the bishop's lungs.

Gudmundson was still young and athletic. As Hiram turned to try to elbow the man, and maybe get his knife into play again, Gudmundson dropped, falling from his grasp, and rolling away across the stone.

Hiram took a moment to regain his balance after the sudden disappearance of his target, and when he turned, knife up defensively, Gudmundson was charging.

Now it was the younger man who threw elbows and kicks, punching with his left and attempting to push Hiram with his body. Lloyd Preece's dagger seemed to float in the air like a lure, forever draining Hiram's attention, but slipping back out of reach and drawing his own knife in response rather than ever attacking. Hiram felt mesmerized, like a prairie dog in front of a rattlesnake.

Gudmundson kicked Hiram's ankle out from underneath him, and Hiram fell. He hit the stone hard and rolled away, narrowly avoiding losing his head to a vicious stomp attack from the other man, and then his guts to a long running slash with the knife. Werewolves scattered, making room, and he thought for a moment that an avenue of escape might open up—
the rock floor fell away beneath him.

Hiram slid on his belly. His hand rattled on stone and he feared he'd lose the dagger, but he closed his fist tight around the hilt and held on.

Arms spread-eagled, he slowed his descent and came to a stop partway down the rock.

Gudmundson bounded down the slope, stomping. Hiram threw himself sideways, which meant skidding a few more yards down, but also saved him from being crushed. While Gudmundson struggled to slow his descent, and then turned and scrambled back up, Hiram climbed the slickrock to again put himself within the ring.

"Whip him, Pap." Michael's voice was surprisingly calm. "Jupiter is with you. Can't you feel it?"

Gudmundson threw a rock. The stone was the size of Hiram's head, but Gudmundson threw it easily, as if skipping a dollar-sized wafer over a pond.

Hiram ducked, and then Gudmundson was immediately stabbing at him again. Hiram caught the blow and counterattacked, and he did indeed feel strong. Pushing with his legs, he hooked one arm through the bishop's elbow and tossed the man to the ground.

"Surrender," Hiram growled. "Confess to the murder, and everyone else goes free."

Gudmundson rolled away and stood. The werewolves growled uncertainly about him.

"I'm tired of this," he said.

Turning, his flesh bulged, thighs swelling, arms swelling, as hair sprouted from his skin. His belt burst. He grew taller, leaner, his face elongating. Teeth lengthened. Fingernails became talons and where a man stood before, now was the form of a hunched man-wolf, furry and yellow-eyed and snarling.

Why had Gudmundson fought him in human form at all? To show his power, to Hiram or to the pack?

The pack howled.

"That's fear, Pap."

Gudmundson might be afraid, but that didn't ease Hiram's worries. He backed away from the large slavering teeth and the low, swinging tail. The wolf-man's bite seemed more fearful to him than the stab of the bishop's dagger.

The werewolf snapped once, and then again, and Hiram leaped away. He felt strong and agile, and he moved quickly, but he feared the bite.

"Pap," Michael said. "He's afraid of you."

Gudmundson the wolf-man leaped at Michael. Hiram leaped, too, but he was too far away, and in his mind's eye he saw the beast's jaws closing on Michael's throat—

only Hiram got there in time. He knocked the werewolf away with his shoulder, sending the big beast into its packmates with a yowl.

Gudmundson came rushing back immediately, and Hiram met him in the center of the killing floor. He stabbed and dodged, stabbed and dodged, but could neither connect, nor see any hope of escape.

The fighters came apart and circled. The howling of the wolves became louder still, and Hiram heard the clatter of deer hooves on stone beyond.

What of the coming dawn, and the disappearance of Jupiter?

A chill struck Hiram's heart. Would the agility and strength and speed that flowed through his body now, transmitted through Scorpio from the planet Jupiter, disappear?

If that happened, he was doomed.

How soon until sunrise?

"Pap!" Michael called. "He can't hurt you!"

He can't hurt you.

Was it true?

But the Jupiter knife—if it worked for Hiram—would harm and even kill a member of the Pack. Gudmundson had killed Clem with it. The muscles of Hiram's belly tightened.

There was only one test to make.

Hiram charged the beast-man. This time, once Gudmundson had dodged his attack and leaped to bite Hiram on the shoulder, Hiram stood still to take the charge. The werewolf's jaws clamped onto Hiram's shoulder, close to his throat. Hiram pulled the monster closer with his left arm, feeling sharp toenails scratch at his belly and thighs. He brought the Jupiter knife up behind the wolf—

then slashed.

The blade caught the wolf-bishop in the neck, and it cut through with ease. In a single swift motion, Hiram cut off Gudmund Gudmundson's head.

Chapter Thirty

BLOOD GUSHED DOWN HIRAM'S CHEST.

The weight of the werewolf's body disappeared, and a naked human trunk crashed to the stone. The head came away in Hiram's arms, and he found himself holding it.

Mercifully, the head retained the wolf's form.

The howling stopped instantly. The clatter of the running deer-men continued for a few seconds, and then a stunned hush fell over the entire amphitheater.

The Jovial light shed over the scene seemed to throb.

Michael stepped to Hiram's side, turning to stand shoulder to shoulder.

Would the beast-men all attack Hiram and his son now?

Hiram dug his fingers into the thick fur, now slick with blood, behind the wolf's ears, and raised the severed head high. The monsters stared at him, and their muzzles drooped.

Hiram slowly raised the Jupiter knife, pointing its tip toward the nearest wolf-man. He met the beast's gaze, and stared until the creature flinched and looked away. Then he stared down the next, and the next, turning slowly and displaying his trophy until every one of the wolves was cowed and shrinking.

The deer-men fled before the wolves had finished submitting.

When all the werewolves crouched low, Hiram tossed the wolf-bishop's head to the ground beside the naked human body of Gudmund Gudmundson. Only when the head touched the stone did it finally revert to the shape of Gudmundson's human skull, with its broad face and its strong chin. Hiram was grateful that shadow obscured the man's facial expression.

In a stray skein of starlight, Hiram could see that one of the bishop's feet was missing toes.

Hiram lowered the Jupiter knife. "Sheriff Del Rose."

Del Rose shifted from wolf form; the sheriff crouched, kneeling naked like some sort of perverse parody of a medieval knight. He kept his eyes down as he addressed Hiram.

"I'm here."

"Leave the body where it lies. Bishop Gudmundson disappeared while walking on the Monument tonight. Go home."

Del Rose assumed his monstrous form and padded off into the night. The other werewolves followed him.

"I want you to know," Michael said, "that I feel like saying all kinds of cuss words, but I'm not doing it. Science has a lot to say for itself, but tonight, it's the chaste and sober mind that wins."

"You haven't totally quit cussing."

"No. But I'm getting better."

Hiram should have been trembling from the

aftermath of the fight. Instead, he felt strong and vital. He wiped the Jupiter knife clean on his own shirt, which was already bloodstained. He then retrieved the sheath off Gudmundson's broken belt. He stuck the dagger into his pants pocket.

He couldn't quite bring himself to wear it. Not yet. Maybe not ever.

Lloyd Preece's knife lay on the stone beside the bishop. Hiram handed it to Michael.

"I think there's someone down the canyon who would like to see this corpse," Michael said.

Hiram clapped his son on the arm. "I hadn't forgotten. I'm glad you hadn't, either."

They waited a few minutes to let the blood pouring from the body dwindle. Hiram found his strength was enough to hoist the body across his shoulders, severed neck away from himself to keep the blood from getting on him too much. He carried Gudmundson's head in the crook of his arm.

"What kind of burial do we give Gudmundson?" Michael asked.

It was a good question. Hiram didn't want to consecrate a grave, because he didn't want to seal this murderer up to the resurrection or make him any spiritual promises. On the other hand, leaving the corpse lying in the open felt indecent. It felt as if it might have been the burial Gudmundson wanted, too, his predator corpse finally picked clean by carrion eaters, and Hiram didn't want to give him that satisfaction.

Also, a grave felt like a sort of quarantine. Whatever evil residue might ooze from this man's body and spirit, Hiram felt it should be contained.

"I need to think about that," he told his son.

Down in the wash, a fire continued to burn. Some of the embers from Hiram's wall had gotten into a thicket, farther up the canyon. This thicket was isolated, and there wasn't enough wind to spread the fire, but for the moment there was fuel and to spare, and the fire was growing.

Good. Hiram could use the flames. Perhaps for more than one end.

He dumped the body beside the fire. This was near enough where he'd had his vision of Jimmy Udall— within a hundred feet or so.

"Are we going to talk to him?" Michael whispered.

Hiram nodded. "Would you like to do it? You're the hero of the hour."

Michael snorted. "Pap . . ."

"It was your craft that figured out the Jupiter knife," Hiram pointed out. "It was your book-lore, in fact, your astrology, your mastery of knowledge that has always been out of my reach, that did it. And then it was your plan that tricked the knife out of Gudmundson's hands. And that's not even to mention your interrogation of Green, and your use of the clay balls to discover Diana's guilt."

"Yeah," Michael said, "and then it was you that kicked his . . . you took all the beating."

Hiram chuckled. "That's what a father is for."

Michael was silent for long moments. "You talk to him."

"Jimmy," Hiram said. "We know you're here. We hope you saw what happened tonight. We believe the man who killed you has been brought to justice."

The fire crackled as the last tree in the thicket took flame.

"Jimmy, I think you can hear my voice, but I know

you can see the fire. Reach into the fire, Jimmy. It's not heavy, you can push it, you've done this before."

Michael seemed to be holding his breath.

"I'm going to ask questions, Jimmy," Hiram said. "If the answer is *yes*, make the fire move. Is that okay with you?"

The bonfire snapped sideways. *Yes*.

"Jimmy, this man, Gudmund Gudmundson . . . is he the one who killed you?"

Yes.

"Is he the only one who killed you?"

Yes.

Hiram hesitated, afraid of what answer he might get to this next question. "Can you rest now, Jimmy?"

Yes.

"Holy smokes, Pap."

One moment, Hiram and Michael were alone with the blaze, and the next, Jimmy was standing beside them. The young boy looked down at the headless corpse at his feet, and Hiram thought he saw compassion in the ghostly eyes.

Then Jimmy raised his arms over his head. His sleeves fell, and Hiram again saw the circular bitemarks, the tooth impressions that looked like they had been made by a human mouth. Slowly, they twisted, becoming elongated and deepening, rearranging themselves into the pattern of a beast's long muzzle.

And then they faded entirely, and Jimmy's flesh was unmarked.

Jimmy Udall smiled at Hiram and Michael, and then he was gone.

"That's what you saw before." Michael's voice was barely above a whisper. "In your dream."

"Or maybe not a dream," Hiram said. "Yes."

They stood awhile, alone together with the fire and the wonder.

Then Hiram picked up Gudmundson's body and heaved it into the flames. He kicked the head deep into the embers, not wanting to touch it with his hands or look into its eyes.

Then he sat on a rock and began to unlace his boots.

"Pap," Michael said, "what are you doing?"

"I'm covered in the gore of that monster," Hiram said. "He was a murderer, a child-killer, and he also went to church every Sunday and smiled at his congregation as their bishop. He killed Jimmy Udall and then preached a sermon at the boy's funeral. I feel . . . unclean."

"You can wash in the river, when we get there."

"I'll do that, too. Here, hold these." Hiram handed his son his Zippo lighter, his bloodstone, and Gudmundson's Jupiter knife.

"What if the werewolves come back?"

Hiram thought about the daunted looks in the monsters' eyes as they had submitted to him. "They won't."

"What do we do about the *Blót*?" Michael asked. "Those guys might be scared of you now, but I don't see them giving up their evil ways once you and I go back to Lehi."

Hiram nodded. "I have an idea about that. There's a telegram I need to send."

Hiram set aside his Redwing Harvesters, and then stripped off all his clothing. Overalls, socks, and long johns all went into the fire. Then Hiram lay down in the sand and rolled around. He took handfuls of it and scoured his skin where he thought he was covered in blood, and when he was finally as clean as he could get, he laced his boots back on.

"Pap," Michael said. "You look like a madman."

Hiram shrugged and chuckled. "Well, appearances can be absolutely correct."

Michael held out his fedora. "I found this. It must have fallen off when you were coming up the canyon."

Hiram took his hat into his hands and grinned. "It needs a good dusting-off. Maybe I should throw a hat-brush into the toolbox."

"Only if you can use it to, I don't know, brush a man to sleep or brush away wounds. We need all the space in that toolbox for our charms stuff. I found the rifle and shotgun, too. No ammo, though. I guess we'd better get walking," Michael said. "We don't want to run into anyone when you're like this."

Hiram laughed. "Well, it wouldn't be my preference, but it wouldn't be the end of the world, either. I want to stay and make sure the fire burns out. And first, I want to say a prayer over Bishop Gudmundson's body."

Michael nodded and folded his arms.

Hiram hesitated, then removed the widow's Uranus cross from around his neck and threw it into the flames. Then he set his hat aside and raised his arms to the heavens. He was conscious of the spectacularly odd scene he made, but he felt clean.

"Great God of Heaven," he said. "We beg thee to forgive this man, Gudmund Gudmundson, as much as thou canst. And what cannot be forgiven, we beg thee to burn it up in fire, that it may no more stain this land or trouble this people. Amen."

"Amen."

They stood and watched the flames. Gudmundson's corpse took fire and burned like a fat taper, sputtering and glowing a deeper red than the trees and brush around it. Hiram chanted assorted Bible verses about fire and corruption, to help the process along.

"I found the money," Michael said, as the fire was crumbling into its last embers, and the sky in the east was beginning to turn pale. "Lloyd Preece's cash. It was hidden inside his mirror, in the cabin."

Hiram laughed. "And that's what he meant about there being a fortune to be had in a man's good opinion of himself. Adelaide Tunstall will be pleased."

"She's not going to be very pleased when I tell her that I was dumb enough to let Diana Artemis take it from me."

"When did that happen?"

"Well, I offered to pay her to help rescue you, and she agreed. But then, just before I got out of the truck back there, she hugged me. I'm pretty sure that's when she took the dough. And that's why she just drove off like she did."

"But not before saving me," Hiram pointed out. "Those flashing lights and the horn led me right to you."

"No, you can't make her good. She just left us to die."

Hiram didn't argue. Instead he laughed. "Well, Adelaide will live. Her dad's lawyer will sell their land, and she'll even live well. I don't think you need to trouble yourself about the bearer bonds."

"And Diana?"

"The widow Artemis took something from both of us,

son, but she doesn't matter anymore. And everything that *does* matter...I have it back, safe and sound."

"Ordinarily," Michael said, "this might be a moment that called for a hug. But I think I'd rather wait until you have clothes on again."

In the yellow light of the rising sun, they began their hike back across the Monument, and back toward civilization.

Chapter Thirty-One

HIRAM WALKED WITH HIS SON OUT OF THE DESERT, heading for town, as the sun rose steadily in the sky.

They stopped at the Udalls' shack to get Hiram some clothes.

Michael knocked on the door, and then explained that they'd found Jimmy's murderer. He'd been brought to justice, and the boy had found peace at last.

Priscilla Udall was too proud to cry in front of them. She told them Jimmy had appeared to her in a dream, just before she awoke, and had told her, "Mamma, I'm happy now."

Moses blew his nose three times and gave Hiram a pair of overalls. He also thanked them, both for news of their boy and for the flour. The overalls barely fit. They rose up to Hiram's mid-calf, and he had to wear them shirtless. When Hiram promised to return the overalls, Moses insisted that Hiram keep them as a token of his respect.

"Mama, I'm happy now," Mrs. Udall was repeating

again and again as Hiram and Michael walked out of earshot.

On their way in to town, Hiram pondered the events of the night before. Hiram had felt the power of the stars and the planets, and specifically Jupiter, and it had humbled him. Michael knew far more about the planets and the stars then he did, and that felt right. Hiram was proud of his son. Adding astrology to their knowledge of how God's power worked in the world could only help them.

And maybe it would lead Michael toward a career in astronomy one day, or even—why not?—piloting a space ship.

Hiram didn't know what kind of reception they would get in town, or if the widow Artemis had not only taken Lloyd Preece's bearer bonds but also their Double-A. Losing the toolbox and the truck would be a blow, and he would require time and money to rebuild his arsenal, as well as to protect a new automobile as the Double-A was protected.

Hiram carried the rifle slung over his shoulder; he felt exposed. Michael walked with the shotgun over the crook of his elbow. They were dusty and exhausted, their vehicle had been stolen and their ammunition spent. Hiram remembered days in the way when he had been similarly filthy, exhausted, and spent, a haggard warrior in a foreign and hostile land.

Michael wasn't Yas Yazzie, but he was a new war buddy and best friend, a fellow fighter in the dark and painful war Hiram fought against the forces of evil. In the morning light, Michael was also the spitting image of his father. A lump stuck in Hiram's throat. He swallowed it down.

They crossed the bridge over the Colorado River

and kept walking the dirt road until they reached the town of Moab. Like always, it seemed like a quiet, sleepy place, full of people working hard and trying their best to make it through the Depression.

The Double-A was parked on Main Street, in front of Banjo & Sons Mercantile.

Hiram hurried forward, leaving Michael behind. To his great relief, the toolbox was there. Going to the cab, he saw the keys in the ignition. Diana had rightly assumed no one would steal it. Why had she left it for them? He doubted he'd ever get the chance to ask her.

Michael ambled up. "Well, darn, I never thought I'd see the day that woman did something nice for us."

"Darn?" Hiram asked.

Michael nodded. "I can't very well cuss and be an instrument for the source of all power." He cocked his head. "And this lust thing. I don't see how you handle that. It's so . . . tough."

"They call them deadly sins for a reason." Hiram peeled down the shoulder-straps of his borrowed overalls to throw on an old shirt that was lying behind the truck's seat. There was still a wide gap showing pale skin between the bottoms of the overalls and the Harvesters.

"Now, what, Pap?" Michael asked.

"I want to get back to camp so I can put some real clothes on. But first, we need a phone."

"The Maxwell House Hotel?"

Hiram grinned. "We might as well go in and see what kind of reception we get. And heck, Leon might not even be around."

"Heck is right," Michael agreed.

They stowed their weapons in the front seat of the truck, along with the toolbox.

Hiram and Michael walked up the steps and into the lobby. Hiram didn't remember when his muscles had ached so much—in addition to the chase and the fight, he and Michael had hiked all night to get out of the Monument. He was also hungry; it was after breakfast time, and Hiram didn't think lunch would be ready for another good hour. Even then, they'd probably had their last delicious meal from Arnie and his father.

Maybe the hotel could spare him an apple.

A man Hiram didn't know stood behind the counter. When Hiram asked for a phone, he pointed to a coin-operated device near the stairs, across from where Erasmus Green had fallen asleep at their table. Those astrological signs would still be under the table; if possible, they should discreetly wipe them away . . . just in case.

Michael provided Hiram the dime. He slipped it in and got an operator. It took a bit, but he finally reached the Utah Highway Patrol. He told them there were at least three bodies to be found up at the Monument. There had been trouble up there overnight, something to do with wild animals. He didn't say more.

The officer on the phone promised they'd send a car down from Price. When he asked about Sheriff Jack Del Rose, Hiram hung up.

Then, true to Hiram's word, they drove to their camp to recover their things—including Hiram's pistol, which they found lying in the dirt of the riverbank—and for Hiram to change into his own clothes.

Later, driving north, Michael sighed. "Hey, Pap, there's something I don't understand."

"Just the one thing?" Hiram squinted against the sun. "This won't take long."

"I hope it doesn't." Michael actually seemed to

squirm behind the wheel. "I had trouble with the divining rod when I was in Preece's cabin because of, well, Diana Artemis. I kept thinking about her. If you know what I'm saying."

Hiram's squint turned into a wince. "It's just another sin. Let's not make too much of it."

"That's the thing," Michael said. "If we separate our biology from the religious connotations of lust, or sin, or any of that, we were created with these urges. It's not a flaw in my character, just as it's not a flaw for horses, pigs, chickens to want to...you know."

Hiram did not want to be talking about this. And yet, it was as unavoidable as it was futile—he was not going to win an argument with his son. Hiram thought maybe if he didn't say anything, another subject would come up. That was wishful thinking.

"There's even that song by Cole Porter," Michael said. "'Birds do it, bees do it...'"

"This is why I don't like jazz."

"The problem doesn't end with the lust, but this whole idea of us being faulty instruments." Michael sighed. "If I'm faulty, it's by God's design. Am I to be punished for His shoddy design? I'm not saying I don't believe, I'm saying...I don't understand."

Hiram took his time answering. "Or perhaps," he finally said, speaking slowly and choosing his words, "you're not faulty. Perhaps you're simply not perfect yet. And perhaps you've come to this earth to become more perfect, as part of a long, long journey that started eons ago and will continue eons from now. And perhaps God will bless you for all the perfection you achieve and the good that you do, and above and beyond your desserts, only you can't even see how much God is blessing you, because your perspective is narrow and human, just like mine."

Michael whistled. "Perfection, huh? What's your charm for achieving that one, Pap?"

"I don't have a charm," Hiram said. "And my only strategy is to try to serve others, as much as I can. If you come across a more effective path, you let me know."

"I guess maybe I should be going to church."

Hiram shrugged. "It's not the *worst* idea. I *do* think you and I need to read the scriptures together a little more. I thought you knew them better." Then he lifted his voice, singing an old hymn:

> *God moves in a mysterious way, his wonders to perform;*
> *He plants His footsteps in the sea and rides upon the storm.*

"Hey," Michael said. "I used that very song to dowse up Lloyd Preece's bearer bonds. Because I, uh, couldn't think of a Bible verse. And it worked."

"You're smart, son." Hiram felt the sun on his skin, the wind in the hair on his arms, and the scent of the last bit of moisture leaving the desert as the sun removed it. "Smart, brave, funny . . . and also doubting, headstrong, and sometimes maybe even lustful. You're human. You're not perfect yet, but you're pretty great."

Hiram thought of the maggots on the Reverend Majestic's right foot, after five years in that boot. Those creatures had kept him alive. God could truly do wonders with some mighty peculiar instruments.

"You don't have all the answers," Michael said finally.

"I hardly have any."

"Pap," Michael said, "I have one last question, and then I won't pester you again until we get to Lehi."

"What is it?"

"You got bitten by a werewolf. Twice. Two different werewolves, actually. Are you going to sprout hair and fangs?"

"If I do," Hiram said, "you'll be the first to know."

By mid-afternoon, they were in Lehi.

They returned to Moab and to the hotel a week later. Hiram would have preferred to come alone, being unsure how the meeting would play out, but he needed Michael to drive. And besides, Michael had earned his place in the meeting.

Inside the lobby of the Maxwell House Hotel, Leon Björnsson, Erasmus Green, and Banjo Johansson sat a table. At a second table sat Sheriff Jack Del Rose and Deputy Pickens. They were all in their best suits, dressed as they had been at Lloyd Preece's wake, and they fidgeted as if they were deeply uncomfortable. Björnsson held the Peteys in a stranglehold and Del Rose drummed his fingers so quickly on the tabletop, he looked as if he was trying to punch a hole in the wood. That put Hiram's mind somewhat at ease—he felt none too comfortable, either.

In the corner, reading a newspaper over a cup of coffee, sat a man in a dark suit and hat.

Hiram scanned the five of them, looked each in turn in the eyes. "No more trouble."

"The *Blót* is over," Green said. "What more trouble could there be?"

"No more trouble," Hiram said again, "*ever.*"

"You called the police, didn't you?" Green asked, glancing at the man in the dark suit.

"I did." Hiram pulled back the edge of his coat so the assembled men could see the bishop's Jupiter Knife, now on Hiram's belt.

Del Rose grimaced. "We shouldn't be talking about the *Blót* in front of strangers."

"I know about your hunt," the stranger in the dark suit said, not looking up from his newspaper.

Michael put in his two cents. "That wasn't who my dad called that morning. He called the Utah Highway Patrol, and he didn't tell them about the *Blót* or any of you."

The five men exchanged glances.

The man in the corner folded his newspaper neatly on the table and stood up. "My employers received a telegram the next day."

Leon petted his dead dogs. "Well, now, I don't know who this fellow is, but I do have one question. It's about Diana Artemis. She cleared out of town the morning after. She gathered up her things and took the first train to Helper. She drove your truck that night on the Monument, didn't she?"

"We had help," Michael answered. "Who it was doesn't matter much."

"She didn't kill Preece, but you knew that," Green itched at his scalp. Dandruff drifted down onto his suit jacket. His hand was bandaged. All three herd members had marks on them, now healing. Banjo had a gash on his good ear. His bad ear had probably been injured in another Tithe, Hiram reflected. Leon favored his left arm, the one bearing the load of Peteys. "I mean, not alone. She helped Gudmundson."

"The meaning of the Tithe," Hiram said. "You pay your tithe by running in the hunt and taking your chances. Some of the deer die, but the rest gain wealth."

Green nodded.

"Gudmund and Clem are gone," Del Rose said. "That's the important thing. They took it too far, it went to their heads."

"You don't care," Green said, "that we . . . as long as no one . . ."

He lapsed into silence.

Michael snorted. "You killed a kid. One that we know of, maybe more."

"I do care that you run around in the desert and kill each other," Hiram said slowly. "There's a way to earn a living in this world, and that's by the sweat of your brow, not by murder and human sacrifice."

The men ground their teeth. Were they sorrowful? Were they defiant?

Green sighed. "Look, the Udall boy was in the wrong place, at the wrong time, though that doesn't excuse what Gudmund did. Preece shouldn't have let anyone live near the arch. Hell, we told him. But Preece had a way about him, an obstinacy, even before he wanted out. He got too rich, I guess. Thought he was above the rules."

"Adelaide Tunstall doesn't know anything about your nonsense," Hiram said sternly. "I swore I'd protect her by ending the cult. I don't take my promises lightly."

Leon chuckled, his jolly demeanor abruptly falling away. "The *Blót* is thousands of years old. We're not going to end it. You're going to go back to your farm, and you're going to forget all about us."

"I thought that might be how you felt." Hiram

nodded. "So I invited one more person to this little meeting."

"And I came, Mr. Woolley." The voice emanating from the stranger in the dark suit and hat who now stepped forward, physically entering the conversation, seemed to echo from across a vast space.

Jack Del Rose sneered. "What are you, some sort of Pinkerton? A cop? What's your name?"

"My name is irrelevant, Mr. Del Rose." The stranger's face was bland, so bland that Hiram didn't think he could describe it if pressed. Dark eyes, he would have said, and a complexion . . . well, dark eyes, and maybe he was Asian, or an Indian. Or was he fair? Suddenly, Hiram wasn't sure. The man stood with his hands unthreateningly at his sides. "I am in the employ of the Rockefeller family."

Erasmus Green trembled and shut his eyes.

"What have the Rockefellers got to do with anything?" Jack Del Rose asked.

"Davison Rock," Green squeaked. "His real name was Rockefeller."

"I am here to give you an order," the stranger said. "Not a suggestion and not a debate, but an order. And then I will make a threat. The order is this: no more *Blót*, ever again. I have been tasked to watch this land, and I will watch it faithfully, for a century. I will know if you run your Tithe. Do not do it. Your old ways die today."

"A century?" Del Rose smirked.

"Uranium is coming, in any case." The stranger smiled. "And other, stranger forms of wealth. This valley will no longer prosper by the law of the Hoof and the Fang."

Michael fidgeted. His face shared, subdued, some of the skepticism that rode on Del Rose's. Hiram touched his son's elbow lightly to hold him back.

"Uranium, my eye." Del Rose stood. "Okay, we have your order, Mr. Rockefeller goon. Now what's the threat? Are you going to come down here with hired muscle like you have some strike to break, and force us into line?" His smile looked wolfish, his teeth long and yellow. "Are you going to beat us up?"

"My threat is this." The stranger's voice was mild and he never quit smiling. He opened his mouth and somehow his jaw seemed to drop a foot, or two feet. The inside of his mouth was pitch black, black as the void between the stars, with no visible teeth or tongue.

The voice that burst from that maw was terrible, and it filled the room. *"Go in unto Pharaoh: for I have hardened his heart, and the heart of his servants, that I might shew these my signs before him: And that thou mayest tell in the ears of thy son, and of thy son's son, what things I have wrought in Egypt, and my signs which I have done among them; that ye may know how that I am the Lord."*

The Book of Exodus. Each word boomed like a terrible bell striking the hour of Armageddon.

The five men began to choke, Fang and Hoof alike, clawing at their throats, lips open, mouths working, slobber dribbling down their chins.

Leon Björnsson dropped the Peteys to claw at his throat.

Erasmus Green's bad scalp turned an angry red even as his lips turned blue, and still, he couldn't get air in.

Jack Del Rose fell, eyes bulging, cheeks becoming a terrible shade of purple.

All were choking, gasping, unable to breathe.

"Pap!" Michael cried out in terror.

Hiram watched in fear. He didn't dare look directly at the man in the dark suit. He had telegraphed the Rockefellers to tell them of the death of Davison Rock, and ask for their help. An answering telegram had promised assistance, and had fixed this appointment.

But who...or what...was this man?

"Stop this!" he called out.

The man in the dark suit, the man with the bland face, clutched an amulet in his fist and said nothing. Or was it a rosary?

Michael had his hands over his eyes.

The man's voice continued to boom.

All five of the stricken men slid from their chairs, kicking at tables, writhing on the floor. They clutched their throats, seconds from death.

Leon finally got onto his knees, and he punched himself in the gut. He shook with the first blow, and then hit himself again, over and over, as if trying to dislodge something from his throat. What was stuck there?

Green's neck bulged weirdly, as if there was an animal trapped inside.

Hiram knew what must be coming, because he recognized the verse from Exodus 10, and he knew its context: the plague of locusts. He was glad his son wasn't looking. He wanted to glance away, but he found he couldn't.

Jack Del Rose opened his mouth. A long, fat grasshopper came tumbling out, staggering left and right across the sheriff's tongue until it tumbled over his lower lip and fell to the flow. Others followed, the stream thicker and thicker, until he was literally vomiting locusts, the swarming column of insects lubricated with food, drink, and bile.

Green, Leon, the others, all ended up on their hands and knees, puking up their lunch and the locusts.

Michael dropped his hands to watch as he heard the men sucking in air again. His eyes were big as headlights.

"That is the threat." The man put his talisman away. He then nodded at his gasping victims. "No more *Blót*, not for a century. I will be watching."

He smiled at Hiram and Michael and then left. Ten seconds after he was gone, Hiram couldn't remember what he looked like, other than the fact that his mouth had been large and he had held something in his hand.

"So, do we help these guys?" Michael asked. "All part of the same eternal family, and all that stuff?"

"I think they've had all the help they can stand." Hiram left the hotel, and Michael followed.

"No more *Blót*," Jack Del Rose wheezed as Hiram walked away.

"No more *Blót*," Green whimpered.

Michael was still shaking as they drove away from Moab again. "I can't believe what I just saw. He did it to them...that guy...he put those grasshoppers inside them. What was he, Pap?"

"I don't know." Hiram wanted to ease his son's mind, but he couldn't.

He had no idea who the man was, or what.

A demon? An angel? A wizard?

And did he work just for the Rockefellers?

They drove in silence for a long time.

Chapter Thirty-Two

BISHOP DAVID SMITH AND BISHOP JOHN WELLS caught Hiram coming out of church the next Sunday.

Despite the heat, Bishop Smith wore his suit, and a shining band of sweat rose from his soaked collar to his Van Dyck beard. Wells wore a loose summer shirt, a short tie, and brown slacks. Both the men's shoes were polished to a high shine; Hiram's own shoes had been polished a glossy black that morning, but after a few hours of exposure to Lehi's dust, they were now powdered a yellowish gray.

Women in dresses chatted in clusters, just as the men gathered together; their children played tag in the dirt parking lot full of cars and trucks. Not a cloud marred the pale blue of the sky.

"Hiram." Bishop Smith exhaled bitterly, through both nostrils simultaneously. "Brother Woolley, what are we going to do with you? You do know we'll have to talk about your dealings in Moab."

"An official inquiry?" Hiram asked.

Bishop Wells slipped his round spectacles off and polished them with a white handkerchief. "According to Grand County Sheriff Jack Del Rose, you were never a suspect for any of the murders." Wells spoke with an English accent, which wasn't all that unusual. Utah still attracted many immigrants, gathering to Zion.

"But there *were* murders," Smith said. "And again, you and your son were there. This doesn't reflect well on you, or on us. We're supposed to be upstanding members of society. You don't see James Anderson getting into such mischief."

Was that a threat? It was at least a reminder of a threat. James Anderson was Hiram's banker, and Bishop Smith had once suggested he could pressure Anderson to call in Hiram's loan if Hiram kept practicing his craft.

Anderson. Had his ancestors come from Iceland? Was he involved in his own form of the *Blót?* Surely at some point in the past, his ancestors had been pagans, and apparently, that might not even have been in a past that was all that distant. Something like the Tithe might explain James Anderson's prosperity.

Or maybe it was simply that he was with a bank that was weathering the storms of the Depression well. Maybe he was a good honest banker, who had also had a little good luck, or been a little blessed.

Hiram shrugged. "I didn't commit any murders. And I wasn't even there on any official errand. I just got asked to help...place a well."

Bishop Smith harrumphed and coughed loudly, as if trying to drown out and ignore Hiram's plain statement that he had been invited down to Moab to dowse for water. "You're getting quite a reputation," he said. "Bishop Cannon is not pleased." Cannon was the third and most senior member of the Presiding Bishopric. "If it comes to an official inquiry, we may not be able to shelter you from the consequences."

Hiram touched the bloodstone in his pants pocket. It was a useful item: it brought rain, stanched blood flow, helped with poison, and could ferret out the truth. Fame was also a part of the package, and Hiram didn't want that. Yet like most things in life, the bad came with the good, entwined. The maggots might keep you alive at the same time as they feasted on your flesh.

"If I can serve God," Hiram said, "then I guess I can accept the consequences of doing so."

"Even if it means being excommunicated?" Smith peered at Hiram closely.

Hiram raised his hands in what he hoped was a peaceful, embracing gesture. "I know the difference between God and the church. If I have to choose between them, it's not a difficult choice."

The three men looked at each other, Smith fiercely, Wells benignly, and Hiram trying not to have any expression on his face at all.

"Did it go well down there?" Bishop Wells finally asked.

Hiram nodded. "All things considered." He reached out a hand.

Wells took it.

Reluctantly, Smith did the same. "Brother Woolley, if not for your sake, then for mine . . . can you be more careful?"

Another nod, and a grin, and then Hiram walked to the Double-A.

When he got home, Michael was at the kitchen table, wiping at his nose with a handkerchief, hunched over the two astrology books he'd gotten during their time in Moab: one from Diana, the other from Mahonri. He had his hand in his hair, in his reading position, scratching at his temples. He didn't glance up. "How was church, Pap?"

"You weren't there, so no one wanted to go ahead. We cancelled the whole thing." Hiram got a glass of buttermilk and sat down at the table.

Michael didn't look up from his reading. "Mmm hmmm," he said. "Next Sunday, I'll be there. I promise."

Hiram believed him.

That night, Hiram woke with a start, climbing out of a dream. He'd dreamed he was at the Provo Train station, the same place where he'd helped Adelaide Preece Tunstall and her family escape the Hoof. There had been a café there, in the dream, and the restaurant was full of flickering candlelight, ebbing with a darkness he felt more than saw.

He was sweating out of fear, clutching his chi-rho amulet, when he crossed the threshold. The tables were full of wolf-shaped men and men-shaped wolves, all shaggy with fur, eyes red and spit dripping from yellow fangs. Their claws scratched at the wooden floor and tables.

Sitting among them was Diana Artemis, in lacy night clothes, revealing more skin than he was comfortable with, even in his dream. Both her legs were of natural flesh and blood. She pointed to the clock, and the hands showed him 10:45 a.m. "If you have a dime for the dance, Hiram. But only if you have a dime for the dance."

When she smiled, she too had yellow fangs.

Hiram managed to get back to sleep, but only after he whispered his sleeping charm, over and over. "In the name of the Father, up and down, the Son and the Spirit upon your crown, the cross of Christ upon your breast, sweetest lady send me rest."

In the morning, he told Michael he had an errand to run. It wasn't a lie, but he wanted his son to forget Diana Artemis as soon as possible. He also didn't want the boy jumping to wrong conclusions about the widow and his father.

At the Provo train station, Hiram found parking next to a Cadillac Roadster and then stepped onto the train platform. There was no café, no candles, just people standing or sitting and waiting for the next train.

It was a little after 10:30 a.m., but there sat Diana Artemis on a little bench, wearing a black dress with a black hat perched on her black hair. This wasn't the hat she'd left at Lloyd's cabin; it looked decidedly more modern, something like a fedora that had been shrunk down, made more form-fitting, and given very feminine swoops and curves. It had to be pinned to her head, to stay fixed in place when she moved.

Hiram swept off his own hat and walked over. He'd fiddle with it while he talked with her. Somehow, this seemed important. Maybe it was his own pride, or maybe he wanted to make sure she wasn't a witch. Best case, she was just a fallen woman, a widow, who had grifted them, and then stolen money. A lot of money. She had helped Michael rescue him, though, and she had given them back the Double-A.

When Diana saw him, she raised a hand. "Mr.

Woolley, so interesting to see you here. Would you like to join me? I can't offer you breakfast, but we can chat." Her green eyes were bright, amused. She didn't seem at all taken aback that he was there. On her right hand was a thick emerald ring. Louisa Parker's ring, which she had stolen as deftly as she'd stolen the wallet out of Michael's coat.

He sat down across from her, hunched over, feeling at the brim of his worn fedora. "I just wanted to compare notes."

"How did you know I was here?" Did her smile dim? Did her eyes turn furtive for a second? It was hard to tell, since her beauty made everything about her a little hazy.

"I dreamed it." He raised his hand to show her his Saturn ring.

"Ah, Saturn gave me away. You'd think devouring his own children would have been enough to satisfy him, but I guess not."

Hiram wasn't sure what she was talking about. "You're not a witch, are you?"

"I prefer the term occultist," she said, a little laughter in her eyes at him. "I'm not that, either. Nor am I one of your cunning women. The show I put on for you, with my crystal ball? I had a wire connected to the drapes. A little sigh from me made the candles flicker. And Michael, dear, sweet Michael, he thought he saw something in my sphere of the spirits."

"He feels bad that you robbed him," Hiram said.

Diana smiled warmly at him. "I thought for sure he'd feel me lift the wallet. But the night was tense, and he was in a state. Out of all my magic tricks, that one was the most real . . . I learned to do it in

Baltimore." She paused. "That's all you and I have, are tricks and flimflam."

"I knew you'd be here. I dreamed it last night. How is that flimflam?"

"Well, now, you're only showing your flimflam is better than mine. World class flimflam, Hiram Woolley. Will you enlighten me?" She seemed genuinely interested, but that was her game, appearing genuine. How could she show no regret, no remorse? "Will you make me pay a dreadful price for the information?"

She narrowed her eyes at him; he supposed it was a seductive look, and he found it had no effect on him at all. He had answers for her, though he doubted she'd believe any of them. "God made the planet Saturn, which governs dreams. God made me and I made this ring, of Saturn-metal and bearing Saturn-signs, after the pattern my Grandma Hettie showed me, which channels true knowledge from Saturn in my dreams. In the end, though, it's God's will."

"No, some person made that ring, and you came across me today by complete luck."

"You don't believe in any magic at all," Hiram said. "You believe in nothing supernatural. You don't believe in God."

"If there is a God, then He has neither the time nor the patience for a woman like me. That was made clear a long time ago. If there is a heaven, I'll find a way in. St. Peter might be a saint, but he's still a man. I don't believe I'd be the first woman to work her way through the Pearly Gates by offering a service in trade."

Hiram didn't reveal his shock. "You don't fear hell?"

Her chuckle came out bitter. "I've been in hell

before. There's always a way out. And you'll pray for me, won't you Hiram? You'll pray your little farmerly heart out. I will count heavily on you when the time comes. You are a good man, Hiram Woolley. I should know. I've met more than my fair share of bad."

Hiram's own laughter was real and it felt good. "I will pray for you, Diana. You can be redeemed and perfected like anyone else."

"I'm Cassandra Seer now. Though I think your God won't be fooled by my entrepreneurial use of names. He'll know who I am. Except that the only god I believe in is Cold Hard Cash. Your great Satanic Truth has gotten me this far in life, and I expect it to see me through to the end."

Hiram sobered. "You believe in more than just money."

She touched her chest. "Do I?"

"You helped Michael that night. Yes, you drove away, but the Lord Divine aided us, and He did it through you. I saw the lights. I heard the horn. It drew me to Michael. You could have picked Michael's pocket before that, or simply taken the money at gunpoint, and you didn't. You stole the money, yes, but first you helped."

For the first time, Diana, or whatever her real name was, showed him a true expression. It was hurt, a little less confident, and she hid it as soon as she realized her mask had slipped. "If there is a God, Hiram, He's the best con artist of all."

He stood. "Good day to you, Cassandra Seer."

"Good day to you, Hiram Woolley."

He started to leave, but turned back. "I'd like your books . . . for Michael. You don't mind if I write Edna?"

"She will be happy to help." The smile on her lips seemed real. "If I need them, I know where to find you. Perhaps I shall darken your doorstep again."

"And if you do, I'll try to lighten that darkness." He put on his hat and tipped the brim at her.

He left her on the bench, surrounded by strangers.

That evening, with sheltering clouds in the sky, Hiram took Michael out to the south forty, a Mosaical Rod in his hand. Carved into the length of wood were the usual crosses and the Tetragrammaton. He handed the rod to Michael. "Do you remember what to say?"

Michael nodded, licked his lips, and gripped the rod. "'Whoso shall hide up treasures in the earth shall find them again no more, because of the great curse of the land, save he be a righteous man and shall hide it up unto the Lord.'" He swung the rod from side to side, and began to go whither it led.

They followed the rod out to the middle of the field, the beets growing around them, watered by the divine hand, a little rain, and a lot of water brought down from the mountains in irrigation ditches. It was different from the hard winter dirt that he'd had to contend with the last time he'd unearthed the chest.

Hiram was ready with a shovel when Michael indicated the spot. He dug, a little shaky and weak after a day of fasting. He removed the box from the hole, a box made of flat stones cemented together. On those stones he'd scratched every warding symbol he knew.

"So a spirit moves the box around?" Michael asked.

"That's right. I never know where it's going to be, and neither does anyone else. I like it that way." He thought of Diana, visiting them again, and prayed she wouldn't. In the same moment, he prayed that she'd find peace and God's mercy.

Some progress along her own path to perfection.

"You know what magic and science have in common?" Michael asked. "Things don't work the way you'd think they would."

Hiram lifted the lid of the stone box. "Sometimes I think the spirit is Grandma Hettie. Sometimes I think it's my mother. I don't really know. It might be someone we don't know at all."

"An angel?"

"Something like that."

Michael shivered. "I can feel it. I can feel something, something bad in there." His eyes were fixed on the objects inside—a skull with horns, a glass bauble, a black candle, and a brown rock with a line of quartz running through the middle. Teancum Kimball's peep-stone.

Hiram placed the Jupiter knives inside. Gudmund Gudmundson's knife was in its sheath, and Lloyd Preece's knife, without a sheath, was wrapped in a length of white cloth.

"Wait, Pap. Those daggers are powerful. We should keep them."

"Both these knives have shed the blood of men," Hiram said. "They're powerful, and we don't know for sure how they work."

"But we can learn how they work," Michael suggested.

"Good." Hiram shut the lid. "That's why we're keeping them. So your job is to learn more about them."

"But not by using them," Michael said.

Hiram nodded. "You'll be spending some time in the

library. That's good. You can prove to Mahonri that I haven't gotten you killed on one of my fool errands."

"Yet."

Hiram laughed, even though that one syllable was more frightening than funny. He glanced up at his son, a young man now, and on his way to becoming a cunning man. But hopefully, Hiram thought, not *only* a cunning man.

The world was changing. The time of the Fang and Hoof, and of similar cults the world over, was ending. The idea comforted Hiram, but at the same time, it troubled him. The *Blót* had taken lives, but it had also brought prosperity to a community in the wilderness. And if the *Blót* fell, what other mysteries would now find themselves on the hangman's scaffold? If all mystery disappeared, if all the old ways vanished, what would be left? Science and logic only? Could they explain a man's life, give him comfort in his time of need, nourishment for his soul? Hiram wasn't sure.

When they had buried the chest, Michael surprised Hiram with a strong hug.

He stepped back. "Thanks, Pap. Thanks for making the world a big, interesting place, full of mystery."

"I didn't make it." Hiram chuckled. "But thank you for seeing the mystery with me."

TIM POWERS

"Other writers tell tales of magic in the twentieth century, but no one does it like Powers."
—*The Orlando Sentinel*

FORCED PERSPECTIVES
HC: 978-1-9821-2440-3 • $25.00 US / $34.00 CAN
Sebastian Vickery and Ingrid Castine are chased by ghosts and gurus as they rush to save Los Angeles from a god-birthing ritual.

DOWN AND OUT IN PURGATORY
PB: 978-1-4814-8374-2 • $7.99 US / $10.99 CAN
Tales of science fiction and metaphysics from master of the trade Tim Powers, with an introduction by David Drake.

EXPIRATION DATE
TPB: 978-1-4814-8330-8 • $16.00 US / $22.00 CAN
PB: 978-1-4814-8408-4 • $7.99 US / $10.99 CAN
When young Kootie comes to possess the ghost of Thomas Edison, every faction in Los Angeles' supernatural underbelly rushes to capture—or kill—boy and ghost.

EARTHQUAKE WEATHER
TPB: 978-1-4814-8351-3 • $16.00 US / $22.00 CAN
PB: 978-1-9821-2439-7 • $8.99 US / $11.99 CAN
Amongst ghosts and beside a man chased by a god, Janis Plumtree and the many personalities sharing her mind must resurrect the King of the West.